Essential Mathematics

Book 7i

David Rayner

Elmwood Press

First published 2001 by
Elmwood Press
80 Attimore Road
Welwyn Garden City
Herts. AL8 6LP
Tel. 01707 333232

Reprinted 2002

British Library Cataloguing in Publication Data

Rayner, David

© David Rayner
The moral rights of the author have been asserted.
Database right Elmwood Press (maker)

ISBN 1 902 214 099

Numerical answers are published in a separate book

Artwork by Stephen Hill

Typeset and illustrated by Tech-Set, Gateshead, Tyne and Wear
Printed and bound by WS Bookwell

PREFACE

Essential Mathematics Books *7i*, *8i* and *9i* are written for pupils in the 'middle' ability range for ages 11 to 14. Most classrooms contain children with a range of abilities in mathematics. These books are written to cater for this situation.

The author is an enthusiastic supporter of the National Numeracy Strategy. The books have been prepared with the cooperation of teachers and pupils in NHS pilot schools. It is encouraging that most teachers are confident that this more structured approach will help to raise standards of understanding and attainment. There is a comprehensive NNS guide at start of the book with references to all topics.

There is no set path through the books but topics appear in the order suggested in the NNS planning charts. Broadly speaking, parts 1 and 2 can be studied in the Autumn Term, parts 3 and 4 in the Spring Term and parts 5 and 6 in the Summer Term.

The author believes that children learn mathematics most effectively by *doing* mathematics. Many youngsters who find mathematics difficult derive much more pleasure and enjoyment from the subject when they are doing questions which help them build up their confidence. Pupils feel a greater sense of satisfaction when they work in a systematic way and when they can appreciate the purpose and the power of the mathematics they are studying.

No text book will have the 'right' amount of material for every class and the author believes that it is better to have too much material rather than too little. Consequently teachers should judge for themselves which sections or exercises can be studied later. On a practical note, the author recommends the use of exercise books consisting of 7 mm squares.

Opportunities for work towards the 'Using and Applying Mathematics' strand appears throughout the book. Many activities, investigations, games and puzzles are included to provide a healthy variety of learning experiences. The author is aware of the difficulties of teaching on 'Friday afternoons' or on the last few days of term, when both pupils and teachers are tired, and suitable activities are included.

The author is indebted to his co-authors David Allman and Laurence Campbell whose work from the first edition of Essential Mathematics has been included where appropriate.

David Rayner

CONTENTS

Using and applying mathematics to solve problems

Applying mathematics and solving problems

2.7 • **Solve word problems and investigate in a**

4.7 **range of contexts:** number, algebra, shape, space and measures, and handling data; compare and evaluate solutions.

6.5 • Identify the necessary information to solve a problem; represent problems mathematically, making correct use of symbols, words, diagrams, tables and graphs.

4.7 • **Break a complex calculation into simpler steps, choosing and using appropriate and efficient operations, methods** and resources, including ICT.

• Present and interpret solutions in the context of the original problem; **explain and justify methods and conclusions**, orally and in writing.

5.7 • Suggest extensions to problems by asking 'What if . . . ?'; begin to generalise and to understand the significance of a counter-example.

Numbers and the number system

Place value, ordering and rounding

1.3 • Understand and use decimal notation and place value; multiply and divide integers and decimals by 10, 100, 1000, and explain the effect.

1.5 • Compare and order decimals in different contexts; know that when comparing measurements they must be in the same units.

1.6 • Round positive whole numbers to the nearest 10, 100 or 1000 and decimals to the nearest whole number or one decimal place.

Integers, powers and roots

5.6 • Understand negative numbers as positions on a number line; order, add and subtract positive and negative integers in context.

3.1 • Recognise and use multiples, factors (divisors), common factor, highest common factor and lowest common multiple in simple cases, and primes (less than 100); use simple tests of divisibility.

3.1 • Recognise the first few triangular numbers, squares of numbers to at least 12×12 and the corresponding roots.

Fractions, decimals, percentages, ratio and proportion

2.1 • Use fraction notation to describe parts of shapes and to express a smaller whole number as a fraction of a larger one; **simplify fractions by cancelling all common factors and identify equivalent fractions;** convert terminating decimals to fractions, e.g. $0.23 = \frac{23}{100}$; use a diagram to compare two or more simple fractions.

2.1 • Begin to add and subtract simple fractions and those with common denominators; calculate simple fractions of quantities and measurements (whole-number answers); multiply a fraction by an integer.

6.2 • Understand percentage as the 'number of parts per 100'; **recognise the equivalence of percentages, fractions and decimals;** calculate

2.5 simple percentages and use percentages to compare simple proportions.

4.2 • Understand the relationship between ratio and proportion; use direct proportion in simple contexts; use ratio notation, reduce a ratio to its simplest form and divide a quantity into two parts in a given ratio; solve simple problems about ratio and proportion using informal strategies.

Calculations

Number operations and the relationships between them

1.2 • Understand addition, subtraction, multiplication and division as they apply to

1.3 whole numbers and decimals; know how to use the laws of arithmetic and inverse operations.

3.2 • **Know and use the order of operations,** including brackets.

Mental methods and rapid recall of number facts

2.6 • Consolidate the rapid recall of number facts, including positive integer complements to 100 and multiplication facts to 10×10, and quickly derive associated division facts.

6.2 • Consolidate and **extend mental methods of calculation to include decimals, fractions and percentages,** accompanied where appropriate by suitable jottings; solve simple word problems mentally.

1.6 • Make and justify estimates and approximations of calculations.

Written methods

1.3 • Use standard column procedures to add and subtract whole numbers and decimals with up to two places.

5.4 • **Multiply and divide three-digit by two-digit whole numbers; extend to multiplying and dividing decimals with one or two places by single-digit whole numbers.** *For calculations with fractions and percentages, see above.*

Calculator methods

3.3 • Carry out calculations with more than one step using brackets and the memory; use the square root and sign change keys.

3.3 • Enter numbers and interpret the display in different contexts (decimals, percentages, money, metric measures).

Checking results

1.6 • **Check a result by considering whether it is of the right order of magnitude** and by working the problem backwards.

Algebra

Equations, formulae and identities

2.4 • **Use letter symbols to represent unknown numbers or variables;** know the meanings of the words *term*, *expression* and *equation*.

2.4 • **Understand that algebraic operations follow the same conventions and order as arithmetic operations**

2.4 • Simplify linear algebraic expressions by collecting like terms; begin to multiply a single term over a bracket (integer coefficients).

4.5 • Construct and solve simple linear equations with integer coefficients (unknown on one side only) using an appropriate method (e.g. inverse operations).

6.3 • Use simple formulae from mathematics and other subjects; substitute positive integers into simple linear expressions and formulae and, in simple cases, derive a formula.

Sequences, functions and graphs

1.1 • Generate and describe simple integer sequences.

1.1 • Generate terms of a simple sequence, given a rule (e.g. finding a term from the previous term, finding a term given its position in the sequence).

6.3 • Generate sequences from practical contexts and describe the general term in simple cases.

6.3 • Express simple functions in words, then using symbols; represent them in mappings.

4.6 • Generate coordinate pairs that satisfy a simple linear rule; **plot the graphs of simple linear functions,** where *y* is given explicitly in terms of *x*, on paper and using ICT; recognise straight-line graphs parallel to the *x*-axis or *y*-axis.

6.4 • Begin to plot and interpret the graphs of simple linear functions arising from real-life situations.

Shape, space and measures

Geometrical reasoning: lines, angles and shapes

4.3 • Use correctly the vocabulary, notation and labelling conventions for lines, angles and shapes.

4.1 • **Identify parallel and perpendicular lines: know the sum of angles at a point, on a straight line and in a triangle,** and recognise vertically opposite angles.

4.1 • Begin to identify and use angle, side and symmetry properties of triangles and quadrilaterals; solve geometrical problems involving these properties, using step-by-step deduction and explaining reasoning with diagrams and text.

1.4 • Use 2-D representations to visualise 3-D shapes and deduce some of their properties.

Transformations

5.1 • Understand and use the language and notation
5.3 associated with reflections, translations and rotations.

• Recognise and visualise the transformation and symmetry of a 2-D shape:

5.2 – reflection in given mirror lines, and line symmetry;

5.1 – rotation about a given point, and rotation symmetry;

5.3 – translation;
explore these transformations and symmetries using ICT.

Coordinates

2.3 • Use conventions and notation for 2-D coordinates in all four quadrants; find coordinates of points determined by geometric information.

Construction

4.3 • Use a ruler and protractor to:
– measure and draw lines to the nearest millimetre and angles, including reflex angles, to the nearest degree;
– construct a triangle given two sides and the included angle (SAS) or two angles and the included side (ASA);
explore these constructions using ICT.

1.4 • Use ruler and protractor to construct simple nets of 3-D shapes, e.g. cuboid, regular tetrahedron, square-based pyramid, triangular prism.

Measures and mensuration

3.4 • Use names and abbreviations of units of measurement to measure, estimate, calculate and solve problems in everyday contexts involving length, area, mass, capacity, time and angle;
convert one metric unit to another (e.g. grams to kilograms); read and interpret scales on a range of measuring instruments.

4.3 • Use angle measure; distinguish between and estimate the size of acute, obtuse and reflex angles.

1.7 • Know and use the formula for the area of a rectangle; calculate the perimeter and area of shapes made from rectangles.

1.7 • Calculate the surface area of cubes and cuboids.

Handling data

Specifying a problem, planning and collecting data

3.5 • Given a problem that can be addressed by statistical methods, suggest possible answers.
   • Decide which data would be relevant to an enquiry and possible sources.

3.5 • Plan how to collect and organise small sets of data; design a data collection sheet or questionnaire to use in a simple survey; construct frequency tables for discrete data, grouped where appropriate in equal class intervals.

3.5 • Collect small sets of data from surveys and experiments, as planned.

Processing and representing data, using ICT as appropriate

5.5 • Calculate statistics for small sets of discrete data:
   – find the mode, median and range, and the modal class for grouped data;
   – calculate the mean, including from a simple frequency table, using a calculator for a larger number of items.

3.5 • Construct, on paper and using ICT, graphs and diagrams to represent data, including:
   – bar-line graphs;
   – frequency diagrams for grouped discrete data;
   use ICT to generate pie charts.

Interpreting and discussing results

3.5 • Interpret diagrams and graphs (including pie charts), and draw simple conclusions based on the shape of graphs and simple statistics for a single distribution.

5.5 • **Compare two simple distributions using the range and one of the mode, median or mean.**

3.5 • Write a short report of a statistical enquiry and illustrate with appropriate diagrams, graphs and charts, using ICT as appropriate; justify the choice of what is presented.

Probability

6.1 • Use vocabulary and ideas of probability, drawing on experience.

6.1 • **Understand and use the probability scale from 0 to 1; find and justify probabilities based on equally likely outcomes in simple contexts;** identify all the possible mutually exclusive outcomes of a single event.

6.1 • Collect data from a simple experiment and record in a frequency table; estimate probabilities based on this data.

6.1 • Compare experimental and theoretical probabilities in simple contexts.

Part 1

1.1 Sequences

- Sequences are lists of numbers (and sometimes letters) which have some underlying pattern to them. Each number in a sequence is called a *term*.

- 2, 9, 4, 7, 6, 41, ... is a list. There is no underlying pattern to the numbers – and so we have no real way of predicting what comes next.

- These are sequences. Their underlying patterns are shown.

Sequence	Structure
3, 5, 7, 9, ...	3 5 7 9 (+2) (+2) (+2) (+2)
20, 17, 14, 11, ...	20 17 14 11 (−3) (−3) (−3) (−3)
5, 8, 12, 17, ...	5 8 12 17 (+3) (+4) (+5) (+6)
2, 2, 4, 12, 48, ...	2 2 4 12 48 (×1) (×2) (×3) (×4) (×5)
15, 14, 16, 13, 17, ...	15 14 16 13 17 (−1) (+2) (−3) (+4) (−5)

Exercise 1

1. The numbers in boxes form a sequence. Find the next term.

(a) 10   12   14   16   ☐

(b) 3   8   13   18   ☐

(c) 11   9   7   5   ☐

Winter

In Questions **2** to **17** write down the sequence and find the next term.

2. 4, 8, 12, 16,   **3.** 2, 5, 8, 11,
4. 21, 17, 13, 9,   **5.** 2, 4, 8, 16,
6. 1, 2, 4, 7, 11,   **7.** 3, 5, 9, 17,
8. 2, 4, 6, 8,   **9.** 1, 4, 8, 13,
10. 80, 40, 20, 10,   **11.** 5, 8, 12, 17,
12. $\frac{1}{2}$, 1, $1\frac{1}{2}$, 2,   **13.** 2, 20, 200, 2000,
14. 45, 36, 28, 21,   **15.** 1, 3, 9, 27,
16. 56, 28, 14, 7,   **17.** 1, 4, 9, 16,

18. Write down the sequence and find the missing number.

(a) | 2 | 6 | ☐ | 14 | 18 |

(b) | 3 | ☐ | 12 | 24 | 48 |

(c) | $\frac{1}{2}$ | 2 | $3\frac{1}{2}$ | 5 | ☐ |

(d) | ☐ | 8 | 4 | 0 | −4 |

spring

19. Copy each sequence and write down the next number
(a) 3·2, 3·4, 3·6, 3·8, ...
(b) 1·76, 1·77, 1·78, 1·79, ...
(c) 0·402, 0·403, 0·404, 0·405, ...

Sequence rules

- For the sequence 10, 13, 16, 19, 22, ..., the first term is 10 and the term-to-term *rule* is 'add 3'.

- For the sequence 3, 6, 12, 24, 48, ..., the term-to-term rule is 'double'.

Exercise 2

1. The first term of a sequence is 20 and the term-to-term rule is 'add 5'. Write down the first five terms of the sequence.

2. You are given the first term and the rule of several sequences. Write down the first five terms of each sequence.

	First term	rule
(a)	8	add 2
(b)	100	subtract 4
(c)	10	double
(d)	64	divide by 2

3. Write down the rule for each sequence.
   (a) 2, 5, 8, 11, 14, ...
   (b) 90, 85, 80, 75, 70, ...
   (c) 1, 3, 9, 27, 81, ...
   (d) 2·2, 2·3, 2·4, 2·5, ...
   (e) 0·1, 0·2, 0·4, 0·8, 1·6, ...
   (f) 0·1, 1, 10, 100, ...

4. The rule for the sequences below is *double and take away 1*. Find the missing numbers

   (a) $3 \rightarrow 5 \rightarrow 9 \rightarrow 17 \rightarrow \boxed{}$

   (b) $\boxed{} \rightarrow 7 \rightarrow 13 \rightarrow 25 \rightarrow 49$

   (c) $\boxed{} \rightarrow 19 \rightarrow \boxed{} \rightarrow 73$

5. The rule for the sequences here is *multiply by 3 and add 1*. Find the missing numbers

   (a) $1 \rightarrow 4 \rightarrow 13 \rightarrow \boxed{}$

   (b) $\boxed{} \rightarrow 7 \rightarrow 22 \rightarrow 67$

   (c) $\boxed{} \rightarrow 2 \rightarrow \boxed{} \rightarrow 22$

6. The rule for three sequences A, B and C is 'double and add 5'. Write down the first four terms of the sequences.

   A: first term = 2

   B: first term = 3

   C: first term = 10.

7. Copy this pattern and write down the next three lines. Do not use a calculator!

$$1 \times 99 = 99$$
$$2 \times 99 = 198$$
$$3 \times 99 = 297$$
$$4 \times 99 = 396$$

8. (a) Copy this pattern and write down the next two lines

$$4 \times 8 = 32$$
$$44 \times 8 = 352$$
$$444 \times 8 = 3552$$
$$4444 \times 8 = 35\,552$$

   (b) Copy and complete $444\,444\,444 \times 8 =$

1.2 Number machines

- A number machine performs an *operation* on numbers.

- A simple *operation* could be   add   (+)
                                    subtract   (−)
                                      multiply   (×)
                        or   divide   (÷)

- The *input* number goes into the machine.   input

- The *output* number comes out of the machine.   output

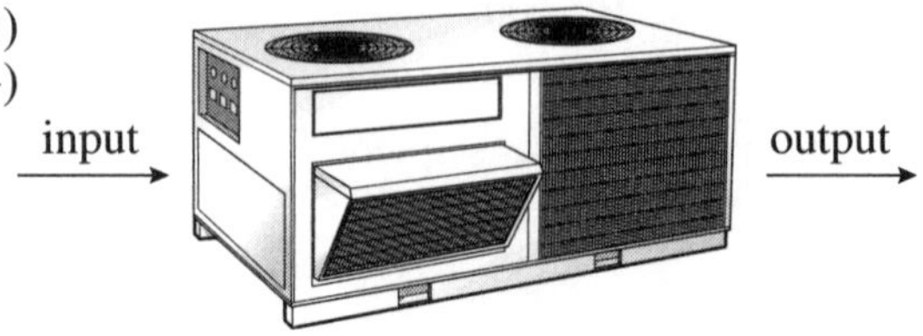

Examples

input	machine	output	output solution	reason
1. 5 →	+ 7	→ ?	? = 12	(5 + 7 = 12)
2. 8 →	− 3	→ ◆	◆ = 5	(8 − 3 = 5)
3. 3 →	× 6	→ ■	■ = 18	(3 × 6 = 18)

Exercise 1

Find the outputs from these number machines.

1.   4 → | + 5 | → ☺

2.   7 → | + 11 | → ◣

3.   10 → | − 3 | → ▮

4.   14 → | − 9 | → ▬

5.   6 → | × 7 | →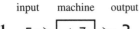

6.   8 → | × 2 | → ⋈

7.   525 → | ÷ 5 | → ?

8.   24 → | ÷ 4 | → ☺

9.   39 → | + 13 | → ▮

10.   7 → | × 9 | → ◣

11.   64 → | − 46 | → ⚁

12.   660 → | ÷ 6 | → 👢

13.   8 → | × 90 | → ⋈

14.   73 → | + 37 | → �

15.   545 → | ÷ 5 | → ◆

16.   51 → | − 15 | → ▮

17.   33 → | × 3 | → ◣

18.   80 → | × 8 | → 🌲

19.   120 → | ÷ 20 | → π

20.   52 → | ÷ 4 | → ∅

Exercise 2

Find the output.

1. 6 → +5 → +2 → ?

2. 3 → +6 → +8 → ●

3. 13 → −9 → −3 → ▲

4. 17 → −8 → −5 → ♦

5. 4 → ×2 → ×5 → π

6. 3 → ×3 → ×3 → ∅

7. 20 → ÷5 → ÷2 → ◢

8. 48 → ÷4 → ÷6 → ◥

9. 17 → +71 → −8 → ■

10. 34 → +43 → −70 → 👢

11. 5 → +4 → ×3 → 🐟

12. 7 → +9 → ×0 → ☺

13. 12 → +6 → ÷6 → ✦

14. 39 → +13 → ÷4 → ▨

15. 89 → −15 → +4 → ▧

16. 73 → −5 → +9 → ▬

17. 42 → −38 → ×7 → 👢

18. 100 → −81 → ×3 → ■

19. 85 → −58 → ÷9 → 🎄

20. 76 → −67 → ÷9 → ⚃

In Questions **21** to **25** there are several operations.

21. 5 → ×3 → −10 → ×2 → ÷10 → ☂

22. 7 → ×9 → ×2 → −66 → ÷12 → ◠

23. 50 → ×10 → −123 → +13 → ÷10 → ÷13 → ↑

24. 17 → ×5 → +25 → ÷11 → ×13 → ÷2 → +7 → ⚑

25. 13 → +84 → ×0 → +14 → ×5 → −15 → ÷11 → !

Inverse operations

- Using the *inverse* (or reverse) we can find the input for any machine, by using the output.

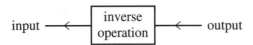

input —← | inverse operation | ←— output

Operation	Inverse operation
+7	−7
−8	+8
×4	÷4
÷6	×6

- Example: Find the input.

$$? \rightarrow \boxed{+9} \rightarrow 20$$

Solution: Change arrows direction and use the inverse operation

$$? \leftarrow \boxed{-9} \leftarrow 20$$

$$? = 11 \text{ since } 20 - 9 = 11$$

Exercise 3

Find the input to these systems

1. ● $\rightarrow \boxed{+6} \rightarrow$ 11

2. ▲ $\rightarrow \boxed{+4} \rightarrow$ 13

3. ⚅ $\rightarrow \boxed{-7} \rightarrow$ 2

4. ◢ $\rightarrow \boxed{-12} \rightarrow$ 24

5. ■ $\rightarrow \boxed{\times 3} \rightarrow$ 18

6. ☺ $\rightarrow \boxed{\times 5} \rightarrow$ 45

7. \$ $\rightarrow \boxed{\div 8} \rightarrow$ 1

8. 👢 $\rightarrow \boxed{\div 7} \rightarrow$ 8

9. 🐟 $\rightarrow \boxed{+14} \rightarrow$ 72

10. ▨ $\rightarrow \boxed{+11} \rightarrow$ 29

11. ◢ $\rightarrow \boxed{-13} \rightarrow$ 31

12. ♦ $\rightarrow \boxed{-72} \rightarrow$ 27

13. ♦ $\rightarrow \boxed{-72} \rightarrow$ 27

14. π $\rightarrow \boxed{\times 9} \rightarrow$ 72

15. ? $\rightarrow \boxed{\div 4} \rightarrow$ 80

16. ◤ $\rightarrow \boxed{\div 60} \rightarrow$ 7

17. ▬ $\rightarrow \boxed{\times 9} \rightarrow$ 54

18. ? $\rightarrow \boxed{\times 8} \rightarrow$ 560

19. ☺ $\rightarrow \boxed{\div 7} \rightarrow$ 7

20. ◢ $\rightarrow \boxed{\div 3} \rightarrow$ 27

Exercise 4

Find the input to these machines

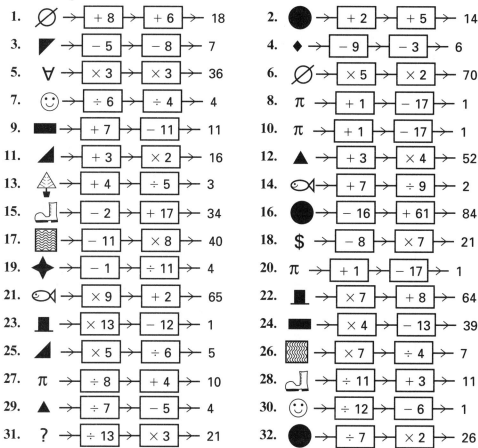

1. ∅ → | + 8 | → | + 6 | → 18
2. ● → | + 2 | → | + 5 | → 14
3. ▟ → | − 5 | → | − 8 | → 7
4. ◆ → | − 9 | → | − 3 | → 6
5. ∀ → | × 3 | → | × 3 | → 36
6. ∅ → | × 5 | → | × 2 | → 70
7. ☺ → | ÷ 6 | → | ÷ 4 | → 4
8. π → | + 1 | → | − 17 | → 1
9. ▬ → | + 7 | → | − 11 | → 11
10. π → | + 1 | → | − 17 | → 1
11. ◢ → | + 3 | → | × 2 | → 16
12. ▲ → | + 3 | → | × 4 | → 52
13. 🎄 → | + 4 | → | ÷ 5 | → 3
14. 🐟 → | + 7 | → | ÷ 9 | → 2
15. 👢 → | − 2 | → | + 17 | → 34
16. ● → | − 16 | → | + 61 | → 84
17. ▨ → | − 11 | → | × 8 | → 40
18. $ → | − 8 | → | × 7 | → 21
19. ◆ → | − 1 | → | ÷ 11 | → 4
20. π → | + 1 | → | − 17 | → 1
21. 🐟 → | × 9 | → | + 2 | → 65
22. ▮ → | × 7 | → | + 8 | → 64
23. ▮ → | × 13 | → | − 12 | → 1
24. ▬ → | × 4 | → | − 13 | → 39
25. ◢ → | × 5 | → | ÷ 6 | → 5
26. ▨ → | × 7 | → | ÷ 4 | → 7
27. π → | ÷ 8 | → | + 4 | → 10
28. 👢 → | ÷ 11 | → | + 3 | → 11
29. ▲ → | ÷ 7 | → | − 5 | → 4
30. ☺ → | ÷ 12 | → | − 6 | → 1
31. ? → | ÷ 13 | → | × 3 | → 21
32. ● → | ÷ 7 | → | × 2 | → 26

Mystery machines

The following inputs go into a mystery machine ...

        3, 6, 27 and 0.

The diagram shows the outputs produced ...

input	machine	output
3 →	?	→ 6
6 →	?	→ 9
27 →	?	→ 30
0 →	?	→ 3

The 'mystery' machine has added three to produce the outputs because it links *all* the inputs to the outputs in the same way.

The mystery machine was ...   input → | +3 | → output

Exercise 5

What operation is taking place in each of these machines?

1.

input	output
1 →[?]→ 5	
2 →[?]→ 10	
3 →[?]→ 15	

2.

input	output
63 →[?]→ 7	
54 →[?]→ 6	
27 →[?]→ 3	

3.

input	output
10 →[?]→ 8	
9 →[?]→ 7	
8 →[?]→ 6	

4.

input	output
3 →[?]→ 6	
8 →[?]→ 11	
7 →[?]→ 10	

5.

input	output
12 →[?]→ 6	
2 →[?]→ 1	
50 →[?]→ 25	

6.

input	output
19 →[?]→ 57	
9 →[?]→ 27	
7 →[?]→ 21	

7.

input	output
26 →[?]→ 11	
40 →[?]→ 25	
91 →[?]→ 76	

8.

input	output
9 →[?]→ 63	
4 →[?]→ 28	
8 →[?]→ 56	

9.

input	output
8 →[?]→ 64	
1 →[?]→ 8	
3 →[?]→ 24	

For Questions **10** to **15** copy and complete the number machines
after working out the operation for each.

10.

input	output
1 →[ ]→ 7	
7 →[ ]→ 13	
13 →[ ]→ ?	
? →[ ]→ 26	
27 →[ ]→ ?	

11.

input	output
2 →[ ]→ 8	
3 →[ ]→ 12	
4 →[ ]→ ?	
10 →[ ]→ ?	
? →[ ]→ 48	

12.

input	output
12 →[ ]→ 5	
7 →[ ]→ 0	
18 →[ ]→ ?	
? →[ ]→ 13	
? →[ ]→ 26	

13.

input	output
0 →⬜→ 11	
3 →⬜→ ?	
12 →⬜→ 23	
? →⬜→ 31	
39 →⬜→ ?	

14.

input	output
3 →⬜→ 1	
9 →⬜→ 3	
? →⬜→ 4	
15 →⬜→ ?	
60 →⬜→ ?	

15.

input	output
0 →⬜→ ?	
5 →⬜→ 50	
? →⬜→ 40	
7 →⬜→ 70	
? →⬜→ 100	

Questions **16** to **20** are more difficult.

16. Find the *single* operation which perfoms the same operation as the two operations shown.

$$In \rightarrow \boxed{+\ 12} - \boxed{-\ 3} \rightarrow Out$$

17. Find the *single* operation which performs the same operation as the three operations shown.

$$In \rightarrow \boxed{\times\ 4} - \boxed{\times\ 3} - \boxed{\div\ 2} \rightarrow Out$$

18. For each chart find the *single* operation which performs the same operation as the three operations shown.

(a) $In \rightarrow \boxed{+\ 5} - \boxed{-\ 2} - \boxed{+\ 10} \rightarrow Out$

(b) $\rightarrow \boxed{-\ 4} - \boxed{+\ 1} - \boxed{-\ 3} \rightarrow$

(c) $\rightarrow \boxed{+\ 2} - \boxed{\times\ 2} - \boxed{-\ 4} \rightarrow$

19. Find the two operations which give *both* the results shown.

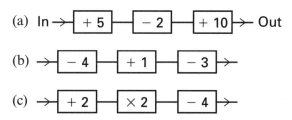

$$4 \rightarrow \boxed{?} - \boxed{?} \rightarrow 9$$

$$9 \rightarrow \boxed{?} - \boxed{?} \rightarrow 19$$

20. Find the two operations which give *both* the results shown.

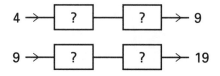

$$5 \rightarrow \boxed{?} - \boxed{?} \rightarrow 14$$

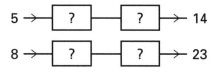

$$8 \rightarrow \boxed{?} - \boxed{?} \rightarrow 23$$

1.3 Arithmetic without a calculator

Place value

- Whole numbers are made up from units, tens, hundreds, thousands and so on.

thousands	hundreds	tens	units
6	3	2	5

- In the number 6325:

> the digit 6 means 6 thousands
> the digit 3 means 3 hundreds
> the digit 2 means 2 tens
> the digit 5 means 5 units (ones)

- In words we write 'six thousand, three hundred and twenty-five'.

Exercise 1

In Questions **1** to **8** state the value of the figure underlined.

1. 3<u>7</u>   **2.** <u>4</u>85   **3.** 60<u>8</u>   **4.** 62<u>7</u>

5. <u>6</u>140   **6.** <u>3</u>2 104   **7.** <u>5</u> 180 000   **8.** <u>7</u>30 111

In Questions **9** to **16** write down the number which goes in each box.

9. $393 = \boxed{} + 90 + 3$ **10.** $527 = 500 + \boxed{} + 7$

11. $834 = 800 + \boxed{} + 4$ **12.** $699 = \boxed{} + 90 + 9$

13. $7317 = \boxed{} + 300 + 10 + 7$ **14.** $5043 = 5000 + \boxed{} + 3$

15. $25\,410 = 20\,000 + 5000 + \boxed{} + 10$

16. $74\,612 = \boxed{} + 4000 + 600 + \boxed{} + 2$

17. Write these numbers in figures.
   (a) Four hundred and nine.
   (b) Six thousand, four hundred and one.
   (c) Sixteen thousand, two hundred and eleven.
   (d) Half a million.
   (e) Four hundred thousand and fifty.
   (f) Three and a half thousand.

18. Here are four number cards:

   (a) Use all the cards to make the largest possible number.
   (b) Use all the cards to make the smallest possible number.

19. Write these numbers in words.
(a) 6200   (b) 90 000   (c) 25 010
(d) 610 400   (e) 7 010 000

20. Here are five number cards:

(a) Use all the cards to make the largest possible *odd* number.
(b) Use all the cards to make the smallest possible *even* number.

21. Write down the number that is ten more than:
(a) 351   (b) 399   (c) 7025

22. Write down the number that is one thousand more than:
(a) 425   (b) 6423   (c) 24100

23. (a) Lisa puts a 2 digit whole number into her calculator.
She multiplies the number by 10.

Fill in *one* other digit which you know must now be
on the calculator.

(b) Lisa starts again with the same 2 digit number and
this time she multiplies it by 1000.
Fill in all five digits on the calculator this time.

24. Write down the numbers in order, from the smallest to the
largest.
(a)   2142   2290   2058   2136
(b)   5329   5029   5299   5330
(c)   25 117   25 200   25 171   25 000   25 500

25. Find a number n so that $5 \times n + 7 = 507$.

26. Find a number p so that $6 \times p + 8 = 68$.

27. Find a pair of numbers a and b for which $8 \times a + b = 807$.

28. Find a pair of numbers p and q for which $7 \times p + 5 \times q = 7050$.

Arithmetic

Here are examples to remind you of non-calculator methods.

(a)
```
    4 2 7
  +5 1 8 6
   5 6 1 3
     1  1
```

(b)
```
  2 7 ⁷8̶ ¹4
  −  6 3 5
   2 1 4 9
```

(c) $57 \times 100 = 5700$

(d)
```
    3 7 4
  ×     6
   2 2 4 4
     4 2
```

(e)
```
        5 4 2
  7)3 7 ²9 ¹4
```

(f)
```
    1 3 8 r 4   or   138⁴⁄₅
  5)6 ¹9 ⁴4
```

Exercise 2

1. 126
  + 37

2. 48
  + 173

3.   9
  17
  + 193

4. 28
  63
  + 205

5. 355
  + 278

6. 573
  + 209

7. 301
  99
  + 257

8. 114
  9
  + 867

9. 501
  397
  + 124

10. 634
  769
  + 127

11. 389
  193
  + 624

12. 371
  567
  + 462

In Questions **13** to **32** set the problems out correctly in columns.

13. $3 + 12 + 109$ **14.** $27 + 260$ **15.** $584 + 617$
16. $39 + 357$ **17.** $3 + 109 + 61$ **18.** $5034 + 69$
19. $201 + 76 + 40$ **20.** $679 + 63 + 4$ **21.** $54 + 507 + 2704$
22. $2030 + 69 + 5$ **23.** $6006 + 708 + 99$ **24.** $842 + 67 + 2011$
25. $1089 + 891 + 19 + 9$ **26.** $5867 + 321 + 45 + 9$ **27.** $8647 + 198$
28. $873 + 2316 + 473$ **29.** $2644 + 55685$ **30.** $26\,514 + 749$
31. $45\,609 + 20\,047$ **32.** $67\,508 + 95\,607 + 436$

Exercise 3

Copy each of the following problems and perform the calculation.
(No calculators.)

1. 49
  − 15

2. 76
  − 7

3. 83
  − 67

4. 92
  −17

5. 50
  − 26

6. 421
  − 59

7. 368
  − 274

8. 573
  − 94

9. 900
  − 487

10. 1001
  − 697

In Questions **11** to **30** write the numbers in columns and then
subtract.

11. $33 - 16$ **12.** $24 - 7$ **13.** $57 - 19$ **14.** $40 - 13$ **15.** $167 - 78$
16. $319 - 234$ **17.** $743 - 517$ **18.** $800 - 342$ **19.** $965 - 877$ **20.** $2001 - 416$

21. Two hundred and four take away forty-eight.
22. Five hundred and thirteen take away one hundred and twenty-five.
23. Two hundred and eight take away thirty-one.
24. Six hundred and nineteen take away two hundred and twenty-seven.
25. Seven hundred and fifty take away three hundred and ninety-one.
26. One thousand take away six hundred and sixty-one.
27. Nine hundred and twelve take away four hundred and fifty.
28. Five hundred and one take away one hundred and eighty.
29. One hundred and eleven take away eighty-nine.
30. One thousand take away one hundred and eleven.

Multiplying

- Multiplication is a quick method of adding together the same number ...
  $7 + 7 + 7 + 7 + 7 + 7 + 7 + 7 + 7$ is the same as 9×7 and $9 \times 7 = 63$.

- Your ability to solve multiplication problems will be greatly improved if you learn your multiplication tables up to 12×12 thoroughly.

Exercise 4

Copy each multiplication and insert the correct answer.

1. $12 \times 5 = ?$	**2.** $6 \times 6 = ?$	**3.** $9 \times 5 = ?$	**4.** $7 \times 6 = ?$
5. $8 \times 5 = ?$	**6.** $8 \times 6 = ?$	**7.** $7 \times 5 = ?$	**8.** $9 \times 6 = ?$
9. $6 \times 5 = ?$	**10.** $12 \times 6 = ?$	**11.** $5 \times 5 = ?$	**12.** $7 \times 7 = ?$
13. $12 \times 4 = ?$	**14.** $8 \times 7 = ?$	**15.** $9 \times 4 = ?$	**16.** $9 \times 7 = ?$
17. $8 \times 4 = ?$	**18.** $12 \times 7 = ?$	**19.** $7 \times 4 = ?$	**20.** $8 \times 8 = ?$
21. $6 \times 4 = ?$	**22.** $9 \times 8 = ?$	**23.** $5 \times 4 = ?$	**24.** $12 \times 8 = ?$
25. $4 \times 4 = ?$	**26.** $9 \times 9 = ?$	**27.** $12 \times 3 = ?$	**28.** $12 \times 9 = ?$
29. $9 \times 3 = ?$	**30.** $12 \times 10 = ?$	**31.** $8 \times 3 = ?$	**32.** $11 \times 11 = ?$
33. $7 \times 3 = ?$	**34.** $12 \times 11 = ?$	**35.** $6 \times 3 = ?$	**36.** $12 \times 12 = ?$
37. $5 \times 3 = ?$	**38.** $3 \times 3 = ?$	**39.** $10 \times 10 = ?$	**40.** $4 \times 3 = ?$

Exercise 5

Speed Test 1.
Copy and complete the grids on the next page. Time yourself on grid 1. Try to improve your time on grid 2.

×	7	2	12	8	6	3	11	9	4	5
7	49									
2										
12										
8										
6				48						
3						9				
11										
9										
4										
5										

×	2	9	6	3	5	11	12	8	7	4
2										
9										
6										
3										
5										
11										
12										
8										
7										
4										

Exercise 6

Work out

1. 32×5

2. 61×4

3. 35×3

4. 48×2

5. 26×6

6. 51×8

7. 62×9

8. 89×7

9. 241×2

10. 416×4

11. 513×3

12. 505×5

13. 267×8

14. 216×6

15. 307×7

16. 199×9

17. 7×345 18. 208×5 19. 6×3143 20. 6082×7

Work out

(a) 42×20
$= 42 \times 2 \times 10$
$= 84 \times 10$
$= 840$

(b) 213×300
$= 213 \times 3 \times 100$
$= 639 \times 100$
$= 63\,900$

(c) 13×5000
$= 13 \times 5 \times 1000$
$= 65 \times 1000$
$= 65\,000$

21. 43×20 **22.** 31×30 **23.** 24×50 **24.** 35×300

25. 52×400 **26.** 63×500 **27.** 600×211 **28.** 7000×21

29. 407×70 **30.** 312×600 **31.** 162×4000 **32.** $521 \times 30\,000$

Exercise 7

Copy and complete the following division problems.

1. $6 \div 3 = ?$ **2.** $8 \div 4 = ?$ **3.** $48 \div 8 = ?$ **4.** $88 \div 11 = ?$

5. $16 \div 2 = ?$ **6.** $10 \div 2 = ?$ **7.** $49 \div 7 = ?$ **8.** $90 \div 9 = ?$

9. $20 \div 5 = ?$ **10.** $99 \div 11 = ?$ **11.** $50 \div 5 = ?$ **12.** $96 \div 12 = ?$

13. $24 \div 6 = ?$ **14.** $14 \div 7 = ?$ **15.** $54 \div 6 = ?$ **16.** $100 \div 10 = ?$

17. $28 \div 4 = ?$ **18.** $15 \div 3 = ?$ **19.** $55 \div 5 = ?$ **20.** $108 \div 9 = ?$

21. $48 \div 6 = ?$ **22.** $16 \div 4 = ?$ **23.** $56 \div 7 = ?$ **24.** $110 \div 10 = ?$

25. $72 \div 9 = ?$ **26.** $18 \div 6 = ?$ **27.** $60 \div 5 = ?$ **28.** $120 \div 10 = ?$

29. $60 \div 12 = ?$ **30.** $20 \div 4 = ?$ **31.** $63 \div 7 = ?$ **32.** $121 \div 11 = ?$

33. $70 \div 7 = ?$ **34.** $22 \div 11 = ?$ **35.** $64 \div 8 = ?$ **36.** $132 \div 11 = ?$

37. $84 \div 7 = ?$ **38.** $24 \div 4 = ?$ **39.** $55 \div 11 = ?$ **40.** $144 \div 12 = ?$

41. $88 \div 11 = ?$ **42.** $27 \div 3 = ?$ **43.** $66 \div 6 = ?$ **44.** $33 \div 11 = ?$

45. $96 \div 8 = ?$ **46.** $28 \div 7 = ?$ **47.** $70 \div 10 = ?$ **48.** $66 \div 11 = ?$

49. $5 \div 1 = ?$ **50.** $45 \div 9 = ?$ **51.** $0 \div 7 = ?$ **52.** $5\frac{1}{2} \div 5\frac{1}{2} = ?$

Dividing larger numbers

- The order in which you divide numbers *is* important. For example $12 \div 3$ is *not* the same as $3 \div 12$.

- Here is a 'pencil and paper' method for dividing.

  (a) $625 \div 5$

  $$5\overline{)6^12^25}$$ with answer $1\,2\,5$

  (b) $936 \div 4$

  $$4\overline{)9^13^16}$$ with answer $2\,3\,4$

  (c) $3073 \div 7$

  $$7\overline{)3^30^27^63}$$ with answer $0\,4\,3\,9$

Exercise 8

Work out

1. $3\overline{)99}$ **2.** $2\overline{)42}$ **3.** $4\overline{)48}$ **4.** $7\overline{)84}$

5. $5\overline{)65}$ **6.** $6\overline{)72}$ **7.** $7\overline{)847}$ **8.** $9\overline{)558}$

9. $8\overline{)128}$ **10.** $9\overline{)729}$ **11.** $2\overline{)678}$ **12.** $6\overline{)3372}$

13. $3\overline{)729}$ **14.** $5\overline{)725}$ **15.** $4\overline{)1028}$ **16.** $8\overline{)1856}$

17. $6\overline{)1296}$ **18.** $7\overline{)343}$ **19.** $9\overline{)6561}$ **20.** $6\overline{)2796}$

21. $8\overline{)2056}$ **22.** $5\overline{)1025}$ **23.** $6\overline{)7776}$ **24.** $7\overline{)5082}$

25. $3050 \div 10$ **26.** $1387 \div 1$ **27.** $38\,199 \div 7$ **28.** $14\,032 \div 8$

29. $31\,386 \div 6$ **30.** $3490 \div 5$ **31.** $28\,926 \div 9$ **32.** $15\,638 \div 7$

Remainders

- Suppose you need to share 267 cakes between 5 people.

  Work out $267 \div 5$:

  $$\begin{array}{r} 5\,3 \text{ remainder } 2 \\ 5\overline{)2\,6\,^17} \end{array}$$

- Each person gets 53 cakes and there are 2 left over.

  Sometimes it is better to write the remainder as a fraction.
  In the calculation above the answer is $53\frac{2}{5}$.
  So each person could get $53\frac{2}{5}$ cakes.

- Work out $432 \div 7$:

  $$\begin{array}{r} 6\,1 \text{ remainder } 5 \\ 7\overline{)4\,3\,^12} \end{array}$$

  The answer is '61 remainder 5' or $61\frac{5}{7}$.

Exercise 9

Write the answer: (a) with a remainder,   (b) as a mixed fraction.

1. $5\overline{)432}$ **2.** $4\overline{)715}$ **3.** $6\overline{)895}$ **4.** $3\overline{)164}$

5. $8\overline{)514}$ **6.** $9\overline{)375}$ **7.** $5\overline{)2642}$ **8.** $2\overline{)7141}$

9. $4079 \div 7$ **10.** $2132 \div 5$ **11.** $4013 \div 8$ **12.** $235 \div 6$

13. $657 \div 10$ **14.** $8327 \div 10$ **15.** $85\,714 \div 6$ **16.** $4826 \div 9$

17. $2007 \div 7$ **18.** $9998 \div 9$ **19.** $6732 \div 11$ **20.** $84\,563 \div 7$

Think about the remainder

- How many teams of 5 can you make from 113 people?

  Work out $113 \div 5$.

  $$\begin{array}{r} 2\,2 \text{ remainder } 3 \\ 5\overline{)1\,1\,^13} \end{array}$$

  Here we round *down*. You can make 22 teams and there will be 3
  people left over.

- An egg box holds 6 eggs. How many boxes do you need for 231 eggs?

  Work out $231 \div 6$.

  $$\begin{array}{r} 3\,8 \text{ remainder } 3 \\ 6\overline{)2\,3\,^51} \end{array}$$

  Here we round *up* because you must use complete boxes. You need 39
  boxes altogether.

Exercise 10

In these questions you will get a remainder. Decide whether it is more sensible to round *up* or to round *down*.

1. Tins of spaghetti are packed 8 to a box. How many boxes are needed for 913 tins?

2. A prize consists of 10 000 one pound coins. The prize is shared between 7 people. How many pound coins will each person receive?

3. There are 23 children in a class. How many teams of 4 can be made?

4. Eggs are packed six in a box. How many boxes do I need for 200 eggs?

5. Tickets cost £6 each and I have £80. How many tickets can I buy?

6. I have 204 plants and one tray takes 8 plants. How many trays do I need?

7. There are 51 children in the dining room and a table seats 6. How many tables are needed to seat all the children?

8. I have 100 cans of drink. One box holds 8 cans. How many boxes can I fill?

9. Five people can travel in one car and there are altogether 93 people to transport. How many cars are needed?

10. There are 332 children in a school. One coach holds 50 children. How many coaches are needed for a whole school trip?

11. I have 300 packets of crisps. One box holds 42 packets. How many boxes can I fill? (You can do this without 'long division'.)

12. How many 9 p stamps can I buy with a £5 note?

13. Find the missing numbers

(a) $\dfrac{7\ 1\ 4\ \text{r}\ \boxed{}}{8)\overline{5\ 7\ 1\ 4}}$ (b) $\dfrac{5\ 6\ \text{r}\ 4}{7)\overline{3\ 9\ \boxed{}}}$ (c) $\dfrac{8\ 1\ 2\ \text{r}\ 7}{9)\overline{7\ 3\ 1\ \boxed{}}}$

Mixed arithmetic

Exercise 11

Work out, without a calculator.

1. $317 + 228$	**2.** $2208 + 329$	**3.** $35 + 214 + 206$	**4.** $4186 + 25\,804$
5. $487 - 177$	**6.** $314 - 206$	**7.** $649 - 68$	**8.** $1024 - 837$
9. 85×10	**10.** 6×1000	**11.** 73×5	**12.** 314×4
13. 206×8	**14.** 1023×7	**15.** $340 \div 4$	**16.** $1944 \div 6$
17. $5295 \div 5$	**18.** $2600 \div 8$	**19.** $365 \div 7$	**20.** $920 \div 10$
21. $289 + 15 + 2009$	**22.** $9704 - 8816$	**23.** $6001 - 5994$	**24.** 54×20
25. $2906 - 1414$	**26.** $4716 \div 9$	**27.** 105×8	**28.** $1504 \div 8$
29. $6 + 1609 + 25$	**30.** $309 + 154 - 78$	**31.** $7 + 295 - 48$	**32.** 47×400

Magic squares

In a magic square the sum of the numbers in each column, row and main diagonal are equal. Here is an example of a magic square. The sum of each column, row and diagonal is 18.

9	5	4
1	6	11
8	7	3

Exercise 12

Copy and complete the following magic squares

1.

4	3	
	5	
		6

2.

		3
	6	
9		4

3.

	10	8
	7	
	4	

4.

		11
5	12	7

5.

6		2
	5	
8		

6.

6	7	
13	8	
	9	

7.

	6	10	15
16		5	4
	12	8	
		11	

8.

9	14		
		16	7
12	3	15	8
6			

9.

11			10
2	13	16	
		4	
7	12		6

Word problems

Exercise 13

1. There were one hundred and eighty-six crisps in a bag. Forty-nine were eaten. How many crisps were left over?

2. There are eight hundred and one pupils in a school. If there are three hundred and eighty-three boys, how many girls are in the school?

3. Four dinosaurs each laid the same number of eggs. Altogether there are 104 eggs. How many eggs did each dinosaur lay?

4. Davy, Dozy, Beaky, Mick and Tich are 5 dogs sharing a large tin of 'Muttmeat' which contains 215 delicious chunks. How many chunks does each dog get if it is shared out equally?

5. A solid fuel stove uses 23 kilograms of coal per day. How much does it use in seven days?

6. Suppose you save 5 pence for every day you attend school (190 days). How much money will you have saved?

7. If you count on thirty-seven from sixty-five, what number will you reach?

8. How much do seventy-seven and eighty-nine make altogether?

9. (a) The *product* of 5 and 7 is 35 [$5 \times 7 = 35$].
   (b) Find the product of 6 and 9.

10. I am a 2-digit number. The sum of my digits is 6.
    The product of my digits is 9.
    What number am I?

11. 'Guzzintas' fizzy drink, comes in six-can packets. Ellen has to pack them into a box which holds 216 cans. How many six-packs of 'Guzzintas' will the box hold?

12. A monster bouncy castle can hold a maximum of 1000 children. There are 223 children bouncing around inside. How many fewer than the maximum is this?

Exercise 14

1. Jake has to share his 'Megamunch' crisps with Max and Joe. He has 243 crisps in his packet. How many will Jake, Max and Joe get each if they are shared out equally?

2. What is the product of nine and seven?

3. A bus has 42 seats. How many passengers can carried by a fleet of 6 buses?

4. How many times does 4 go into 64?

5. How many lots of 3 are there in 78?

6. Woody has 240 matchsticks which he must divide into groups of 3. How many groups will he have?

7. What number is thirty-nine more than eighty-seven?

8. What is the total of one hundred and twenty-four and two hundred and seventy-eight?

9. Vicky's book was 900 pages long. She had read 529 pages. How many pages does she still have to read to finish the book?

10. What is the difference between 152 and 480?

11. Geoff grows peas with exactly eleven peas per pod. Geoff picks 77 pods. How many peas will Geoff have to eat?

12. Find the sum of the three numbers: two and a half million, eighty-eight thousand and three and a half thousand.

13. Copy and complete this multiplication square.

×	3	5		
		40		16
			28	
4	12			8
				18

14. One subtraction, using the digits 2, 3, 4, 5, 6, is $\boxed{642-35}$.

Which subtraction using all the digits 2, 3, 4, 5, 6 has the smallest positive answer?

Exercise 15

1. How many 5p coins are worth the same as a hundred 2 p coins?

2. A man has £1000. How much has he left after buying a television for £217 and a video recorder for £399?

3. How many spots are there on 20 ordinary dice?

4. Geoff grows peas with exactly eleven peas per pod. Geoff picks 77 pods. How many peas will Geoff have to eat?

5. Copy and complete this multiplication square.

×	3	7		
		35		45
8			32	
11	33			
				54

6. You are looking for a mystery number.
   Use the clues to find it.

   - the sum of the digits is 10
   - the number reads the same forwards as backwards
   - the number is less than 2000
   - the number has no zeros
   - the number has four digits

7. A man died in 1993 aged 58. In what year was he born?

8. A bird remains airborne for five days. How many hours is that?

9. How many £10 notes are in (a) £1000, (b) £2500, (c) £140 000?

10. How many £100 notes are in (a) £1800, (b) £200 000, (c) £5 million?

11. How many 1p coins are in (a) £10, (b) £500, (c) £2700?

12. Copy and complete these two sentences:

   (a) Multiplying by 100 is the same as multiplying by ☐ and again by ☐.

   (b) Multiplying by 1000 is the same as multiplying by ☐, again by ☐ and again by ☐.

13. Cans of coke at 55p each are put in packs of 10.
Ten packs are put in a box.
One hundred boxes are put in a container.
Find the cost of:
(a) 1 pack
(b) 1 box
(c) 1 container
(d) 100 containers.

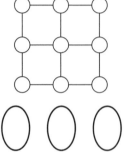

14. Magazines costing £2 each are wrapped in packs of 10.
Ten packs are put in a box.
Ten boxes are put in a van.
Find the cost of:
(a) 1 pack
(b) 1 box
(c) 1 van load
(d) 1000 van loads.

15. Write the numbers 1 to 9 in the circles so that each side of the square adds up to 12. [Hint: Put '7' in the middle.]

16. Here are three eggs. Arrange the numbers 1, 2, 3, ... 9 so that the numbers in each egg add up to 15. Put three numbers in each egg.
Try to find different ways of doing it.

17. Choose 3 digits from 2, 3, 5, 7.

☐☐ + ☐ = 32

Put them in the boxes to make a true statement.

18. If you have 20 video tapes each of 360 minutes duration, how many minutes of taping can you do?

19.* Mike knows that $221 \times 31 = 6851$. Explain how he can use this information to work out 222×31.

20.* Given that $357 \times 101 = 36\,057$, work out 358×101 without multiplying.

Divisibility tests: an investigation

Whole numbers are divisible by:

2 if the number is even
3 if the sum of the digits is divisible by 3
4 if the last *two* digits are divisible by 4
5 if the last digit is 0 or 5
6 if the number is even and also divisible by 3
8 if half of it is divisible by 4
9 if the sum of the digits is divisible by 9
10 if _____ (fill in the space)

A   Copy and complete the table below, using $\sqrt{}$'s and ×'s.

Number	Divisible by						
	2	3	4	5	6	8	9
363	×	$\sqrt{}$					
224							
459							
155							
168							
865							
360							
2601							

B   You will notice that there is no test above for divisibility by 7.
Investigate the following test for four-, five- or six-digit numbers:

Test 18 228

Find the difference between the last 3 digits and the digits at the
front. $228 - 18 = 210$

If this difference is divisible by 7, then the original number is
divisible by 7.

Try the test on these numbers:

37 177, 8498, 431 781, 42 329, 39 579, 910 987.

Now choose some numbers of your own.

C   *Investigate* to find out whether or not a similar test works for
divisibility by 11.

Crossnumber Puzzle

Copy the grid below. Fill in the grid using the clues.

1		2		3	4				5
		6	7						
8	9		10	11			12	13	
							14		
15			16		17	18			
		19			20				21
22	23						24		
			25	26		27			
28		29		30					
		31					32		

Clues across

1. $536 + 219$
3. $2511 - 699$
6. 5×15
8. $637 \div 7$
10. $591 \div 3$
12. 64×8
14. $11 \times 11 \times 4$
15. $101 - 39 + 7$
16. $2000 - 238$
19. 3×14
20. $180 - 135$
22. 809×7
24. $96 + 79$
25. $182 - 139$
27. $3 \times 3 \times 3$
28. $1000 - 599$
30. $4657 + 2732$
31. $15 \times 5 \times 3$
32. 2×30

Clues down

1. $9 \times 9 \times 9$
2. 3×19
4. $1001 - 114$
5. 8×128
7. $100 - 49$
9. 13×13
11. $1000 - 83$
12. 3×18
13. 4×45
15. 5×127
16. $9999 - 8765$
17. 8×80
18. $1000 \div 40$
19. $19 + 17 + 10$
21. $3 \times 50 \times 10$
23. $6100 \div 10$
24. $2000 - 204$
26. $750 - 375$
27. $112 \div 4$
28. 7×7
29. $132 \div 11$

Number messages

Instructions:-

1. Start in the box marked X.
2. Work out the answer to the question at the bottom of the box.
3. Find the box which has the answer in the top right hand corner.
4. Write down the letter in this box. Now work out the answer to the question in that box.
5. Look for the answer as in (3.) Don't forget to record the letter!
6. Continue this process until you arrive back at box X.
7. Read the message.

1.

100 X 8 + 17	61 A 77 + 12	40 U 21 + 35	62 D 27 + 33	71 F 37 + 22
25 O 63 + 8	4 G 49 + 51	70 N 2 + 2	89 N 45 + 17	23 S 14 + 17
91 N 38 + 25	60 R 12 + 19	88 P 16 + 75	22 O 16 + 24	56 R 17 + 8
27 H 27 + 24	52 I 21 + 49	31 U 82 + 9	99 B 48 + 33	85 J 65 + 33
20 Y 13 + 9	3 W 12 + 80	59 F 28 + 33	63 N 37 + 15	17 A 27 + 11

2.

100 X 27 − 19	48 B 25 − 16	26 W 19 − 8	29 A 51 − 17	22 O 81 − 40
16 A 47 − 29	31 R 50 − 30	17 T 65 − 43	43 S 80 − 17	5 U 27 − 11
39 N 42 − 13	46 O 13 − 8	1 A 101 − 1	28 E 98 − 81	15 H 60 − 19
41 P 75 − 27	40 L 71 − 70	70 G 43 − 24	38 M 16 − 7	77 N 71 − 42
99 Q 43 − 29	9 A 94 − 17	18 R 41 − 13	34 N 2 − 1	8 Y 66 − 20

3.

100 X 3 × 5	41 B 3 × 2	24 O 2 × 9	42 A 7 × 8	27 C 7 × 7
81 C 6 × 7	32 A 2 × 8	51 S 7 × 4	83 T 6 × 8	21 K 7 × 9
20 E 3 × 10	14 R 3 × 8	56 L 3 × 9	7 E 2 × 7	45 O 1 × 1
15 L 6 × 4	49 U 10 × 5	18 O 3 × 7	16 T 5 × 9	1 R 10 × 10
64 O 9 × 9	72 P 10 × 9	90 H 9 × 8	50 L 4 × 8	63 N 8 × 8

4.

100 X 20 ÷ 5	20 E 9 ÷ 3	5 T 49 ÷ 7	21 H 8 ÷ 4	14 A 39 ÷ 3
12 A 99 ÷ 9	16 M 21 ÷ 3	3 H 15 ÷ 15	18 C 51 ÷ 17	11 B 20 ÷ 10
9 G 3 ÷ 1	13 S 60 ÷ 5	15 T 30 ÷ 6	8 R 12 ÷ 2	7 O 70 ÷ 7
10 N 100 ÷ 1	4 B 24 ÷ 3	19 P 81 ÷ 3	20 E 57 ÷ 3	21 D 30 ÷ 5
1 T 28 ÷ 2	25 Y 100 ÷ 50	17 S 99 ÷ 3	2 U 30 ÷ 2	6 I 90 ÷ 10

5.

100 X 12 × 7	19 I 9 × 9	96 E 18 ÷ 3	6 P 12 × 8	81 S 7 × 8
95 S 54 + 7	144 D 10 × 10	121 F 84 ÷ 7	61 R 7 × 5	116 T 43 − 17
84 O 20 ÷ 4	91 R 71 − 49	29 Y 0 × 7	0 C 32 − 7	22 L 12 × 12
12 T 38 + 47	35 A 2 ÷ 1	26 O 11 × 11	9 O 49 + 42	8 H 16 ÷ 4
56 W 72 ÷ 8	37 U 22 + 7	5 U 67 + 49	10 I 8 × 5	85 H 58 − 39

Inverse operations: find the missing digits

The word inverse means 'opposite'.

- The inverse of adding is subtracting $\quad 7 + 11 = 18, \quad 7 = 18 - 11$
- The inverse of subtracting is adding $\quad 20 - 8 = 12, \quad 20 = 12 + 8$
- The inverse of multiplying is dividing $\quad 8 \times 4 = 32, \quad 8 = 32 \div 4$
- The inverse of dividing is multiplying $\quad 30 \div 5 = 6, \quad 30 = 6 \times 5$

Find the missing digits.

(a) $\boxed{}2 \div 4 = 23$

Work out 23×4 because multiplying is the inverse of dividing.
Since $23 \times 4 = 92$, the missing digit is 9.

(b) $3\,\boxed{}\,7 \times 8 = 2616$

Work out $2616 \div 8$ because dividing is the inverse of multiplying.
Since $2616 \div 8 = 327$, the missing digit is 2.

(c)
```
   1 □ 6
 + 4 4 □
 ─────────
 □ 2 9
```

Start from the right. $\quad 6 + 3 = 9$
Middle column. $\quad 8 + 4 = 12$
Check
```
      1 8 6
    + 4 4 3
    ───────
      6 2 9
         1
```

Exercise 16

Find the missing digits.

1. (a)
```
   3 1 4
 + □ 6 3
 ───────
 7 □ □
```

(b)
```
   3 5 □
 + □ 2 4
 ───────
 9 □ 8
```

(c)
```
   □ 5 8
 + 1 4 □
 ───────
 5 □ 2
```

2. (a)
```
   5 3 6
 + 2 □ 4
 ───────
 □ 5 □
```

(b)
```
   2 □ 6
 + 3 5 7
 ───────
 □ 0 3
```

(c)
```
   6 3 4
 + □ 8 □
 ───────
 9 □ 8
```

3. (a)
```
     3 □
 ×     5
 ───────
 1 8 5
```

(b)
```
     4 □
 ×     9
 ───────
 4 2 3
```

(c)
```
   □ □ 4
 ×     8
 ───────
 2 9 9 2
```

4. (a) $\boxed{} \div 7 = 33$ (b) $\boxed{} \times 11 = 143$

(c) $12 \times \boxed{} = 108$ (d) $\boxed{} \div 6 = 153$

5. (a)
$$
\begin{array}{r}
8\ \boxed{}\ 6 \\
-\ 3\ \ 2\ \boxed{} \\
\hline
\boxed{}\ \ 3\ \ 2
\end{array}
$$
(b)
$$
\begin{array}{r}
8\ \boxed{}\ 2 \\
-\ \boxed{}\ 1\ \boxed{} \\
\hline
4\ \ 1\ \ 7
\end{array}
$$
(c)
$$
\begin{array}{r}
\boxed{}\ 4\ \boxed{} \\
-\ 2\ \boxed{}\ 8 \\
\hline
3\ \ 5\ \ 7
\end{array}
$$

6. (a) $\boxed{} \times 8 = 440$ (b) $\boxed{} \times 11 = 231$

(c) $400 \div \boxed{} = 50$ (d) $\boxed{} \div 6 = 163$

7. (a) $\boxed{} + 48 = 127$ (b) $\boxed{} - 49 = 463$

(c)
$$
\begin{array}{r}
\boxed{}\ 5\ \ 3 \\
-\ 4\ \boxed{}\ 7 \\
\hline
1\ \ 6\ \boxed{}
\end{array}
$$
(d)
$$
\begin{array}{r}
8\ \ 7\ \ 5 \\
-\ 5\ \ 7\ \boxed{} \\
\hline
\boxed{}\ \boxed{}\ 6
\end{array}
$$

8. There is more than one correct answer for each of these questions. Ask a friend to check your solution.

(a) $\boxed{4}\,\boxed{5} + \boxed{}\,\boxed{} - \boxed{}\,\boxed{} = 45$

(b) $\boxed{7}\,\boxed{2} - \boxed{}\,\boxed{} + \boxed{}\,\boxed{} = 71$

(c) $\boxed{2}\,\boxed{2} \times \boxed{} \div \boxed{} = 11$

(d) $\boxed{6}\,\boxed{0} \times \boxed{}\,\boxed{} \div \boxed{} = 600$

9. Each of these calculations has the same number missing from all three boxes. Find the missing number in each calculation.

(a) $\boxed{} \times \boxed{} - \boxed{} = 12$

(b) $\boxed{} \div \boxed{} + \boxed{} = 9$

(c) $\boxed{} \times \boxed{} + \boxed{} = 72$

10. In the circle write $+$, $-$, $\times$ or $\div$ to make the calculation correct.

(a) $9 \times 5 \bigcirc 3 = 48$ (b) $8 \times 5 \bigcirc 2 = 20$

(c) $8 \bigcirc 9 - 5 = 67$ (d) $12 \bigcirc 2 + 4 = 10$

(e) $60 \div 3 \bigcirc 5 = 15$

11. Write the following with the correct signs.

(a) $5 \times 4 \times 3 \bigcirc 3 = 63$

(b) $5 + 4 \bigcirc 3 \bigcirc 2 = 4$

(c) $5 \times 2 \times 3 \bigcirc 1 = 31$

1.4 Three dimensional objects

Three dimensional objects have three dimensions ... length, width and depth.
Three dimensional is abbreviated to '3D'.
3D objects are often referred to as 'solids' or 'solid objects'.

Special Names are given to certain 3D solid objects ...

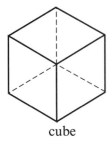

cube

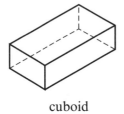

cuboid

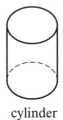

cylinder

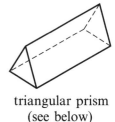

triangular prism
(see below)

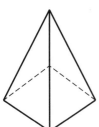

square based
pyramid

cone

sphere

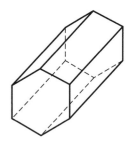

hexagonal prism
(see below)

- A *prism* has the same cross section throughout its length. Here is a triangular prism.

  If you cut through the prism parallel to its end, (the face marked A in the diagram) you produce a shape exactly the same as A (marked A').

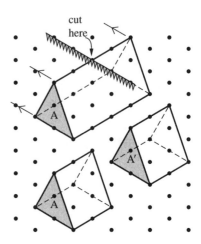

Exercise 1

Below are drawn ten 3D objects labelled A to J.

1. Write down the letters of all objects that are prisms and write next to the letter the name of the object.

2. Write down the letters of all the objects that are non-prisms and write next to the letter the name of the object.

3. For the 10 objects given, sort the objects into two groups (other than prisms and non-prisms). Write down your two groups and how you chose your groups.

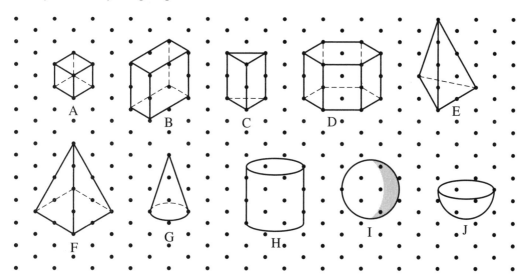

Faces, edges and vertices

Many three-dimensional shapes have *faces*, *edges* and *vertices* (plural of *vertex*). The diagram opposite shows a cuboid.

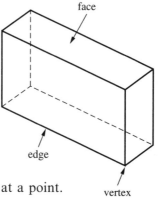

The *faces* of the cuboid are the flat surfaces on the shape.
There are 6 faces on a cuboid.
The *edges* of the cuboid are the lines that make up the shape.
There are 12 edges on a cuboid.
The vertices of the cuboid are where the edges meet at a point.
There are 8 vertices on a cuboid.

Visualising 3-D shapes

Exercise 2

1. For objects B and C in the last exercise state the number of faces, edges and vertices.

2. Imagine a large cube which is cut in half along the dotted lines. Describe the two new solids formed.
   How many faces, edges and vertices does each solid have?

3. 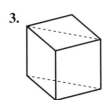 Suppose the same large cube is now cut in half along a different dotted line. Describe the two new solids formed.
   How many faces, edges and vertices does each solid have?

4. Suppose you cut off one corner from a cube. How many faces, edges and vertices has the remaining shape? How about the piece cut off?

5. These diagrams show different solids when viewed from directly above. Describe what each solid could be. [There may be more than one correct response but you only have to give one.]

6. Describe two different ways in which you could cut a cylinder into two identical pieces. Describe and/or sketch the solids you would obtain in each case.

7. For objects A to F in Exercise 1, state the number of faces, edges and vertices. Make a table with columns: shape; faces; edges; vertices.

8. Try to find a connection between the number of faces, edges and vertices which applies to all the objects A to F.

9. Draw 3 pictures of a cube and label them A, B, C.
On A colour in a pair of edges which are parallel.
On B colour in a pair of edges which are perpendicular.
On C colour in a pair of edges which are neither parallel nor
intersect each other.

10. Sit back to back with a partner. Look at one of the models
below but don't tell your partner which one. Tell your partner
how to make the model. Now swap over. With practice you
can design harder models of your own.

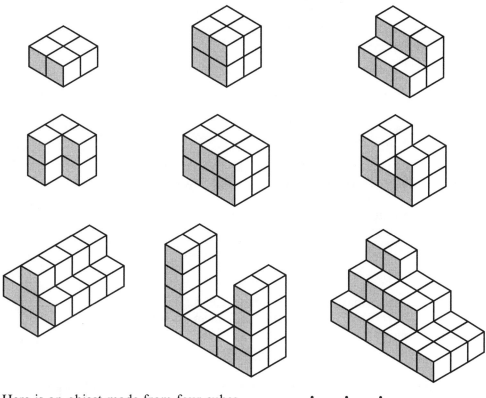

11. Here is an object made from four cubes.
   (a) Copy the drawing on isometric paper.
       (Make sure you have the paper the
       right way round.)

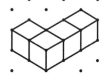

   (b) Make as many *different* objects as you can using four cubes.
       Draw each object on isometric paper.

Nets for making shapes

- If the cube shown was made of cardboard, and you cut along some of the edges and laid it out flat, you would have a *net* of the cube.

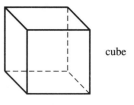

cube

  There is more than one net of a cube as you will see in the exercise below.

- To make a cube from card you need to produce the net shown below complete with the added 'tabs' for glueing purposes.

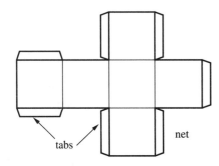

tabs

net

- In this section you will make several interesting 3D objects. You will need a pencil, ruler, scissors and either glue (Pritt Stick) or Sellotape.

  Score all lines before cutting out the net. This makes assembly of the object easier. Don't forget the tabs!

Exercise 3

1. Here are several nets which may or may not make cubes. Draw the nets on squared paper, cut them out and fold them to see which ones do make cubes.

(a)
A	B	C	
	D	E	F

(b)

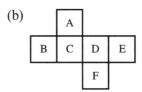

(c)
A		
B	C	
	D	E	F

(d)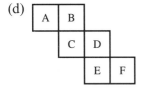

(e)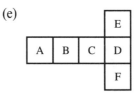

2. For the nets, which *did* make cubes in Question 1, state which of the faces B, C, D, E or F was opposite face A on the cube.

3. Each diagram below shows *part* of the net of a cube. Each net needs one more square to complete the net.

(a)
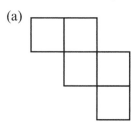

(b)
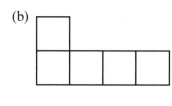

Cut out each of the shapes given and then draw the four possible nets which would make a cube with each one.

4. Draw a net for each of the following:
(a) a closed cuboid measuring $5\,cm \times 3\,cm \times 2\,cm$
(b) a square-based pyramid.

5. Some interesting objects can be made using triangle dotty paper. The basic shape for the nets is an equilateral triangle. With the paper as shown the triangles are easy to draw.

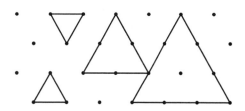

Make the sides of the triangles 3 cm long so that the objects are easy to make. Here is the net of a tetrahedron. Draw it and then cut it out.

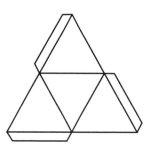

6. Here are two more.
(a) Octahedron (octa: eight; hedron: faces)

(b) Icosahedron (an object with 20 faces)

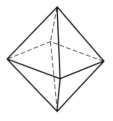

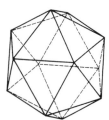

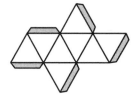

1.5 Decimals 1

- Decimals are used with money and with
  measurements of lengths, weights, times.
  The number 3.745 is 'three point seven four five', *not* 'three point
  seven hundren and forty-five'.
  £1.67 is spoken as 'one pound sixty-seven'.
  £2.05 is spoken as 'two pounds and five pence'.

- The diagram below shows numbers we would see if we could
  'zoom in' on an imaginary ruler.

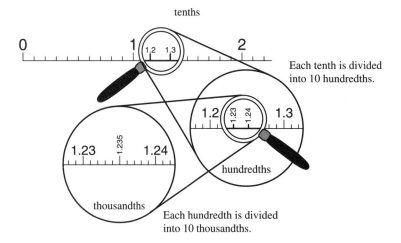

The numbers between 1·2 and 1·3 go up by 0·01 at a time:
   1·21, 1·22, 1·23, 1·24 ...
The numbers between 1·23 and 1·24 go up by 0·001 at a time:
   1·231, 1·232, 1·233, 1·234, 1·235 ...

- Here are some decimal numbers.

Number	Hundreds H	Tens T	Units U	•	Tenths $\frac{1}{10}$	Hundredths $\frac{1}{100}$	Thousandths $\frac{1}{1000}$
538·1	5	3	8	•	1		
42·63		4	2	•	6	3	
0·04			0	•	0	4	
7·125			7	•	1	2	5

Ordering decimals

Consider these three decimals ...

0·09, 0·101, 0·1.

Which is the correct order from lowest to highest?

- When ordering decimals it is always helpful to write them with the same number of figures after the decimal point.

0·09   ⟶ 0·090   Empty spaces can be
0·101 ⟶ 0·101   filled with zeros.
0·1   ⟶ 0·100

Now we can clearly see the correct order of these decimals from lowest to highest ... 0·090, 0·1, 0·101.

Exercise 1

In Questions **1** to **16** answer True (T) or False (F).

1. 0·7 is less than 0·71

2. 0·61 is more than 0·16.

3. 0·08 is more than 0·008

4. 0·5 is equal to 0·500

5. 0·613 is less than 0·631

6. 7·0 is equal to 0·7.

7. 6·2 is less than 6·02

8. 0·09 is more than 0·1.

9. 2·42 is equal to 2·420

10. 0·63 is less than 0·36

11. 0·01 is more than 0·001

12. 0·78 is less than 0·793

13. 8 is equal to 8·00

14. 0·4 is more than 0·35

15. 0·07 is less than 0·1

16. 0·1 is equal to $\frac{1}{10}$.

17. Here is a pattern of numbers based on 3. ⟶

Write a similar pattern based on 7 and extend it from 70 000 000 down to 0·0007. Write the numbers in figures and in words

three thousand	3000
three hundred	300
thirty	30
three	3
nought point three	0·3
nought point nought three	0·03

18. What does the digit 7 in 3·271 represent?
And the 2? And the 1?

19. What does the digit 3 in 5·386 represent?
And the 6? And the 8?

20. Write the decimal number equivalent to:
(a) three tenths   (b) seven hundredths
(c) eleven hundredths   (d) four thousandths
(e) sixteen hundredths   (f) sixteen thousandths.

21. Write down the single operation needed [+,−] when you change:
For example, to change 0·24 to 0·28, you *add 0·04*.
(a) 5·32 to 5·72   (b) 11·042 to 11·047
(c) 0·592 to 0·392   (d) 0·683 to 0·623.

Exercise 2

In Questions **1** to **20**, arrange the numbers in order of size, smallest first.

1. 0·21, 0·31, 0·12.   **2.** 0·04, 0·4, 0·35.

3. 0·67, 0·672, 0·7.   **4.** 0·05, 0·045, 0·07.

5. 0·1, 0·09, 0·089.   **6.** 0·75, 0·57, 0·705.

7. 0·41, 0·041, 0·14.   **8.** 0·809, 0·81, 0·8.

9. 0·006, 0·6, 0·059.   **10.** 0·15, 0·143, 0·2.

11. 0·04, 0·14, 0·2, 0·53.   **12.** 1·2, 0·12, 0·21, 1·12.

13. 2·3, 2·03, 0·75, 0·08.   **14.** 0·62, 0·26, 0·602, 0·3.

15. 0·5, 1·3, 1·03, 1·003.   **16.** 0·79, 0·792, 0·709, 0·97.

17. 5·2 m, 52 cm, 152 cm   **18.** £1·20, 75p, £0·8

19. 200 m, 0·55 km, $\frac{1}{2}$ km   **20.** 1·2 mm, 0·1 cm, 2 mm

21. Here are numbers with letters
(a) Put the numbers in order, smallest first. Write down just the letters.
(b) Finish the sentence using letters and numbers of your own. The numbers must increase from left to right.

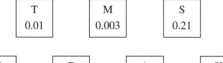

T	M	S
0.01	0.003	0.21

C	E	A	H
0.06	0.015	0.03	0.061

R	Y	E
0.2	0.007	0.08

I
0.201

22. Increase the following numbers by $\frac{1}{10}$th:
(a) 3·27   (b) 14·8   (c) 0·841

23. Increase the following numbers by $\frac{1}{100}$th:
(a) 11·25   (b) 1·294   (c) 0·382

24. Increase the following numbers by $\frac{1}{1000}$th:
(a) 3·142   (b) 2·718   (c) 1·414

25. Write the following amounts in pounds:
(a) 11 pence.   (b) 2 pence.   (c) 5 pence.
(d) 10 pence.   (e) 20 pence.   (f) 50 pence.

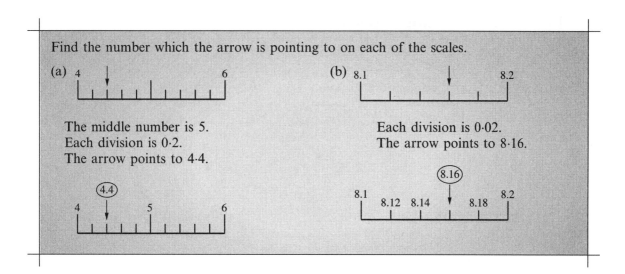

Find the number which the arrow is pointing to on each of the scales.

(a) 4   6   (b) 8.1   8.2

The middle number is 5.
Each division is 0·2.
The arrow points to 4·4.

Each division is 0·02.
The arrow points to 8·16.

Exercise 3

Work out the value indicated by the arrow.

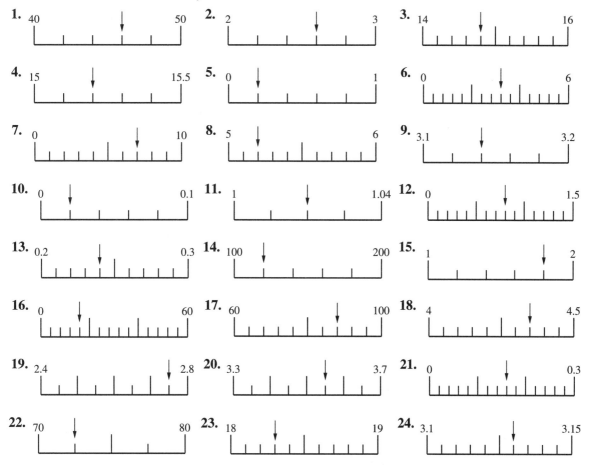

Adding and subtracting decimals

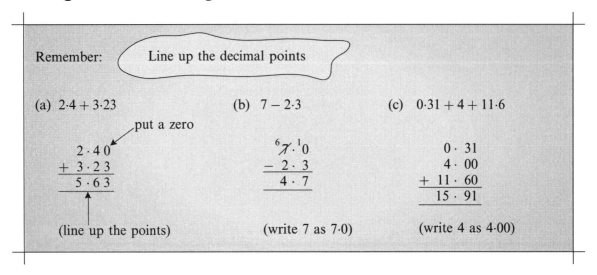

Remember: Line up the decimal points

(a) 2·4 + 3·23   (b) 7 − 2·3   (c) 0·31 + 4 + 11·6

put a zero

$$
\begin{array}{r}
2\cdot40\\
+\ 3\cdot23\\
\hline
5\cdot63
\end{array}
$$

$$
\begin{array}{r}
{}^{6}\not{7}\cdot{}^{1}0\\
-\ 2\cdot3\\
\hline
4\cdot7
\end{array}
$$

$$
\begin{array}{r}
0\cdot31\\
4\cdot00\\
+\ 11\cdot60\\
\hline
15\cdot91
\end{array}
$$

(line up the points)   (write 7 as 7·0)   (write 4 as 4·00)

Exercise 4

1. 5 + 0·26   **2.** 2·9 + 4·37   **3.** 8·62 + 7·99

4. 0·078 + 2·05   **5.** 10·04 + 3·005   **6.** 13·47 + 27·084

7. 1·97 + 19·7   **8.** 4·56 + 7·890   **9.** 456·7 + 8·901

10. 16·374 + 0·947 + 27   **11.** 3·142 + 2·71 + 8   **12.** 0·03 + 11 + 8·74

13. 29·6 − 14   **14.** 59·2 − 34·8   **15.** 81·8 − 29·9

16. 8 − 2·7   **17.** 6·7 − 4·29   **18.** 47·2 − 27·42

19. 94·63 − 5·9   **20.** 2·97 − 1·414   **21.** 25·52 − 1·436

22. 3·142 − 1·414   **23.** 2·718 − 1·732   **24.** 12 − 3·74

25. Find the missing digits

(a)
$$
\begin{array}{r}
\boxed{}\cdot5\,\boxed{}\\
-\ 4\cdot\boxed{}\,3\\
\hline
3\cdot7\ 3
\end{array}
$$

(b)
$$
\begin{array}{r}
4\cdot\boxed{}\,7\\
+\ \boxed{}\cdot9\,\boxed{}\\
\hline
9\cdot0\ 3
\end{array}
$$

(c)
$$
\begin{array}{r}
3\cdot1\ 7\ \boxed{}\\
-\ \boxed{}\cdot4\,\boxed{}\,8\\
\hline
0\cdot\boxed{}\,4\ 8
\end{array}
$$

26. David has £3·20 and wants to buy articles costing £1·10, 66 p, £1·99 and 45 p. How much more money does he need?

27. Which six different coins make £1·78?

28. Jane went to a shop and bought a book for £2·95 and a compact disc for £10·95. She paid with a £50 note. What change did she receive?

29. Geri bought her local team's replica football kit, shirt costing £10·75, shorts costing £3·99 and socks for £2·59. How much did she spend?

30. Winston spent £5·15 in the supermarket and £10·99 in the music shop. How much change did he get from £20?

31. What must be added to £5·63 to make £18?

32. Which five different coins make a total of £1·37?

33. David has £3·20 and wants to buy articles costing £1·10, 66 p, £1·99 and 45 p. How much more money does he need?

34. Which six different coins make £1·78?

35. Jane went to a shop and bought a book for £2·95 and a compact disc for £10·95. She paid with a £50 note. What change did she receive?

Top Banana!   The Banana man of Tesco's.

The following article is a true story. Read the article (which deliberately contains blanks) and then answer the questions below.

He is called the Banana man of Tesco. In a special offer Phil Calcott bought almost half a ton of bananas. He then gave it all away and still made a profit on the deal. In a way Mr Calcott made his local store pay him to take away its own fruit.

The offer said that if you bought a 3 lb bunch of bananas at £1.17, you would gain 25 Tesco 'Club Card' points. These points could be used to buy goods worth £1.25.

Mr Calcott asked the store to load up his Peugeot 205 with bananas.

'I took a car load at a time because even with the back seat down and the boot full I could only fit in 460 lbs of bananas,' he said.

He returned for another load the next day and altogether spent £ ___ buying 942 lbs of the fruit. This earned him almost ___ ,000 Tesco 'Club Card' points.

1. How much would it cost to buy ten 3 lb bunches of bananas?

2. How many Tesco Club Card points would you get?

3. How much would the points be worth?

4. How much profit would you make on this deal?

5. Do you like bananas?

6. Write down the paragraph, which starts 'He returned ...' and fill in the missing numbers.

1.6 Rounding numbers

Here are cuttings from two newspapers:

A. '1074 bus shelters were vandalised last
   year at a total cost of £517,638.'

B. '1000 bus shelters were vandalised at a
   cost of over £500,000.'

In B the figures have been *rounded off* because the reporter thinks
that his readers will not be interested in the exact numbers in the
report.

Rules for rounding

- Rounding to the nearest whole number.

  If the first digit after the decimal point
  is *5 or more* round *up*.
  Otherwise round down.

  $$57\cdot3 \to 57$$
  $$89\cdot8 \to 90$$
  $$5\cdot5 \to 6$$

- Rounding to the nearest 100.

  If the digit in the tens column
  is 5 or more round up.
  Otherwise round down.

  $$593 \to 600$$
  $$247 \to 200$$
  $$2643 \to 2600$$

- Rounding to the nearest 10.

  If the digit in the units column
  is 5 or more round up.
  Otherwise round down.

  $$27 \to 30$$
  $$42 \to 40$$
  $$265 \to 270$$

- Rounding to the nearest 1000.

  If the digit in the hundreds column
  is 5 or more round up.
  Otherwise round down.

  $$1394 \to 1000$$
  $$502 \to 1000$$
  $$11\,764 \to 12\,000$$

Exercise 1

1. Round off these numbers to the nearest 10.
   (a) 73   (b) 58   (c) 24   (d) 99
   (e) 56   (f) 127   (g) 242   (h) 18
   (i) 29   (j) 589   (k) 37   (l) 51

2. Round off these numbers to the nearest 100.
   (a) 584   (b) 293   (c) 607   (d) 914
   (e) 285   (f) 655   (g) 222   (h) 1486

3. Round off these numbers to the nearest 1000.
   (a) 4555   (b) 757   (c) 850   (d) 2251
   (e) 614   (f) 2874   (g) 25712   (h) 13568

4. Work out these answers on a calculator and then round off the
    answer to the *nearest whole number*.
    (a) 235 ÷ 17   (b) 4714 ÷ 58   (c) 2375 ÷ 11   (d) 999 ÷ 17
    (e) 5·62 × 7·04   (f) 19·3 × 1·19   (g) 53·2 × 2·3   (h) 12·6 × 0·93
    (i) 119·6 ÷ 5·1   (j) 109 ÷ 0·7   (k) 63·4 ÷ 11   (l) 1·92 ÷ 0·09

5. How long is this rod to:
    (a) the nearest cm   (b) the nearest 10 cm   (c) the nearest metre

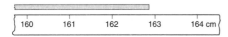

Decimal places

• Using a calculator to work out 25 ÷ 9, the
   answer is 2·777777.
   On a number line we can see that the answer
   is nearer to 2·8 than to 2·7. We will *round off*
   the answer to 2·8 correct to 1 *decimal place*.

• Using a calculator to work out 11% of 21·23,
   the answer is 2·3353.
   On a number line we can see that the answer
   is nearer to 2·3 than to 2·4. So the answer is
   2·3, correct to 1 decimal place (1 d.p. for
   short).

• Suppose the calculator shows 1·75. This number is exactly half
   way between 1·7 and 1·8. Do we round up or not?
   The rule for rounding off to 1 decimal place is:

> If the figure in the 2nd decimal place is 5 or more, round
> up. Otherwise do not.

Examples: 3·7538 = 3·8 to 1 d.p.
                  ↑
              14·287 = 14·3 to 1 d.p.
                  ↑
              17·9582 = 18·0 to 1 d.p. (We need the zero!)
                  ↑

• 7·96 rounded to the nearest whole number is 8

   7·96 rounded to 1 decimal place is 8·0 [The zero is needed.]

Exercise 2

1. Round these numbers to 1 decimal place.
   (a) 2·41   (b) 8·94   (c) 4·65   (d) 12·47

2. Round these numbers to 1 decimal place.
   (a) 1·924   (b) 4·065   (c) 9·997   (d) 65·374

3. Write the following numbers correct to 1 decimal place.
   (a) 18·7864   (b) 3·55   (c) 17·0946   (d) 0·7624
   (e) 5·421   (f) 11·27   (g) 10·252   (h) 7·084

4. Write the following numbers correct to the nearest whole number.
   (a) 3·75821   (b) 11·64412   (c) 0·38214   (d) 138·2972
   (e) 11·444   (f) 7·058   (g) 6·5781   (h) 5·3092

5. Round each number:
   (a) to the nearest whole number,
   (b) to one decimal place
       (i) 8·41   (ii) 0·782   (iii) 7·92   (iv) 4·95

6. Work out the following on a calculator and write the answer correct to 1 decimal place.
   (a) 11 ÷ 7   (b) 213 ÷ 11   (c) 1·4 ÷ 6   (d) 29 ÷ 13
   (e) 1·3 × 0·95   (f) 1·23 × 3·71   (g) 97 ÷ 1·3   (h) 0·95 × 8·3

7. Measure the lines below and give the lengths in cm correct to one decimal place.

   (a) ————————————————————————————

   (b) ——————————

   (c) ————————————————————————————————

   (d) —————————————————————

   (e) ————————————————————————————————————

8. Measure the dimensions of the rectangles below.
   (a) Write down the length and width in cm, correct to one decimal place.
   (b) Work out the area of each rectangle and give the answer in cm^2, correct to one decimal place.

   (i)   (ii)

Calculating with estimates, checking results

- Hazim worked out $38{\cdot}2 \times 10{\cdot}78$ and wrote down $41{\cdot}1796$. He can check his answer by working with estimates.
  Instead of $38{\cdot}2$ use 40, instead of $10{\cdot}78$ use 10.

    So $40 \times 10 = 400$.

  Clearly Hazim's answer is wrong. He put the decimal point in the wrong place.

- Here are three more calculations with estimates.

  (a) $27{\cdot}2 \times 51{\cdot}7$
      $\approx 30 \times 50$
      ≈ 1500

  (b) $78{\cdot}9 \div 1{\cdot}923$
      $\approx 80 \div 2$
      ≈ 40

  (c) 12% of £411·55
      $\approx$ 10% of £400
      $\approx$ £40

Exercise 3

Do not use a calculator. Decide, by estimating, which of the three answers is closest to the exact answer. Write the calculation and the approximate answer for each question (use $\approx$).

	Calculation	A	B	C
1.	$102{\cdot}6 \times 9{\cdot}7$	90	500	1000
2.	$7{\cdot}14 \times 11{\cdot}21$	30	70	300
3.	$1{\cdot}07 \times 59{\cdot}2$	6	60	200
4.	$2{\cdot}21 \times 97{\cdot}8$	200	90	20
5.	$8{\cdot}95 \times 42{\cdot}1$	200	400	4000
6.	$4{\cdot}87 \times 6{\cdot}18$	15	10	30
7.	$789 \times 12{\cdot}3$	8000	4000	800
8.	$978 \times 9{\cdot}83$	1 million	100 000	10 000
9.	$1{\cdot}11 \times 28{\cdot}7$	20	30	60
10.	$9{\cdot}8 \times 82463$	8 million	1 million	800 000
11.	$307{\cdot}4 \div 1{\cdot}97$	50	100	150
12.	$81{\cdot}2 \div 0{\cdot}99$	8	0·8	80
13.	$6121 \div 102{\cdot}4$	60	300	600
14.	$59{\cdot}71 \div 3{\cdot}14$	10	20	180
15.	$1072 \div 987{\cdot}2$	0·2	1	10
16.	$614 - 297{\cdot}4$	300	100	3000
17.	$0{\cdot}104 + 0{\cdot}511$	0·06	0·1	0·6
18.	$8216{\cdot}1 + 1{\cdot}44$	800	4000	8000
19.	51% of £8018·95	£40	£400	£4000
20.	9% of £205·49	£10	£20	£200

21. A new band's first demo tape was sold at £2·95 per copy. Estimate the total cost of 47 copies.

22. David has to pay £208·50 per month for 2 years towards the cost of his car. Estimate the total cost of his payments.

23. Two hundred and six people share the cost of hiring a train. Roughly how much does each person pay if the total cost was £61 990?

In Questions **24** and **25** there are six calculations and six answers. Write down each calculation and insert the correct answer from the list given. Use estimation.

24. (a) $6·9 \times 7·1$ (b) $9·8 \div 5$ (c) $21 \times 10·2$
      (d) $0·13 + 15·2$ (e) $3114 \div 30$ (f) $4·03 \times 1·9$

Answers: 1·96, 15·33, 48·99, 103·8, 7·657, 214·2.

25. (a) $103·2 \div 5$ (b) $7·2 \times 7·3$ (c) $4·1 \times 49$
      (d) $3·57 \div 3$ (e) $36·52 \div 4$ (f) $1·4 \div 10$

Answers: 52·56, 1·19, 9·13, 200·9, 20·64, 0·14.

1.7 Area and perimeter

We use area to describe how much *surface* a shape has.

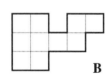

B contains 10 squares.

B has an area of 10 squares.

C has an area of $12\frac{1}{2}$ squares.

D has an area of 12 squares.

Rectangles

A 2 cm by 3 cm rectangle may be split into 6 squares as shown.

The area of each square is one square centimetre ($1 \, \text{cm}^2$), so the area of the rectangle is $6 \, \text{cm}^2$.

This result can be obtained by multiplying the *length* by the *width*.

     Area of rectangle $= (3 \times 2) \, \text{cm}^2$

                    $= 6 \, \text{cm}^2$

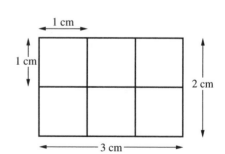

Exercise 1

Find the area of each shape. The lengths are in cm.

1.    8, 5

2.    11, 2

3. 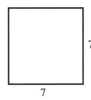   7, 7

4. 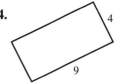   4, 9

5. Measure the length and width of these rectangles and then work out the area of each one.

Length

Find the area of each shape. The lengths are in cm.

6. 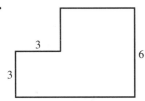   3, 3, 6, 8

7. 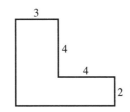   3, 4, 4, 2

8. 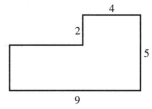   4, 2, 5, 9

9. 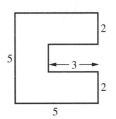   2, 5, 3, 2, 5

10. 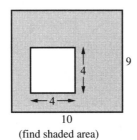   4, 4, 9, 10
(find shaded area)

11.   5, 3, 4, 2, 4, 5
(find shaded area)

12. 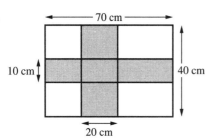 Calculate the area of the shaded cross.

13. A rectangle measuring 20 cm by 11 cm is split into four smaller rectangles. Work out the area of each small rectangle. Check that the total area of the four rectangles is equal to the area of the 20 × 11 rectangle.

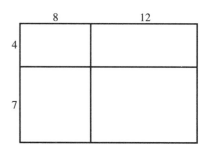

In Questions **14** to **17** the area is written inside the shape. Calculate the length of the side marked x.

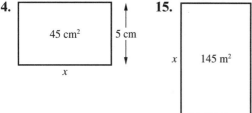

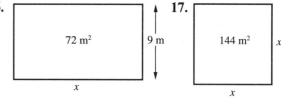

18. A square has an area of 81 cm². How long are the sides of the square?

In Questions **19** to **22** write each sentence and choose the number which is the best estimate.

19. The cover of this book has an area of about [50 cm², 500 cm², 5 m²]

20. The playground has an area of about [5 m², 1000 m², 1 km²]

21. A postage stamp has an area of about [5 mm², 5 cm², 50 cm²]

22. The area of the classroom floor is about [50 m², 500 m², 1000 m²]

Triangles

This triangle has base 6 cm, height 4 cm and a right angle at A.

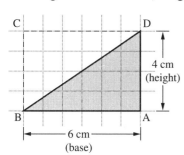

Area of rectangle ABCD $= (6 \times 4)\,\text{cm}^2$
$$= 24\,\text{cm}^2.$$

Area of triangle ABD = area of triangle CDB.

$\therefore$ Area of triangle ABD $= 24 \div 2$
$$= 12\,\text{cm}^2$$

For a right-angled triangle: Area $= \frac{1}{2}(\text{base} \times \text{height})$

Exercise 2

Find the area of each triangle. Lengths are in cm.

1.
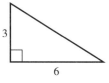

2.
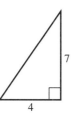

3.
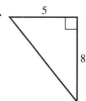

4.
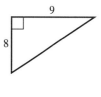

In Questions **5** to **7** find the total area.

5.
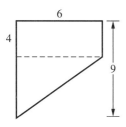

6.
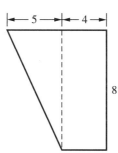

7.
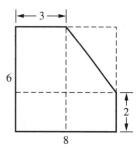

8. Find the shaded area.

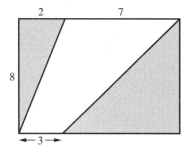

9. Find the shaded area.

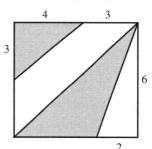

Perimeter

The perimeter of a shape is the distance around its outline.

(a) The perimeter of this rectangle
is $4 + 10 + 4 + 10 = 28$ cm

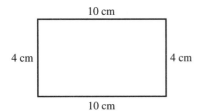

(b) The perimeter of this triangle
is $7 + 5 + 9 = 21$ cm.

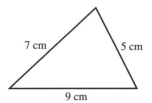

Exercise 3

1. Measure the sides of these shapes and work out the perimeter of
each one.

(a) 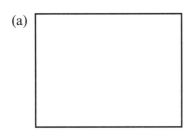   (b)    (c)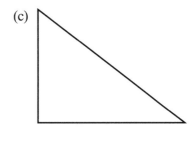

2. Find the perimeter of these pictures.

(a)    (b)    (c)

3. Find the perimeters of these shapes

   (a) rectangle 7·5 cm by 4 cm   (b) square of side 6 cm

   (c) equilateral triangle of side 7 cm   (d) rectangle 3·5 cm by 2·5 cm

   (e) square of side 20 m   (f) regular hexagon of side 5 cm

The shapes in Questions **4** to **11** consist of rectangles joined together. Find the missing lengths and then work out the perimeter of each shape. The lengths are in cm.

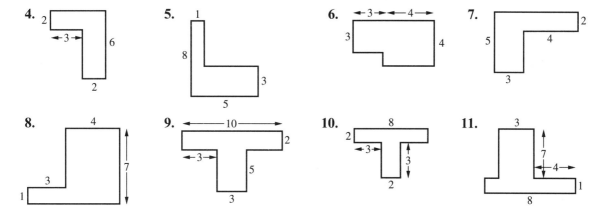

4.

5.

6.

7.

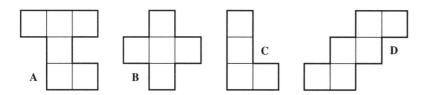

8.

9.

10.

11.

Questions **12** onwards are about perimeter *and* area.

12. Here are four shapes made with centimetre squares.

A   B   C   D

(a) Which shape has an area of $5\,cm^2$?
(b) Which two shapes have the same perimeter?

13. Each of the shapes here has an area of $2\,cm^2$.
(a) On square dotty paper draw three more shapes with area $2\,cm^2$
(b) Draw three shapes with area $3\,cm^2$.
(c) Draw one shape with area $4\,cm^2$ *and* perimeter 10 cm.

14. A picture frame has its length twice its height.
The total length of wood used in the frame is 132 cm.
Work out the length of the frame.

height

length

15. Here are five shapes made from equilateral triangles of side 1 cm.

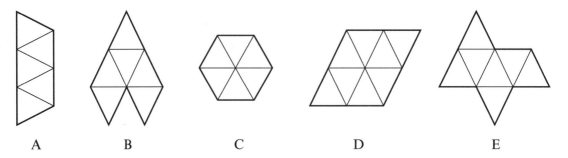

A   B   C   D   E

(a) Which shape has the longest perimeter?
(b) Which shape has the smallest area?
(c) Which shape has the same perimeter as D?

16. The perimeter of a rectangular lawn is 40 m. The shortest side is 7 m. How long is the longest side?

17.* The diagram shows the areas of 3 faces of a rectangular box. What are the measurements of the box?

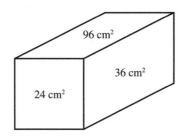

Area and perimeter: an investigation

A ● Draw *four* different rectangles which all have a *perimeter* of 24 cm.

B ● Draw *three* different rectangles which all have an *area* of 24 cm².

C ● Draw at least four rectangles which have a perimeter of 20 cm.
   ● Work out the area of each rectangle.
   ● Which of your rectangles has the largest area?

D ● The perimeter of a new rectangle is 32 cm.
   ● Try to *predict* what the sides will be for the rectangle with the largest possible area.
   ● Now check to see if your prediction was correct.

E* ● Explain why you cannot find a rectangle with perimeter 32 cm which has the *smallest* possible area. [Neither length nor width can be zero.]

Part 2

2.1 Fractions

- Express the shaded part of the diagram as a fraction of the whole.

  3 out of 8 sections are shaded.
  The fraction shaded $= \frac{3}{8}$.

- It is not possible to express the shaded part in this diagram as a fraction of the whole. This is because the shape has not been divided equally.

Exercise 1

In each of the following diagrams, express the shaded part of the diagram as a fraction of the whole where possible.

1.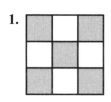
2.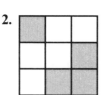
3.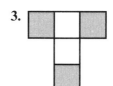
4.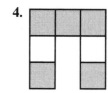

5.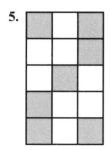
6.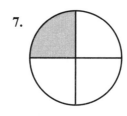
7.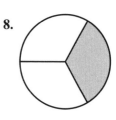
8.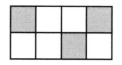

9.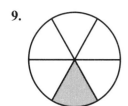
10.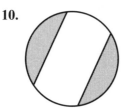
11.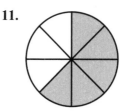
12.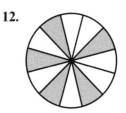

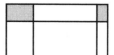

Writing fractions in their simplest form

- A fraction is composed of two numbers:

  The top number is called the   ⟶   Numerator

  The bottom number is called the   ⟶   Denominator.

  The method of changing a fraction into a simpler form is known as '*cancelling down*'.

  The fraction $\frac{15}{20}$ *cancels down* to $\frac{3}{4}$.

  To do this, use the following method ...

  > Find the **highest** possible number that divides exactly into **both** the numerator and denominator

  $$\frac{15 \div 5}{20 \div 5} = \frac{3}{4}$$ The highest possible number that divides exactly into 15 and 20 is 5.

- In the diagram $\frac{4}{12}$ of the shape is shaded. You can also see that $\frac{1}{3}$ of the shape is shaded.

  By cancelling down, $\frac{4}{12} = \frac{1}{3}$ (÷4)

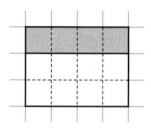

Exercise 2

Copy and complete the table below to cancel down each fraction into its simplest form:

No.	Fraction	Method of cancelling down	Simplest form of fraction
1.	$\frac{9}{12}$	3 goes into 9: ___ times 3 goes into 12: ___ times	――
2.	$\frac{6}{24}$	6 goes into 6: ___ time 6 goes into 24: ___ times	――
3.	$\frac{8}{10}$	2 goes into 8: ___ times 2 goes into 10: ___ times	――

Express each fraction in its simplest form:

4. $\frac{8}{20}$ **5.** $\frac{9}{36}$ **6.** $\frac{8}{12}$ **7.** $\frac{9}{15}$ **8.** $\frac{6}{18}$

9. $\frac{7}{21}$ **10.** $\frac{32}{36}$ **11.** $\frac{24}{30}$ **12.** $\frac{4}{12}$ **13.** $\frac{4}{18}$

14. $\frac{20}{30}$ **15.** $\frac{12}{18}$ **16.** $\frac{14}{42}$ **17.** $\frac{20}{24}$ **18.** $\frac{6}{15}$

19. $\frac{27}{45}$ **20.** $\frac{56}{64}$ **21.** $\frac{18}{30}$ **22.** $\frac{28}{36}$ **23.** $\frac{18}{63}$

24. $\frac{44}{55}$ **25.** $\frac{24}{60}$ **26.** $\frac{54}{81}$ **27.** $\frac{45}{90}$ **28.** $\frac{18}{72}$

29. $\frac{72}{108}$ **30.** $\frac{75}{100}$

Exercise 3

Cancel down or scale up the following fractions as required:

1. $\frac{6}{8} = \frac{\square}{4}$ **2.** $\frac{2}{6} = \frac{\square}{3}$ **3.** $\frac{6}{10} = \frac{\square}{5}$ **4.** $\frac{6}{9} = \frac{\square}{3}$

5. $\frac{9}{12} = \frac{\square}{4}$ **6.** $\frac{12}{15} = \frac{\square}{5}$ **7.** $\frac{15}{20} = \frac{\square}{4}$ **8.** $\frac{25}{30} = \frac{\square}{6}$

9. $\frac{2}{6} = \frac{\square}{3} = \frac{\square}{9}$ **10.** $\frac{3}{4} = \frac{\square}{8} = \frac{\square}{12}$ **11.** $\frac{8}{12} = \frac{\square}{6} = \frac{\square}{3}$ **12.** $\frac{1}{5} = \frac{\square}{10} = \frac{\square}{20}$

13. $\frac{7}{10} = \frac{\square}{30} = \frac{14}{\square}$ **14.** $\frac{1}{4} = \frac{\square}{16} = \frac{8}{\square}$ **15.** $\frac{7}{12} = \frac{\square}{24} = \frac{21}{\square}$ **16.** $\frac{6}{15} = \frac{\square}{5} = \frac{24}{\square}$

17. $\frac{\square}{10} = \frac{3}{5} = \frac{\square}{25}$ **18.** $\frac{\square}{21} = \frac{3}{7} = \frac{15}{\square}$ **19.** $\frac{\square}{3} = \frac{6}{18} = \frac{\square}{15}$ **20.** $\frac{21}{\square} = \frac{\square}{30} = \frac{7}{15}$

Equivalent fraction anagrams

Example: In the table given below, pick out all the letters above the fractions which are equivalent to one half ($\frac{1}{2}$).

C	Q	E	A	Y	P	R	N	H	F	letters
$\frac{5}{10}$	$\frac{3}{4}$	$\frac{2}{4}$	$\frac{21}{42}$	$\frac{1}{3}$	$\frac{3}{5}$	$\frac{6}{12}$	$\frac{3}{6}$	$\frac{4}{7}$	$\frac{5}{10}$	fractions

The letters are C, E, A, R, N, F
because ... $\frac{5}{10}$, $\frac{2}{4}$, $\frac{21}{42}$, $\frac{6}{12}$, $\frac{3}{6}$, $\frac{5}{10}$ are all the same as $\frac{1}{2}$.

Now rearrange the letters to make the name of a country.

C, E, A, R, N, F $\longrightarrow$ FRANCE

Exercise 4

As in the example above, find the fractions in the table which are equivalent to the given fraction. Rearrange the letters to make a word using the clue.

1. ($\frac{1}{3}$, city)

L	P	A	U	R	I	D	N	S	B
$\frac{3}{9}$	$\frac{2}{8}$	$\frac{5}{7}$	$\frac{4}{12}$	$\frac{7}{20}$	$\frac{6}{18}$	$\frac{8}{24}$	$\frac{10}{30}$	$\frac{3}{5}$	$\frac{5}{15}$

2. ($\frac{1}{4}$, fruit)

B	O	P	A	E	I	H	C	R	T
$\frac{2}{7}$	$\frac{4}{16}$	$\frac{11}{44}$	$\frac{2}{8}$	$\frac{3}{9}$	$\frac{10}{40}$	$\frac{6}{25}$	$\frac{5}{20}$	$\frac{12}{48}$	$\frac{3}{12}$

3. ($\frac{3}{4}$, sport)

R	O	F	G	A	U	B	D	Y	J
$\frac{8}{10}$	$\frac{6}{8}$	$\frac{15}{25}$	$\frac{5}{7}$	$\frac{21}{32}$	$\frac{9}{12}$	$\frac{30}{45}$	$\frac{15}{20}$	$\frac{66}{99}$	$\frac{75}{100}$

4. ($\frac{1}{10}$, drink)

R	E	F	E	F	T	O	W	C	A
$\frac{2}{20}$	$\frac{5}{60}$	$\frac{9}{108}$	$\frac{5}{50}$	$\frac{12}{96}$	$\frac{3}{30}$	$\frac{4}{20}$	$\frac{10}{100}$	$\frac{6}{50}$	$\frac{7}{70}$

5. ($\frac{2}{3}$, country)

A	N	E	R	S	B	I	Z	Q	L
$\frac{4}{6}$	$\frac{9}{12}$	$\frac{14}{22}$	$\frac{60}{90}$	$\frac{16}{25}$	$\frac{8}{12}$	$\frac{22}{33}$	$\frac{20}{30}$	$\frac{32}{49}$	$\frac{12}{18}$

6. ($\frac{1}{2}$, animal)

N	C	U	E	A	N	T	Y	R	B
$\frac{5}{10}$	$\frac{3}{18}$	$\frac{7}{14}$	$\frac{6}{9}$	$\frac{1}{3}$	$\frac{17}{34}$	$\frac{5}{12}$	$\frac{25}{50}$	$\frac{5}{15}$	$\frac{9}{18}$

7. Now make up your own question and test it on a friend.

Equivalent fraction pairs: an activity

This is an activity for 2, 3 or 4 players using the equivalent fraction cards.

How to play:

- Shuffle the cards, place them face down in a pattern of 6 rows by 4 columns.

- Decide who will go first.

- Each turn requires a player to turn over a pair of cards.

- If the pair of cards are equivalent such as $\frac{1}{5}$ and $\frac{2}{10}$ the player keeps the pair. If the cards are not equivalent turn the cards face down again.

- Try to remember which cards are where!

- If you find a pair you get another go, the player with the most pairs when no cards are left is the winner.

- Teacher's note. The fraction cards can be photocopied from the answer book. Alternatively many teachers prefer to have the cards made by pupils.

Proper and improper fractions

- A *proper* fraction is one in which the *numerator* (top number) is less than the *denominator* (bottom number).

  The fractions $\frac{1}{2}$, $\frac{2}{3}$, $\frac{3}{4}$ and $\frac{99}{100}$ are all examples of *proper* fractions.

- An *improper* fraction is one in which the *numerator* is larger than the *denominator*. They are sometimes called 'top-heavy' fractions.

  The fractions $\frac{3}{2}$, $\frac{4}{3}$, $\frac{8}{5}$ and $\frac{100}{33}$ are all examples of *improper* fractions.

- A *mixed number* is one which contains both a whole number and a fraction. *Improper* fractions can be changed into *mixed numbers* and vice versa.

(a) $\frac{3}{2} = 1\frac{1}{2}$ Step 1. 2 into 3 goes once, giving the whole number 1.
Step 2. The remainder is 1 which is written as $\frac{1}{2}$.

(b) $\frac{16}{3} = 5\frac{1}{3}$ Step 1. 3 into 16 goes five times, giving the whole number 5.
Step 2. The remainder is 1, which is written $\frac{1}{3}$.

(c) $2\frac{1}{2} = \frac{5}{2}$ Step 1. 2 times 2, gives 4 (4 halves).
Step 2. Add 1 from the numerator to 4 giving 5.
Step 3. Express 5 as a fraction of 2 which is $\frac{5}{2}$.

(d) $3\frac{5}{6} = \frac{23}{6}$ Step 1. 3 times 6 is 18 (18 sixths).
Step 2. There are 5 sixths to add from the numerator giving 23.
Step 3. Express 23 as a fraction of 6 which is $\frac{23}{6}$.

Exercise 5

Change the following improper fractions to mixed numbers or whole numbers where applicable.

1. $\frac{7}{2}$ **2.** $\frac{5}{3}$ **3.** $\frac{7}{3}$ **4.** $\frac{5}{4}$ **5.** $\frac{8}{3}$

6. $\frac{8}{6}$ **7.** $\frac{9}{3}$ **8.** $\frac{9}{2}$ **9.** $\frac{9}{4}$ **10.** $\frac{10}{2}$

11. $\frac{10}{6}$ **12.** $\frac{10}{7}$ **13.** $\frac{13}{8}$ **14.** $\frac{35}{15}$ **15.** $\frac{42}{21}$

16. $\frac{120}{10}$ **17.** $\frac{22}{7}$ **18.** $\frac{15}{9}$ **19.** $\frac{12}{5}$ **20.** $\frac{150}{100}$

In Questions **21** to **35** change the mixed numbers to improper fractions.

21. $1\frac{1}{4}$ **22.** $1\frac{1}{3}$ **23.** $2\frac{1}{4}$ **24.** $2\frac{2}{3}$ **25.** $1\frac{7}{8}$

26. $1\frac{2}{3}$ **27.** $3\frac{1}{7}$ **28.** $2\frac{1}{6}$ **29.** $4\frac{3}{4}$ **30.** $7\frac{1}{2}$

31. $3\frac{5}{8}$ **32.** $4\frac{2}{5}$ **33.** $3\frac{2}{5}$ **34.** $8\frac{1}{4}$ **35.** $1\frac{3}{10}$

Mixed questions

Exercise 6

1. How many halves are in: (a) $1\frac{1}{2}$,   (b) $2\frac{1}{2}$,   (c) $10\frac{1}{2}$?

2. How many thirds are in: (a) $1\frac{2}{3}$,   (b) $3\frac{1}{3}$,   (c) $5\frac{2}{6}$?

3. How many quarters are in: (a) $2\frac{1}{4}$,   (b) $3\frac{1}{2}$,   (c) $4\frac{3}{4}$?

4. Copy each sequence and write down the next four numbers

     (a) $\frac{1}{2} = \frac{2}{4} = \frac{3}{6} = \frac{4}{8} = \frac{5}{10} = \ldots\ldots$

     (b) $\frac{1}{3} = \frac{2}{6} = \frac{3}{9} = \frac{4}{12} = \frac{5}{15} = \ldots\ldots$

5. Write down the first five numbers in the sequence which starts
$\frac{1}{5} = \frac{2}{10} = \ldots\ldots$

6. Draw these fraction charts, using squared paper.

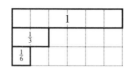

7. Use your fraction charts to answer the following:

(a) $\frac{3}{4} = \frac{?}{8}$ (b) $\frac{3}{5} = \frac{?}{10}$ (c) $\frac{1}{2} + \frac{1}{4} = \frac{?}{4}$

(d) $\frac{1}{5} + \frac{1}{10} = \frac{?}{10}$ (e) $\frac{2}{3} + \frac{1}{6} = \frac{?}{6}$ (f) $\frac{1}{4} + \frac{2}{8} = ?$

8. What fraction of the months of the year begin with the letters J, A or M?

9. What fraction of one kilogram is 200 grams?

10. What fraction of one complete turn is two right-angles?

11. What fraction of one minute is ten seconds?

12. What fraction of £1 is 60 p?

13. In a class of 30 pupils writing an essay, 23 are right-handed. What fraction are left-handed?

14. What fraction of the numbers from zero to ninety-nine contain the number 7?

15. Here are four numbers   2   4   7   11
You can use two of the numbers to make a fraction less than one (e.g. $\frac{4}{7}, \frac{2}{7} \ldots$)
(a) What is the smallest fraction you can make?
(b) What is the largest fraction you can make?

16. What number is half way between $3\frac{1}{4}$ and $3\frac{1}{2}$?

17. What fraction of the square is shaded?

18. Find six ways of adding two fractions to make one.

19. The fraction $\frac{6}{12}$ has three digits 6, 1 and 2. It is equal to $\frac{1}{2}$.

    (a) Find all the three-digit fractions that are equal to $\frac{1}{2}$

    (b) Find all the three-digit fractions that are equal to:

        (i) $\frac{1}{3}$ (ii) $\frac{1}{4}$ (iii) $\frac{1}{5}$.

20. Write each statement with either $>$, $<$ or $=$ in the space.

    (a) $\frac{3}{5}$ ☐ $\frac{1}{2}$ (b) $2\frac{1}{2}$ ☐ $\frac{5}{2}$ (c) $\frac{1}{7}$ ☐ $\frac{1}{6}$

    (d) $3\frac{2}{3}$ ☐ $\frac{10}{3}$ (e) $\frac{7}{35}$ ☐ $\frac{1}{5}$ (f) $\frac{2}{11}$ ☐ $\frac{1}{5}$

Fraction of a number

- If a prize of £50 is shared equally between two people, each person receives $\frac{1}{2}$ of £50.

  This is £50 ÷ 2 = £25 each

  > To find one *half* of a quantity, divide the quantity by *two*

  Similarly: To find $\frac{1}{3}$ of a quantity, divide the quantity by 3

Exercise 7

1. Copy and complete this table.

No.	Fraction of quantity required	Divide the quantity by ...
(a)	$\frac{1}{2}$	2
(b)	$\frac{1}{3}$	
(c)	one quarter	
(d)		10
(e)	$\frac{1}{5}$	

In Question **2** to **19** copy and complete.

2. $\frac{1}{2}$ of £8 = ? **3.** $\frac{1}{4}$ of 28 litres = ? **4.** $\frac{1}{3}$ of 60 kg = ?

5. $\frac{1}{4}$ of 20 kg = ? **6.** $\frac{1}{2}$ of 16 kg = ? **7.** $\frac{1}{3}$ of 60 kg = ?

8. $\frac{1}{2}$ of 150 cm = ? **9.** $\frac{1}{3}$ of 27 cm = ? **10.** $\frac{1}{4}$ of 280 cm = ?

11. $\frac{1}{5}$ of £10 = ? **12.** $\frac{1}{10}$ of £100 = ? **13.** $\frac{1}{5}$ of 45 litres = ?

14. $\frac{1}{10}$ of 250 cm = ? **15.** $\frac{1}{8}$ of £72 = ? **16.** $\frac{1}{20}$ of 300 cm = ?

17. $\frac{1}{12}$ of 288 m = ? **18.** $\frac{1}{9}$ of 729 kg = ? **19.** $\frac{1}{100}$ of £5000 = ?

20. The calculations in each row are all the same. Copy and complete the table

$\frac{1}{2}$ of 18	$\frac{1}{2} \times 18$	$18 \times \frac{1}{2}$	$18 \div 2$
$\frac{1}{3}$ of 12	$\frac{1}{3} \times 12$	$\square \times \frac{\square}{\square}$	$\square \div \square$
		$15 \times \frac{1}{5}$	
			$20 \div 4$
	$\frac{1}{6} \times 30$		

(a) In a mixed school with 364 pupils, $\frac{3}{7}$ of the pupils are girls. How many girls are there?

We need to work out $\frac{3}{7}$ of 364.

$\frac{1}{7}$ of $364 = 364 \div 7$
$\qquad = 52$

$\left[Working: \quad 7\overline{)3\,6\,^14} \;\; ^{5\,2} \right]$

So $\frac{3}{7}$ of $364 = 52 \times 3$
$\qquad = 156$

There are 156 girls in the school.

$\left[Because\ \frac{3}{7}\ of\ 364\ is\ 3\ times\ as\ many\ as\ \frac{1}{7}\ of\ 364. \right]$

(b) Work out $\frac{2}{5}$ of £560

$\frac{1}{5}$ of $560 = 560 \div 5$
$\qquad = 112$

$5\overline{)5\,6\,^10} \;\; ^{1\,1\,2}$

So $\frac{2}{5}$ of $560 = 112 \times 2$
$\qquad = 224$

Answer: £224.

Exercise 8

Copy and complete these problems. (Use a calculator if needed)

1. $\frac{3}{8}$ of £24 = ?   2. $\frac{2}{5}$ of £15 = ?   3. $\frac{3}{4}$ of £36 = ?

4. $\frac{4}{7}$ of £84 = ?   5. $\frac{5}{9}$ of £108 = ?   6. $\frac{2}{3}$ of £216 = ?

7. $\frac{3}{4}$ of 20 kg = ?   8. $\frac{2}{3}$ of 30 kg = ?   9. $\frac{7}{10}$ of 30 g = ?

10. $\frac{5}{8}$ of 480 cm = ?   11. $\frac{4}{5}$ of 80 cm = ?   12. $\frac{2}{3}$ of 120 cm = ?

13. $\frac{2}{5}$ of 30 p = ?   14. $\frac{5}{8}$ of 64 p = ?   15. $\frac{3}{10}$ of 150 p = ?

16. $\frac{2}{7}$ of 140 m = ?   17. $\frac{5}{12}$ of 60 km = ?   18. $\frac{8}{9}$ of 72 litres = ?

19. In a maths test full marks were 120. How many marks did Ben
    get if he got $\frac{7}{10}$ of full marks?

20. A petrol tank in a car holds 56 litres when full.
    How much petrol is in the tank when it is $\frac{3}{4}$ full?

21. A rose garden is home to 2600 ladybirds.
    If $\frac{3}{100}$ of these are male, how many females are
    there?

22. Mario has an order for 600 pizzas. If $\frac{5}{12}$ of his
    pizzas must be vegetarian, how many will be non-vegetarian?

23. If a book has 440 pages and you have read $\frac{3}{8}$ so far, how many
    more pages do you still have to read?

24. Here are calculations with letters.
    Put the answers in order of size,
    smallest first.
    Write down the letters to
    make a word.

R	A	P
$\frac{2}{7}$ of 49	$\frac{1}{11}$ of 165	$\frac{2}{3}$ of 27

M	Y	D	I
$\frac{4}{9}$ of 45	$\frac{3}{4}$ of 16	$\frac{5}{6}$ of 300	$\frac{5}{8}$ of 96

25. A television is bought for £287 and sold at a car bootsale for $\frac{3}{7}$
    of the original price. What was the selling price?

26. Draw a copy of the rectangle.
    (a) Shade in $\frac{1}{3}$ of the squares.
    (b) Draw crosses in $\frac{1}{5}$ of the unshaded squares.
    (c) How many squares are neither shaded nor
        have crosses in them?

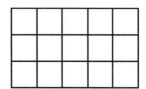

Adding and taking away

- Fractions can be added when they have the same denominator (bottom number).

- Here are some easy ones.

  $\frac{1}{5} + \frac{2}{5} = \frac{3}{5}$, $\frac{2}{7} + \frac{3}{7} = \frac{5}{7}$, $\frac{1}{10} + \frac{5}{10} = \frac{6}{10}$

- In these questions one of the fractions has to be changed to an equivalent fraction

  (a) $\frac{1}{2} + \frac{1}{4}$ (b) $\frac{1}{6} + \frac{1}{3}$ (c) $\frac{5}{8} - \frac{1}{4}$

      $= \frac{2}{4} + \frac{1}{4}$ $= \frac{1}{6} + \frac{2}{6}$ $= \frac{5}{8} - \frac{2}{8}$

      $= \frac{3}{4}$ $= \frac{3}{6}$ $= \frac{3}{8}$

Exercise 9

Work out

1. $\frac{1}{5} + \frac{2}{5}$ 2. $\frac{2}{7} + \frac{1}{7}$ 3. $\frac{1}{6} + \frac{4}{6}$ 4. $\frac{1}{8} + \frac{3}{8}$

5. $\frac{2}{9} + \frac{3}{9}$ 6. $\frac{3}{10} + \frac{4}{10}$ 7. $\frac{3}{11} + \frac{2}{11}$ 8. $\frac{1}{25} + \frac{2}{25}$

In Questions **9** to **24** change one of the fractions to an equivalent fraction. [e.g. $\frac{1}{2} = \frac{2}{4}$]

9. $\frac{1}{4} + \frac{1}{2}$ 10. $\frac{1}{8} + \frac{1}{4}$ 11. $\frac{3}{8} + \frac{1}{2}$ 12. $\frac{1}{16} + \frac{1}{2}$

13. $\frac{3}{4} - \frac{1}{2}$ 14. $\frac{5}{8} - \frac{1}{4}$ 15. $\frac{1}{4} - \frac{1}{8}$ 16. $\frac{5}{8} - \frac{1}{2}$

17. $\frac{1}{6} + \frac{2}{3}$ 18. $\frac{4}{5} + \frac{1}{10}$ 19. $\frac{2}{5} + \frac{3}{10}$ 20. $\frac{1}{6} + \frac{1}{3}$

21. $\frac{7}{8} - \frac{1}{2}$ 22. $\frac{2}{3} - \frac{1}{6}$ 23. $\frac{1}{10} - \frac{1}{20}$ 24. $\frac{3}{4} - \frac{3}{8}$

25. (a)

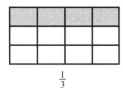 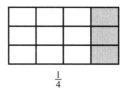 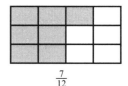

         $\frac{1}{3}$ $+$ $\frac{1}{4}$ $=$ $\frac{7}{12}$

   (b) Draw similar diagrams to show that $\frac{2}{3} + \frac{1}{4} = \frac{11}{12}$.

26. The fraction sum $\frac{1}{3} + \frac{4}{6}$ is made from four different digits and the sum is 1.

   Find other fraction sums using four different digits so that the sum is 1.

2.2 Two dimensional shapes

Lines and angles

- A straight line can be considered to have infinite length.
  A *line segment* is a part of a straight line and has finite length.
  Here is a line segment with end-points M and N.　M————————————N

- Lines that meet at a point ...

  ... or cross each other ...

  ... create angles.

- Lines which are at right angles are *perpendicular* to each other.

- Lines like these which never meet
  are called *parallel*. To show that
  lines are parallel we draw arrows.

- A *horizontal* line is parallel to the horizon.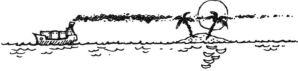

- A *vertical* line is perpendicular to the surface of the earth.

Look around the classroom. Where can you see parallel lines?
Where can you see *perpendicular* lines?

Can you see anything which is *vertical*? Is there anything which is
horizontal?

Builders sometimes use a plumb line or a spirit level.
What is a plumb line?
What is a spirit level?

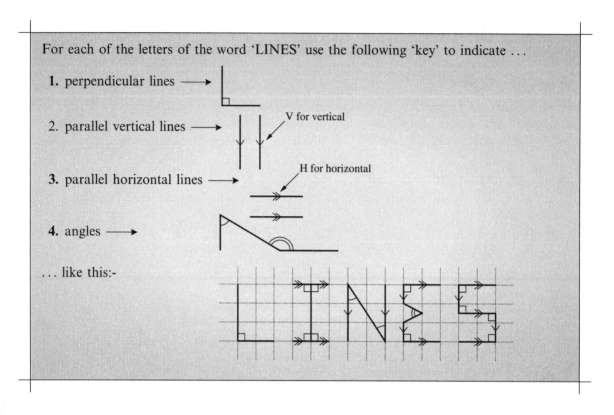

For each of the letters of the word 'LINES' use the following 'key' to indicate . . .

1. perpendicular lines ⟶

2. parallel vertical lines ⟶   V for vertical

3. parallel horizontal lines ⟶   H for horizontal

4. angles ⟶

. . . like this:-

Exercise 1

Copy out the key given in the above example and the stencil of the alphabet below onto squared paper. Use the key to show on all the letters any:
(a) perpendicular lines   (b) parallel vertical lines   (c) parallel horizontal lines   (d) angles.

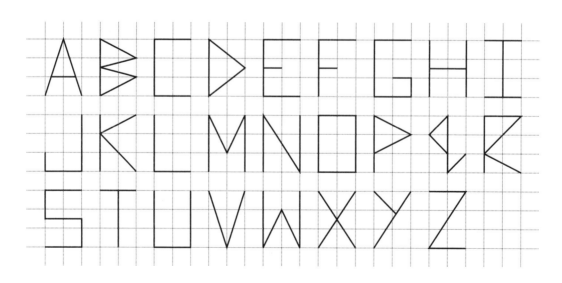

Exercise 2

In Questions **1** to **3** write the sentence choosing the correct word.

1. AB is (parallel/perpendicular) to CD.

2. 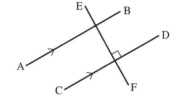 LM is (parallel/perpendicular) to MN.
ON is (parallel/perpendicular) to LM.
OL is (parallel/perpendicular) to MN.

3. CD is _____ to EF.

AB is _____ to CD.

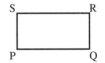

4. In the rectangle PQRS, RQ is perpendicular to SR.
(a) Which other line is perpendicular to PQ?
(b) Which line is parallel to PQ?

5. Find out which lines are perpendicular.

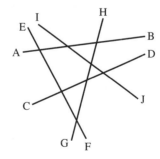

6. Use the sides of a ruler to draw a quadrilateral with two pairs of parallel sides. Mark the parallel sides with arrows.

7. Copy the diagram on the right.
(a) Draw a line through C which is perpendicular to AB
(b) Draw a line through D which is parallel to AB
(c) Draw a line through D which is perpendicular to the line AB.

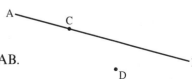

8. 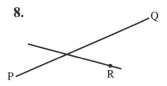   Copy the diagram on the left.
(a) Draw a line through R which is parallel to PQ.
(b) Draw a line through R which is perpendicular to PQ.

9.* Answer true or false (Think carefully).
(a) Two vertical lines are always parallel.
(b) Two horizontal lines are always parallel.

Triangles

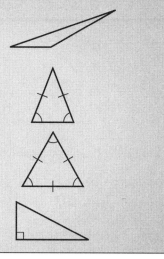

- A plane figure with three sides and angles is a triangle.

- A triangle with three different sides and three different angles is a *scalene* triangle.

- A triangle with two sides the same length and two angles the same is an *isosceles* triangle.

- A triangle with three sides the same length and three equal angles is an *equilateral* triangle.

- A triangle which contains a right angle is a *right angled* triangle.

Exercise 3

For each of the following triangles state whether it is scalene, isosceles, equilateral or right angled. (Lines of the same length are indicated by dashes and equal angles are marked.)

1. 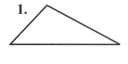   **2.** 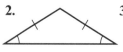   **3.**    **4.**   **5.**

6. 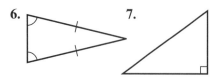   **7.**   **8.** 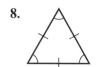   **9.** 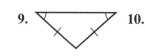   **10.**

Quadrilaterals

- A plane figure with four sides and angles is a *quadrilateral*

Here are some special types of quadrilaterals:

1. A *square* has all its sides equal in length and all its angles are right angles.

2. A *rectangle* has pairs of opposite sides equal in length and all its angles are right angles.

3. A *parallelogram* has its opposite sides equal in length and parallel. Its opposite angles are equal.

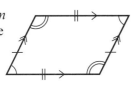

4. A *rhombus* is a parallelogram with all its sides equal.

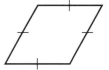

5. A *trapezium* has one pair of opposite sides parallel.

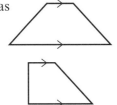

6. A *kite* is a quadrilateral with two pairs of adjacent sides equal in length. (Adjacent means 'next to'.)

Polygons

A polygon is a plane figure with straight sides. A polygon can have any number of sides from 3 upwards.

Here is a five-sided polygon or pentagon.

If a polygon is described as *regular*, then all its sides and angles are equal. Here is a regular pentagon.

Here are the names of other common polygons:
Hexagon = 6 sides; Heptagon = 7 sides; Octagon = 8 sides;
Nonagon = 9 sides; Decagon = 10 sides.

Exercise 4

Write down the name for each shape. If the shape has a special name like 'parallelogram' or 'kite' write that name. Otherwise write 'quadrilateral', 'hexagon', 'regular pentagon' and so on.

1.

2.

3.

4.

5.

6.

7.

8.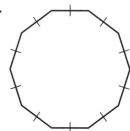

9.

10.

11.

12.

13.

14.

15.

16.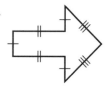

17.

18.

19.

20.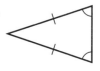

21. Draw any rectangle. Make a statement about the diagonals of a rectangle.

22. Draw any rhombus. Make a statement, with as many facts as possible, about the diagonals of a rhombus.

Shapes investigation

On a square grid of 9 dots it is possible to draw several different triangles with vertices on dots. A vertex (plural vertices) is where two lines meet. Look at the three examples below:

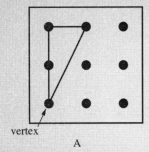 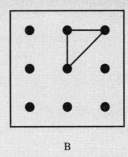 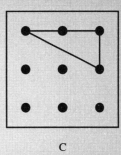

vertex
    A   B   C

A and B are different triangles but C is the same as A. If a triangle could be cut out and placed exactly over another triangle then the two triangles are the same. The two triangles are called *congruent*.

1. Copy A and B above and then draw as many different triangles as you can. Check carefully that you have not repeated the same triangle.

2. On a grid of 9 dots it is also possible to draw several different *quadrilaterals*.

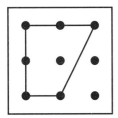 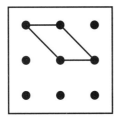 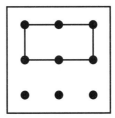

Copy the three shapes above and then draw as many other different quadrilaterals as possible. You are doing well if you can find 12 shapes but there are a few more!

Check carefully that you have not repeated the same quadrilateral. (Congruent shapes are not allowed.)

2.3 Coordinates

- To get to the point P on this grid we go **across** 1 and **up** 3 from the bottom corner.
  The position of P is (1, 3).
  The numbers 1 and 3 are called the **coordinates** of P.
  The coordinates of Q are (4, 2).
  The *origin* is at (0, 0).

  We call the first coordinate the *x*-coordinate and the second coordinate the *y*-coordinate.

- The *across* coordinate is always *first* and the *up* coordinate is *second*.
  Remember: 'Along the corridor and up the stairs'.

- Notice also that the *lines* are numbered, *not* the squares.

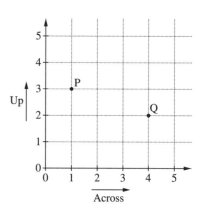

Exercise 1

1. Write down the coordinates of all the points marked like this: A(5, 1) B(1,4)

   Don't forget the brackets.

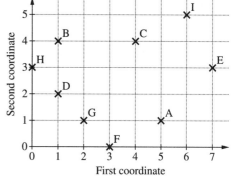

2. The map below shows a remote Scottish island used for training by the S.A.S.

   Write down the coordinates of the following places:
   (a) Rocket launcher
   (b) H.Q.
   (c) Hospital A
   (d) Rifle range
   (e) Officers' mess
   (f) Radar control

3. Make a list of the places which are at the following points:
   (a) (2, 8)   (b) (7, 8)   (c) (3, 3)
   (d) (6, 4)   (e) (2, 6)   (f) (6, 2)
   (g) (2, 4)   (h) (9, 1)

4. Make up your own map and mark points of interest.

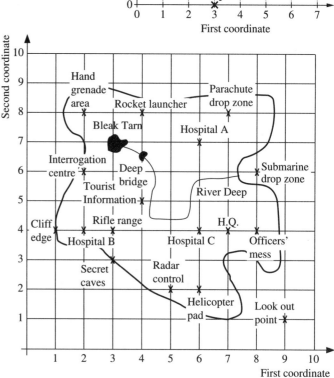

Negative coordinates

The *x* axis can be extended to the left and the *y* axis can be extended downwards to include the negative numbers −1, −2, −3 etc.

The name 'FALDO' can be found using the letters in the following order:
(2, 3),   (−2, −1),   (−1, 2),   (2, −2),   (−2, −3).

Similarly the coordinates of the points which spell out the word 'LOAD' are (−1, 2),   (−2, −3), (−2, −1),   (2, −2)

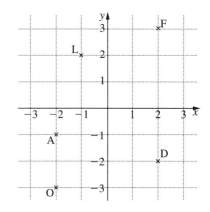

Exercise 2

The letters from A to Z are shown on the grid.
Coded messages can be sent using coordinates.

For example (−4, −2)   (−4, 2)   (−4, 2)   (4, 2) reads 'FOOD'.

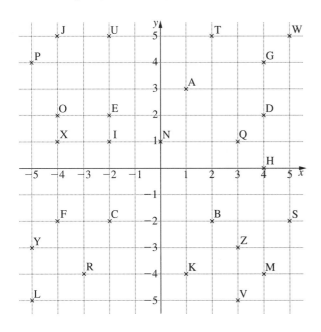

Decipher the following messages

1. (5, 5) (4, 0) (1, 3) (2, 5) # (4, 2) (−4, 2) # (−5, −3)
   (−4, 2) (−2, 5) # (−2, −2) (1, 3) (−5, −5) (−5, −5) #
   (1, 3) # (4, −4) (1, 3) (0, 1) # (5, 5) (−2, 1) (2, 5) (4, 0) #
   (1, 3) # (5, −2) (−5, 4) (1, 3) (4, 2) (−2, 2) # (−2, 1)
   (0, 1) # (4, 0) (−2, 1) (5, −2) # (4, 0) (−2, 2) (1, 3)
   (4, 2) ? # (4, 2) (−4, 2) (−2, 5) (4, 4) !

2. Change the seventh word to: (5, 5) (−2, 1) (2, 5) (4, 0)
   (−4, 2) (−2, 5) (2, 5).
   Change the last word to: (4, 2) (−4, 2) (−2, 5) (4, 4)
   (−5, −5) (1, 3) (5, −2).

3. (5, 5) (4, 0) (1, 3) (2, 5) # (4, 2) (−4, 2) # (−5, −3)
   (−4, 2) (−2, 5) # (−2, −2) (1, 3) (−5, −5) (−5, −5) #
   (1, 3) # (4, 2) (−2, 2) (1, 3) (4, 2) # (−5, 4) (1, 3) (−3, −4)
   (−3, −4) (−4, 2) (2, 5) ? # (−5, 4) (−4, 2) (−5, −5) (−5, −3)
   (4, 4) (−4, 2) (0, 1) !

4. (5, 5) (−2, 1) (2, 5) (4, 0) # (5, 5) (4, 0) (1, 3) (2, 5) #
   (4, 2) (−4, 2) # (−5, −3) (−4, 2) (−2, 5) # (5, −2) (2, 5)
   (−2, 5) (−4, −2) (−4, −2) # (1, 3) # (4, 2) (−2, 2) (1, 3)
   (4, 2) # (−5, 4) (1, 3) (−3, −4) (−3, −4) (−4, 2)
   (2, 5) ? # (−5, 4) (−4, 2) (−5, −5) (−5, −3) (−4, −2) (−2, 1)
   (−5, −5) (−5, −5) (1, 3) !

5. Write a message or joke of your own using coordinates. Ask a
   friend to decipher your words.

Coordinate pictures

Plot the points below and join them up in order.
(a) (2, 4), (8, 1), (6, 3), (4, 4),
    (2, 6), (2, 4), (0, 3), (6, 2).
(b) (5, $3\frac{1}{2}$), (4, 5), ($3\frac{1}{4}$, $4\frac{2}{3}$).

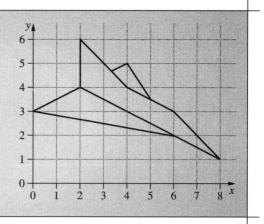

Exercise 3

Plot the points given and join them up in order.
Write on the grid what the picture is.

1. Draw x and y axes with values from 0 to 14.
   (a) (6, 13), (1, 3), (2, 1), (12, 1), (8, 9), (6, 5),
       (4, 5), (8, 13), (6, 13), (8, 13), (13, 3), (12, 1).

   (b) (1, 3), (9, 3), (7, 7), (6, 5), (8, 5).
       Now colour in the shape.

2. Draw *x* and *y* axes with values from 0 to 10.
  (a) (3, 2), (4, 2), (5, 3), (3, 5), (3, 6), (2, 7), (1, 6),
      (1, 8), (2, 9), (3, 9), (5, 7), (4, 6), (4, 5), (6, 4)
      (8, 4), (8, 5), (6, 7), (5, 7).
  (b) (7, 4), (9, 2), (8, 1), (7, 3), (5, 3).
  (c) (1, 6), (2, 8), (2, 9), (2, 7).
  (d) Draw a dot at (3, 8).
      Colour in the shape.

3. Draw *x* and *y* axes with values from 0 to 16
  (a) (4, 9), (1, 11), (3, 8), (1, 5), (4, 7), (6, 5), (7, 5), (8, 3),
      (9, 5), (11, 5), (12, 7), (15, 9), (15, 10), (12, 11), (9, 11),
      (8, 14), (7, 11), (6, 11), (4, 9).
  (b) (15, 12), (16, 12), (16, 13), (15, 13), (15, 12).
  (c) (14, 14), (13, 14), (13, 15), (14, 15), (14, 14).
  (d) (12, 8), (13, 8).
  (e) Draw a dot at (13, 10).
      Colour in the shape.

4. Draw axes with both *x* and *y* from 0 to 17.
  (a) (5, 1), (6, 6), (6, 3), (7, 2), (6, 2), (5, 1).
  (b) (8, 11), (8, 8), (10, 10), (11, 12), (11, 15).
  (c) (2, 14), (1, 14), (1, 15), (2, 15).
  (d) (12, 1), (11, 2), (10, 2), (10, 4), (9, 6), (8, 7), (7, 10),
      (8, 11), (9, 13), (11, 15), (10, 17), (8, 17), (7, 16), (4, 16),
      (2, 15), (2, 14), (3, 13), (5, 13), (6, 12), (4, 7), (4, 2),
      (3, 2), (2, 1), (12, 1).
  (e) (7, 16), (7, 15).
  (f) (5, 13), (6, 13).

5. Draw axes with both *x* and *y* from 0 to 11.
  (a) (7, 1), (3, 1), (1, 10), (2, 11), (3, 10), (4, 11), (5, 10),
      (6, 11), (7, 10), (8, 6), (8, 5), (9, $4\frac{1}{2}$), (9, 4), (8, 4), (9, 3),
      (5, 3), (5, 2), (7, 1).
  (b) (5, 5), (4, 6), (5, 7), (6, 6), (7, 7), (8, 6), (7, 5), (6, 6), (5, 5).
  (c) (5, 2), (6, 2), (6, $1\frac{1}{2}$).
  (d) (7, 5), (8, 5).
  (e) (7, 4), (8, 4).
  (f) (3, 7), (2, $6\frac{1}{2}$), (3, 6).
  (g) Put dots at (5, 6) and (7, 6).

6. Draw axes with both *x* and *y* from 0 to 18.
  (a) (0, 3), (1, 4), (2, 6), (4, 8), (6, 8), (8, 9), (12, 9), (13, 11),
      (12, 12), (12, 14), (14, 12), (15, 12), (17, 14), (17, 12),
      (16, 11), (17, 10), (17, 9), (16, 9), (15, 8), (14, 9), (13, 9).
  (b) (16, 9), (16, 7), (14, 5), (14, 1), (15, 1), (15, 6), (13, 4),
      (13, 1), (12, 1), (12, 4), (11, 5), (9, 5), (9, $6\frac{1}{2}$), (9, 4), (8, 3),
      (8, 1), (7, 1), (7, 4), (6, 6), (6, 4), (5, 3), (5, 1), (6, 1), (6, 3),
      (7, 4), (6, 6), (6, 7), (3, 2), (1, 2), (0, 3).

7. Design your own coordinates picture.

Complete the shape

Two sides of a rectangle are drawn.

Find   (a) the coordinates of the fourth vertex of the
           rectangle
       (b) the coordinates of the centre of the rectangle.

The complete rectangle is shown.
(a) Fourth vertex is at (6, 3)
(b) Centre of rectangle is at $(3\frac{1}{2}, 3)$

Exercise 4

1. The graph shows several
   incomplete quadrilaterals.
   Copy the diagram and
   complete the shapes.
   (a) Write down the
       coordinates of the fourth
       vertex of each shape.
   (b) Write down the
       coordinates of the centre
       of each shape.

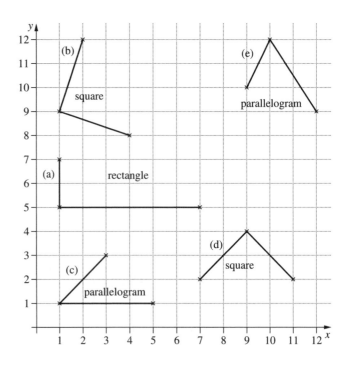

2. Copy the graph shown.
(a) A, B and F are three corners of a square. Write down the coordinates of the other corner.
(b) B, C and D are three corners of another square. Write down the coordinates of the other corner.
(c) D, E and F are three corners of a rectangle. Write down the coordinates of the other corner.

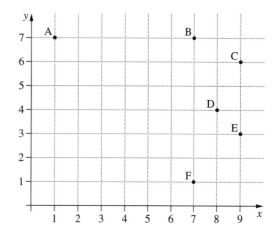

3. Draw a grid with values from 0 to 10. Plot the three points given and then find the coordinates of the point which makes a square when the points are joined up.
(a) (1, 2) (1, 5) (4, 5)
(b) (5, 6) (7, 3) (10, 5)
(c) (0, 9) (1, 6) (4, 7)

4. You are given the vertices but not the sides of two parallelograms P and Q.

For each parallelogram find *three* possible positions for the fourth vertex.

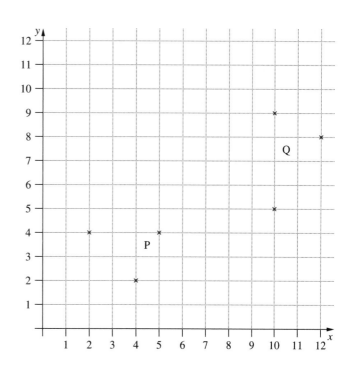

5. Copy the graph shown.

(a) A, B and C are three corners of a square. Write down the coordinates of the other corner.

(b) C, A and D are three corners of another square. Write down the coordinates of the other corner.

(c) B, D and E are three corners of a rectangle. Write down the coordinates of the other corner.

(d) C, F and G are three vertices of a parallelogram. Write down the coordinates of the other vertex.

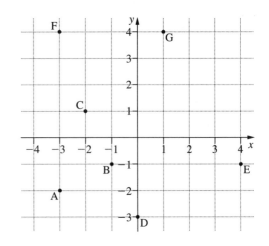

6.

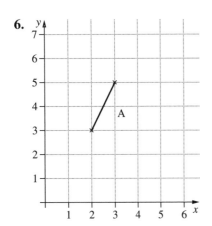

The crosses mark two vertices of an isosceles triangle A.

Find as many points as you can, with whole number coordinates, for the third vertex of the triangle. [There are, in fact, 12 possible points for the third vertex. Find as many as you can.]

7. The diagram shows one side of an isosceles triangle B.

(a) Find *six* possible points, with whole number coordinates, for the third vertex of the triangle.

(b) Explain how you could find the coordinates of several more positions for the third vertex.

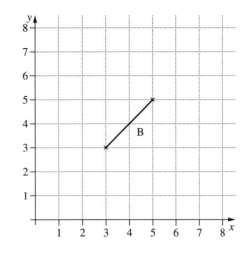

2.4 Rules of algebra

Using letters for numbers

Many problems in mathematics are easier to solve when letters are used instead of numbers. This is called using *algebra*.

It is important to remember that the *letters stand for numbers*.

- Here is a square with sides of length l cm
  The perimeter of the square in cm is $l+l+l+l$.
  If we use p cm to stand for the perimeter,
  we can write $\qquad p = l+l+l+l$
  or $\qquad\qquad\quad p = 4l$ (This means $4 \times l$)

- Suppose there are a number of people in a room. Call this number N. If one more person enters the room there will be $N+1$ people in the room. $N+1$ is an *expression*. An expression has no equals sign whereas an equation does have an equals sign.

- Suppose there are x cows in a field. After the farmer puts 3 more cows in the field there are $x+3$ cows in the field.

- Suppose a piece of wood is l centimetres long.
  If you cut off 5 cm the length left is $l-5$ cm.

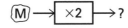

$x+3$ and $l-5$ are expressions

- Suppose there are y people on a bus. At a bus stop n more people get on the bus. Now there are $y+n$ people on the bus.

- If I start with a number N and then double it, I will have $2N$. If I then add 7, I will have $2N+7$.

- When you multiply, write the number before the letter. So write $2N$, *not* $N2$.

Exercise 1

In Questions **1** to **10** find the expression I am left with.

1. I start with M and then double it.

2. I start with N and then add 6.

3. I start with e and then take away 3.

4. I start with d and then add 10.

5. I start with N and then multiply by 3.

6. I start with x, double it and then add 3.

7. I start with y, double it and then and then take away 7.

8. I start with k, treble it and then add 10.

9. I start with s and multiply by 100.

10. I start with t, multiply it by 6 and then add 11.

11. (a) The perimeter p of the square is
$$p = x + x + x + x$$
or $p = 4x$.
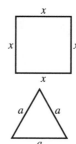
    (b) Find the perimeter, p of this triangle.
Write '$p = \ldots$'

In Questions **12** to **17** find the perimeter p of the shape.

12.

13.

14.

15.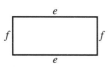

16.

17.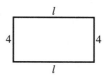

18. Draw and label a rectangle whose perimeter p is given by the formula $p = 2t + 2m$.

19. Draw and label a triangle whose perimeter is given by the formula $p = 2y + 7$.

20. Draw and label a pentagon (5 sides) whose perimeter p is given by the formula $p = 2a + 3b$.

Exercise 2

In Questions **1** to **8** find what expression I am left with.

1. I start with x, add y and then take away 3.

2. I start with N, double it and then add T.

3. I start with p, add t and then take away x.

4. I start with b, treble it and then add c.

5. I start with M, divide it by 2 and then add 7.

6. I start with $3x$, take away z and then add 3.

7. I start with $5N$, double it and then add M.

8. I start with p, treble it and then take away $2x$.

9. A piece of string is l cm long. If I cut off a piece 4 cm long, how much string remains?

10. A piece of rope is 25 m long. How much remains after I cut off a piece of length x m?

11. When a man buys a small tree it is h cm tall. During the year it grows a further t cm and then he cuts off 30 cm. How tall is it now?

12. A brick weighs w kg. How much do six bricks weigh?

13. A man shares a sum of N pence equally between four children. How much does each child receive?

14. On Monday there are n people in a cinema. On Friday there are three times as many people plus another 50. How many people are there in the cinema on Friday?

15. A prize of £x is shared equally between you and four others. How much does each person receive?

Simplifying expressions

The expression $5a + 2a$ can be *simplified* to $7a$. This is because $5a + 2a$ means five a's plus two a's, which is equivalent to seven a's.

(It can also be remembered as '5 *apples* + 2 *apples* = 7 *apples*'.)

Similarly, the expression $7c - 3c$ can be simplified to $4c$.

The expression $10x + x$ can be thought of as $10x + 1x$ which can be simplified to $11x$.

Similarly, $9a - a$ can be thought of as $9a - 1a$ which can be simplified to $8a$.

Notice that when we simplify an expression we are not finding its value when a is a particular number. We are just rewriting the expression in a simpler form.

Some expressions cannot be simplified.

The expression $7x + 2x$ consists of two *terms*, $7x$ and $2x$.

The expression $5x + 3y$ consists of two *terms*, $5x$ and $3y$.

$7x$ and $2x$ are called *like* terms.
$5x$ and $3y$ are called *unlike* terms.

An expression which is the sum or difference of two terms can only be simplified if the terms are *like* terms.

Exercise 3

Simplify as many of the following expressions as possible. This exercise could be done orally.

1. $7x - 2x$ 2. $4a + 5a$ 3. $3a + 2b$ 4. $9y - 2y$
5. $5x + 4x$ 6. $5c - 2d$ 7. $4x + 3$ 8. $9d + d$
9. $13y - y$ 10. $6d - 4$ 11. $6x + 3y$ 12. $4h + 2h$
13. $7y - 5y$ 14. $13x - 9x$ 15. $7a + a$ 16. $3a + b$
17. $4 - 2x$ 18. $7d - 3d$ 19. $10a - 4a$ 20. $17t - 2t$
21. $19b + 3b$ 22. $9c + 5c$ 23. $5c - c$ 24. $5c - 5$
25. $9a + a$ 26. $9a + 9$ 27. $11b - 11$ 28. $11b - b$

Collecting like terms

- This pentagon has three sides of length a and two sides of length l. The perimeter of the shape is $a + a + a + l + l$. We can simplify this expression to $3a + 2l$.

  This is called *collecting like terms*.

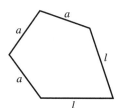

- We follow the conventions below when collecting like terms

  $4 + m + 3 + 3m = 4m + 7$ ← collect in alphabetical order, with letter terms before numbers

  $s + 4 + s + 2 + t = 2s + t + 6$ ←

  $4p - 4$ can not be simplified.

  $3x + y - 3x = y$ ← do not write 0_x do not write $1y$,

- The sign in *front* of the term is part of the term. If we change the order of terms the sign in *front* of each term *stays* with the term. We can emphasise this fact by drawing loops around each term to include the sign.

(a) Simplify $7x + 5y + 2x - 3y$

$(7x)(+5y)(+2x)(-3y) = (7x)(+2x)(+5y)(-3y)$ [group together like terms]
$= 9x + 2y$

$\uparrow$
[no sign means +]

(b) Simplify $5a - 2x - a + 2x$

$(5a)(-2x)(-a)(+2x) = (5a)(-a)(-2x)(+2x)$ [group together like terms]
$= 4a$

Exercise 4

Simplify the following expressions as far as possible by collecting like terms.

1. $7x + 3y + 2x + 5y$
2. $9x + 2y + 3x + y$
3. $5a + 6y - 2a - 4y$
4. $11t + 7 - t - 4$
5. $8y + 3 + y + 7$
6. $9x + 2b - 8x + 7b$
7. $6a + 10 - 2a - 2$
8. $6h - 2y + 3h + 9y$
9. $8y - 3 + y + 9$
10. $4x + 10 - x + 3$
11. $x + 12y + 3x - 2y$
12. $7y + 5 + 7y - 4$
13. $3a - 2c + 5c - 2a$
14. $5x + 2y + 7y + 5x$
15. $7d - 4 + 10 - 6d$
16. $5a + 2c - 2a - 5d$
17. $10x + 7 - 4x + x$
18. $6x - 2y + x + 4$
19. $11y + 3 + 2y - 2$
20. $a - 4c + 2a + 10c$
21. $8d - 5 - 7d + 9$
22. $4a - 11 + 2 + 6a$
23. $14a + 13c - 2a - 8c$
24. $2 + 3y + 7 - 2y$
25. $4y - 2x + 8y + 5x$
26. $6c + 13d - 7d + 4c$
27. $8a + 5y + 2a - y$
28. $9a + c - 8a + c$
29. $5x + 11y - 2y + 9$
30. $6a + 3x - 2a + 10a$

Order of operations

Algebraic operations follow the same conventions and order as numerical operations.

- In the expression $3 + 4n$, the multiplication is performed first.
- In the expression $5 + x^2$, x is squared first and then added to 5.
- In the expression $3(n + 5)$, the operation inside the bracket is performed first.

Inverses

- We know that $3 + 6 = 6 + 3$ and that $a + b = b + a$.
  Also if $a + b = 10$, then $a = 10 - b$.

- We know that $3 \times 5 = 5 \times 3$ and that $a \times b = b \times a$.
  If $a \times b = 30$, then $a = \dfrac{30}{b}$ and $b = \dfrac{30}{a}$.

Exercise 5

In Questions 1 to 12 write down each statement and say whether it is 'True' or 'False' for all values of the symbols used.

1. $n + n = 2n$
2. $n \times n \times n = 3n$
3. $a \times a = a^2$
4. $cd = dc$
5. $p + q = q + p$
6. $n^2 + n^2 = 2n^2$
7. $m - n = n - m$
8. $a \times 4 = 4a$
9. $3n - n = 3$
10. $n \div 2 = 2 \div n$
11. $2n^2 = (2n)^2$
12. $\frac{1}{2}$ of $h = \dfrac{h}{2}$

If you are not sure, try different values for the letter

13. Copy and complete

    (a) If $m + n = 100$, then $m = \boxed{} - \boxed{}$

    (b) If $a \times b = 15$, then $a =$

    (c) If $c - d = 20$, then $c =$

14. Simplify the following expressions.

(a) $a + 3 + 4a - 3$ (b) $n - 2 + 2n$ (c) $m + n + p + n$

(d) $\dfrac{a}{a}$ (e) $\dfrac{3n}{3}$ (f) $\dfrac{a^2}{a}$

> If you are not sure, try different values for the letter

15. Think of two pairs of values for a and b for each equation.

(a) $a + b = 20$ (b) $ab = 100$ (c) $a^2 b = 8$

16. Find the value of each expression, when $n = 3$.

(a) $3n + 2$ (b) $2 + n^2$ (c) $5(n + 1)$

(d) $4(4 + n)$ (e) $(2n)^2$ (f) $2n^2$

Number walls: an investigation

Here we have three bricks with a number written inside each one.

A wall is built by putting more bricks on top to form a sort of pyramid.

The number in each of the new bricks is found by adding together the numbers in the two bricks below like this:

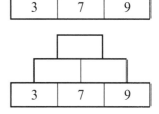

Here is another wall.

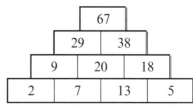

A • If you re-arrange the numbers at the bottom, does it affect the total at the top?
   • What is the largest total you can get using the same numbers?
   • What is the smallest total?
   • *How* do you get the largest total?

B • What happens if the bottom numbers are
   (a) the same? (e.g. 5, 5, 5, 5)
   (b) consecutive? (e.g. 2, 3, 4, 5)
   • Write down any patterns or rules that you notice.

C • What happens if you use different numbers at random? (eg 7, 3, 5, 11)
  • Given 4 numbers at the bottom, can you find a way to predict the top number without finding all the bricks in between?

D • Can you find a rule with 3 bricks at the bottom, or 4 bricks? Can algebra help? [Hint: see diagram]

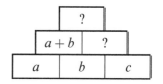

Balance puzzles

In balance puzzles the scales balance exactly.

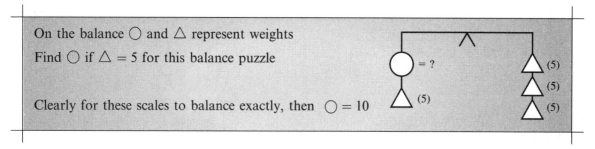

On the balance ○ and △ represent weights

Find ○ if △ = 5 for this balance puzzle

Clearly for these scales to balance exactly, then ○ = 10

Exercise 6

Copy each diagram and find the value of the required symbol.

1. Find □ if △ = 4.

2. Find ○ if △ = 10.

3. Find ○ if □ = 4.

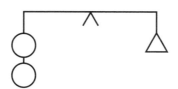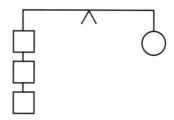

4. Find □ if △ = 12.

5. Find △ if □ = 2.

6. Find △ if ○ = 6.

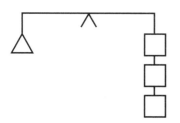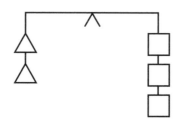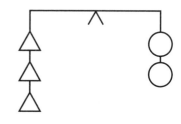

7. Find ☐ if ◯ = 8.

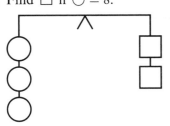

8. Find △ if ☐ = 15.

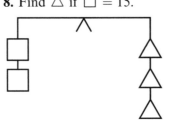

9. Find △ if ◯ = 14.

10. Find ☐ if ◯ = 8.

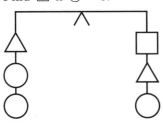

11. Find ◯ if △ = 6.

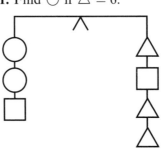

12. Find ◯ if ☐ = 5.

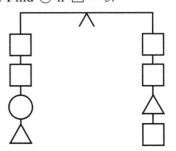

Exercise 7

Copy each diagram and find the value of the unknown symbols.

1. ◯ = 10, find △ and ☐.

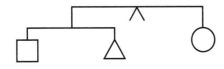

2. △ = 8, find ◯ and ☐.

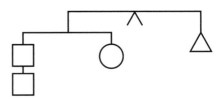

3. ☐ = 14, find ◯ and △.

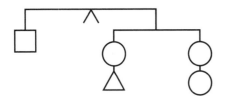

4. ☐ = 6, find ◯ and △.

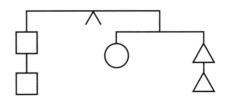

5. ◯ = 8, find ☐ and △.

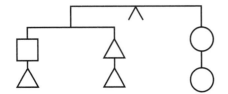

6. ☐ = 4, find ◯ and △.

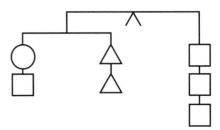

7. △ = 4, find ○ and □.

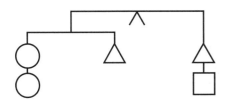

8. ○ = 10, find △ and □.

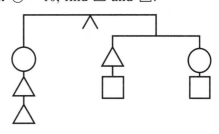

9. △ = 5, find ○ and □.

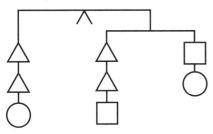

10. □ = 3, find ○ and △.

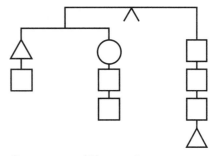

11. □ = 6, find △ and ○.

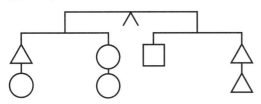

12. ○ = 5, find □ and △.

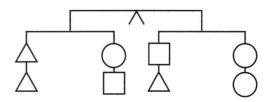

13. △ = 4, find ○ and □.

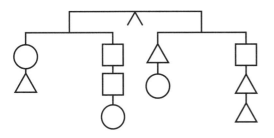

14. ○ = 8, find □ and △.

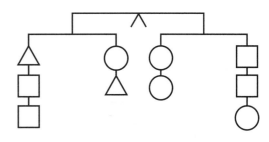

15. □ = 4, find ○ and △.

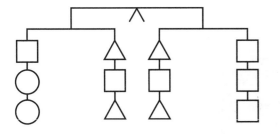

16. ○ = 3, find ✳.

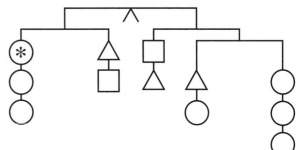

2.5 Percentages

Percentages are fractions with denominator (bottom number) equal to 100.
So 25% means $\frac{25}{100}$, 67% means $\frac{67}{100}$ and so on.

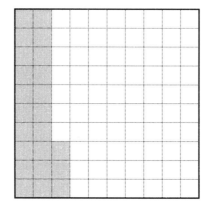

The square contains
100 squares and 23
squares are shaded

Fraction shaded $= \frac{23}{100}$

Percentage shaded $= 23\%$

Exercise 1

1. Draw each square and write underneath it

   (a) what fraction is shaded   (b) what percentage is shaded

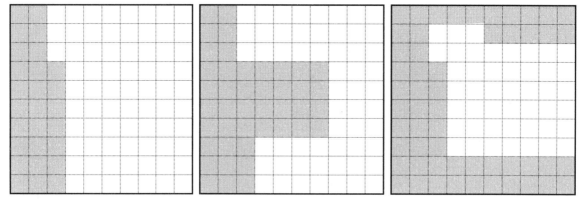

2. If 40% of a square is shaded, what percentage of the square is not shaded?

3. If 73% of a square is shaded, what percentage of the square is not shaded?

4. Approximately 67% of the earth's surface is covered with water. What percentage of the earth's surface is land?

5.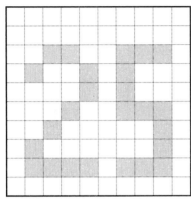

In this square, 25 out of 100 squares are shaded to show 25%.
Draw your own numbers (like 17, 21 or 33) and shade in the correct number of squares to show the percentage. Try to draw the numbers the same size.

6. The diagram shows the percentage of people who took part in activities offered at a sports centre on a Friday night.

(a) What percentage went swimming?
(b) What percentage played squash?
(c) What percentage played a racket sport?
(d) What percentage did not play football?
(e) What percentage played activities involving a ball?

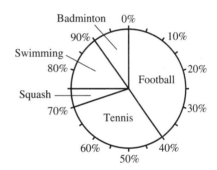

Common percentages

- Some percentages are used a lot and you should learn them.

$$10\% = \frac{10}{100} = \frac{1}{10}, \quad 30\% = \frac{30}{100} = \frac{3}{10}, \quad 70\% = \frac{7}{10}, \quad 90\% = \frac{9}{10}, \quad 20\% = \frac{20}{100} = \frac{1}{5},$$

$$40\% = \frac{40}{100} = \frac{2}{5}, \quad 60\% = \frac{3}{5}, \quad 80\% = \frac{4}{5}, \quad 25\% = \frac{1}{4}, \quad 50\% = \frac{1}{2},$$

$$75\% = \frac{3}{4}, \quad 33\frac{1}{3}\% = \frac{1}{3}, \quad 66\frac{2}{3}\% = \frac{2}{3}$$

$\frac{1}{4} = 25\%$

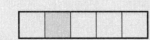

$\frac{1}{5} = 20\%$

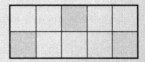

$\frac{3}{10} = 30\%$

Exercise 2

1. For each shape write
  (a) what fraction is shaded   (b) what percentage is shaded.

A   **B**    **C** 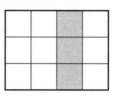   **D**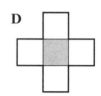

E 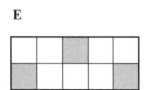   **F** 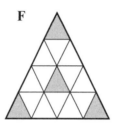   **G** 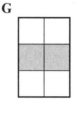   **H**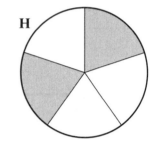

2. Copy these and fill in the spaces.
  (a) $30\% = \frac{\ }{10}$ (b) $\frac{3}{4} = \quad \%$ (c) $\frac{1}{3} = \quad \%$
  (d) $1\% = \frac{\ }{100}$ (e) $80\% = -$ (f) $\frac{1}{10} = \quad \%$

3. These pictures show how much petrol is in a car. E is Empty
and F is Full.
What percentage of a full tank is in each car?

  (a) 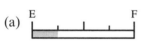   (b)

  (c)    (d)

  (e)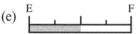

4. What percentage could be used in each sentence?
  (a) Three quarters of the pupils at a school had school dinners.
  (b) Three out of five workers voted for a strike.
  (c) Nicki got 15 out of 20 in the spelling test.
  (d) One in three cats prefer 'Whiskas'.
  (e) Half of the customers at a supermarket thought that prices
      were too high.
  (f) One in four mothers think children are too tidy at home.

5. Draw three diagrams of your own design, like those in Question
1 and shade in:
  (a) 30%   (b) 75%   (c) $66\frac{2}{3}\%$

Percentage of a number

(a) Work out 25% of £60.

25% is the same as $\frac{1}{4}$, $\frac{1}{4}$ of £60 is £15.

(b) In a sale, prices are reduced by 20%. Find the 'sale price' of the dress shown.

20% is the same as $\frac{1}{5}$

$\frac{1}{5}$ of £40 = £8.

Sale price = £40 − £8

= £32.

£40

Exercise 3

1. Work out
   (a) 20% of £50
   (b) 75% of £12
   (c) 10% of £90
   (d) 25% of £4000
   (e) $33\frac{1}{3}$% of £90
   (f) 30% of £40

2. Now do these
   (a) 90% of £100
   (b) 40% of $30
   (c) $66\frac{2}{3}$% of £12
   (d) 50% of $1200
   (e) 1% of £300
   (f) 5% of £100

3. Kate earns £15 for doing a paper round. How much *extra* does she earn when she gets a 20% rise?

4. Full marks in a maths test is 60. How many marks did Tim get if he got 60%?

5. Of the 240 children at a school, 75% walk to school. How many children walk to school?

6. Find the actual cost of the following items in a sale. The normal prices are shown.

   (a) £60

   25% off
   marked price

   (b)  £15

   50% off!

   (c) £24

   $33\frac{1}{3}$% off
   normal
   price

   (d) £40

   10%
   discount
   off price

   (e) £80

   75% off!

   (f) £25

   40%
   discount
   off price

7. In many countries Value Added Tax [V.A.T.] is charged at $17\frac{1}{2}\%$. Here is a method for finding $17\frac{1}{2}\%$ of £4000 without a calculator.

$$17\frac{1}{2}\% \text{ of £4000:} \quad \begin{aligned} 10\% &= £400 \\ 5\% &= £200 \\ 2\frac{1}{2}\% &= £100 \\ \hline 17\frac{1}{2}\% &= £700 \end{aligned}$$

Use this method to work out:

(a) $17\frac{1}{2}\%$ of £6000   (b) $17\frac{1}{2}\%$ of £440   (c) $17\frac{1}{2}\%$ of £86

8. The price of a car was £6600 but it is increased by $17\frac{1}{2}\%$. What is the new price?

9. A car is worth £3400. After an accident its value falls by 30%. How much is it worth now?

10. In a sale the price of a shirt costing £12 is reduced by 25%. Find the reduced price of the shirt.

11. The price of a boat was £36 000 but it is increased by 5%. What is the new price?

12. On the first of March a shopkeeper puts all his prices up by 5%. Find the new prices of the following.
(a) a scarf at £10.
(b) a pair of gloves at £12
(c) a coat at £40.

13. A lizard weighs 500 g. While escaping from a predator it loses its tail and its weight is reduced by 1%. How much does it weigh now?

14. Find the odd one out
(a) 50% of £30   (b) 20% of £50   (c) 25% of £60

15. Find the odd one out
(a) 10% of £70   (b) 25% of £60   (c) 5% of £140

16. A hen weighs 3 kg. After laying an egg her weight is reduced by 2%. How much does she weigh now?

17. A marathon runner weighs 60 kg at the start of a race. During the race his weight is reduced by 5%. How much does he weigh at the end of the race?

Percentages using a calculator

(a) To work out 16% of 210 we can convert the percentage to either an equivalent decimal or fraction.
So 16% of 210 = 0.16 × 210

$$\boxed{0.16} \quad \boxed{\times} \quad \boxed{210} \quad \boxed{=} \qquad \text{Answer: 33.6}$$

(b) Work out 16% of £15.

16% of £15
$= \frac{16}{100} \times \frac{15}{1}$
$= \frac{240}{100} = £2.40$

(c) Work out 23% of £350
(Quick way)
23% = 0·23 as a decimal
So 23% of £350 = 0·23 × 350
$= £80.50$

Exercise 4

1. Copy and complete, using percentages and decimals.

(a) 24% = 0·24   (b) 37% = ☐   (c) 83% = ☐

(d) 8% = ☐   (e) ☐ % = 0·11   (f) ☐ % = 0·07

2. Work out

(a) 55% of £310   (b) 24% of £44   (c) 19% of £1120
(d) 6% of £406   (e) 5% of £12·60   (f) 120% of £400

3. Give the correct units in your answers to the following:

(a) 18% of 28 km   (b) 97% of 4000 kg   (c) 35% of 400 m
(d) 62% of $35 000   (e) 11% of 710 km   (f) 7% of $155

4. Using a calculator we find that 13·2% of £12·65 = £1·6698.

This answer has to be rounded off to the nearest penny, since the penny is the smallest unit of currency.
So 13·2% of £12·65 = £1·67, to the nearest penny.

Work out, to the nearest penny:
(a) 8% of £11·64   (b) 37% of £9·65
(c) 3·5% of £13·80   (d) 12% of £24·52
(e) $3\frac{1}{2}$% of £11·11   (f) 115% of £212·14

2.6 Mental arithmetic

Mental calculation strategies

In this section we will look at strategies for adding and subtracting numbers mentally. The introduction is followed by 12 questions to practise the new techniques.

A. 'Easy-to-add' numbers

When numbers are added the order of the numbers does not matter:

$$23 + 17 \quad\quad = 17 + 23$$
$$41 + 9 + 110 = 110 + 9 + 41$$

Many pairs of numbers are easy to add together mentally

e.g. $17 + 23 = 40,$ $18 + 32 = 50,$ $33 + 7 = 40$

Practice questions

Look for 'easy-to-add' pairs of numbers in the following. If necessary change the order of the numbers in your head and then write down the answer without working.

1. $5 + 17 + 15$	**2.** $8 + 27 + 12$	**3.** $17 + 13 + 16$
4. $22 + 48 + 11$	**5.** $9 + 87 + 11$	**6.** $19 + 41 + 37$
7. $17 + 15 + 25$	**8.** $18 + 2 + 57$	**9.** $16 + 3 + 24$
10. $90 + 110 + 58$	**11.** $75 + 37 + 25$	**12.** $215 + 49 + 51$

B. Splitting the numbers

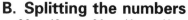

- $23 + 48$: $20 + 40 = \; 60$ and $3 + 8 = 11$
    So $23 + 48 = \; 60 + 11 = 71$

- $255 + 38$: $250 + 30 = 280$ and $5 + 8 = 13$
    So $225 + 38 = 280 + 13 = 293$

- Other way
    $23 + 48 = \; 23 + 40 + 8 = \; 63 + 8 = 71$
    $255 + 38 = 255 + 30 + 8 = 285 + 8 = 293$

    $576 - 43 = 576 - 40 - 3 = 536 - 3 = 533$
    $95 - 48 = \; 95 - 40 - 8 = \; 55 - 8 = 47$

Practice questions

1. $34 + 47$	**2.** $65 + 28$	**3.** $78 + 23$	**4.** $57 + 24$
5. $88 - 31$	**6.** $97 - 42$	**7.** $84 + 17$	**8.** $82 - 35$
9. $66 + 37$	**10.** $58 + 34$	**11.** $62 - 44$	**12.** $206 + 105$

C. Add/subtract

9, 19, 29 ... 11, 21, 31, ..., adjusting by one.

- $54 + 19 = 54 + 20 - 1 = 63$
- $77 + 41 = 77 + 40 + 1 = 118$
- $63 + 59 = 63 + 60 - 1 = 122$
- $54 - 31 = 54 - 30 - 1 = 23$
- $77 - 39 = 77 - 40 + 1 = 38$
- $95 - 29 = 95 - 30 + 1 = 66$

Practice questions

1. $67 + 21$	**2.** $37 + 51$	**3.** $36 + 39$	**4.** $76 + 29$
5. $45 + 29$	**6.** $70 - 21$	**7.** $80 - 41$	**8.** $44 + 58$
9. $33 + 96$	**10.** $91 - 37$	**11.** $53 + 41$	**12.** $48 - 23$

D. Doubling large numbers: work from the left

- double 63 = double 60 + double 3 = 120 + 6 = 126
- double 79 = double 70 + double 9 = 140 + 18 = 158
- double 127 = double 100 + double 20 + double 7 = 200 + 40 + 14 = 254
- double 264 = double 200 + double 60 + double 4 = 400 + 120 + 8 = 528

Practice questions

1. double 54	**2.** double 38	**3.** double 67	**4.** double 73
5. double 28	**6.** double 79	**7.** double 115	**8.** double 126
9. double 87	**10.** double 66	**11.** double 237	**12.** double 342

E. (a) Multiplying by doubling and then halving

- 23×5 $23 \times 10 = 230$ $230 \div 2 = 115$
- 7×45 $7 \times 90 = 630$ $630 \div 2 = 315$
- 11×15 $11 \times 30 = 330$ $330 \div 2 = 165$

(b) To multiply by 50, multiply by 100, then halve the result.

- 23×50 $23 \times 100 = 2300$ $2300 \div 2 = 1150$
- 38×50 $38 \times 100 = 3800$ $3800 \div 2 = 1900$

(c) To multiply by 25, multiply by 100, then divide by 4.

- 44×25 $44 \times 100 = 4400$ $4400 \div 4 = 1100$
- 56×25 $56 \times 100 = 5600$ $5600 \div 4 = 1400$

Practice questions

1. 22×50	**2.** 32×50	**3.** 24×25	**4.** 16×25
5. 8×35	**6.** 8×15	**7.** 7×45	**8.** 9×35
9. 14×50	**10.** 13×20	**11.** 18×50	**12.** 12×25
13. 12×25	**14.** 44×50	**15.** 26×50	**16.** 22×15

Mental arithmetic tests

There are several sets of mental arithmetic questions in this section. It is intended that a teacher will read out each question twice, with all pupils' books closed. The answers are written down without any written working. Each test of 20 questions should take about 20 minutes.

Mental Arithmetic Test 1

1. Write the number six thousand and thirty-one in figures.

2. What number should you subtract from fifty-one to get the answer twenty-four?

3. What is twenty multiplied by ten?

4. What is thirty-five divided by seven?

5. Add together nine, three and eighteen.

6. Write nought point five as a fraction.

7. How many centimetres are there in ninety millimetres?

8. What is two point three multiplied by ten?

9. How many quarters make up two whole ones?

10. The side of a square is four metres. What is the area of the square?

11. If sixty per cent of teachers in a school are female what percentage of teachers are male?

12. A bus journey starts at seven twenty. It lasts fifty-five minutes. At what time does it end?

13. In the morning the temperature is minus three degrees celsius. What will be the temperature after it rises eleven degrees?

14. Write a factor of twenty-four which is greater than one.

15. What is three squared?

16. Write down any multiple of nine.

17. How much change from ten pounds would you get after spending eight pounds and fifty pence?

18. Write down the number that is halfway between fourteen and twenty?

19. Fifty per cent of a number is thirty-two. What is the number?

20. What is the reflex angle between clock hands showing three o'clock?

Mental Arithmetic Test 2

1. Add together seven, three and twelve.

2. Write the number that is thirteen less than one hundred.

3. What is nine multiplied by seven?

4. Write the number two thousand and thirty-seven in figures.

5. Write nought point two five as a fraction.

6. What is two hundred and ten divided by one hundred?

7. Change thirteen centimetres into millimetres.

8. What is double seventeen?

9. How many ten pence coins make three pounds and seventy pence?

10. What is four hundred and fifty-eight to the nearest ten?

11. What number is half way between six and thirteen?

12. A television programme starts at five minutes to seven and lasts thirty-five minutes. At what time does the programme finish?

13. One third of a number is six. What is the number?

14. How many twenty pence coins would you get for ten pounds?

15. What number is eight squared?

16. What is three quarters of one hundred?

17. If seventy-seven per cent of pupils in a school are right-handed, what percentage are left-handed?

18. Write seven tenths as a decimal number.

19. The temperature in Weston-super-Mare was minus two degrees, the temperature in Benidorm was eleven degrees warmer. What was the temperature in Benidorm?

20. David ate one hundred and twenty degrees of a circular wedding cake. Jacqui ate sixty degrees. How many degrees of cake were left?

Mental Arithmetic Test 3

1. Write the number two thousand one hundred and four in figures

2. What number is eight more than thirty-seven?

3. If oranges cost twelve pence each, how many can I buy for one pound?

4. With three darts I score seven, double five and treble eleven. What is my total score?

5. A film lasting one and half hours starts at seven twenty-five p.m. What time does the film finish?

6. If I buy a pen for twenty-eight pence and a note pad for forty-two pence, how much change do I get from one pound?

7. What number is nine less than forty-six?

8. What is half of half of sixty?

9. How many twenty pence coins make five pounds?

10. What is the perimeter of a rectangular lawn fifteen metres by six metres?

11. I am facing South-West and the wind is hitting me on my back. What direction is the wind coming from?

12. If eight per cent of pupils of a school are absent, what percentage of pupils are present?

13. Write nought point nine as a fraction.

14. What is twenty-fifteen in twelve hour clock time?

15. How many degrees are there in three right angles?

16. A quarter of my wages is taken in tax. What percentage have I got left?

17. How many grams are there in half a kilogram?

18. What four coins make seventy-six pence?

19. One angle in an isosceles triangle is one hundred and ten degrees. How large is each of the other two angles?

20. What number is one hundred times bigger than nought point two?

Mental Arithmetic Test 4

1. What are eight twenties?

2. What number is nineteen more than eighty-seven?

3. Write in figures the number six-thousand and eleven.

4. What is one quarter of twenty-eight?

5. What is the sum of sixty-three and twenty-nine?

6. How many sevens are there in eighty-four?

7. A pair of shorts costs £8·99, how much change do you get from a £10 note?

8. Subtract forty-five centimetres from two metres giving your answer in metres as a decimal number.

9. If you have three thousand and eleven pennies, how much do you have in pounds and pence?

10. The perimeter of a square is sixteen centimetres. What is the length of the side of the square?

11. How many metres are there in 1·5 kilometres?

12. What is fifty per cent of fifty pounds?

13. How many sides has a heptagon?

14. I think of a number, double it and the answer is five. What was the number I thought of?

15. What is three thousand four hundred and sixty-nine to the nearest hundred?

16. What is nought point two squared?

17. Two angles of a triangle add up to one hundred and fifty-five degrees. What size is the third angle?

18. Write noon in twenty-four hour clock time.

19. You are facing south and turn through three right angles anti-clockwise, what direction are you now facing?

20. A thermometer in a freezer compartment shows minus five degrees. The temperature outside the freezer is thirteen degrees celsius. What is the difference in temperature between inside and outside?

Mental Arithmetic Test 5

1. What is nought point one as a percentage?

2. How many edges has a triangular based pyramid?

3. What is three quarters of sixty pounds?

4. Change nineteen forty-five into twelve hour clock time.

5. I am facing north-west and turn through one and a half right-angles in a clockwise turn. In which direction am I now facing?

6. What is the product of ten and twenty-five?

7. What is the sum of the numbers 1, 2, 3, 4, 5?

8. How much change from a ten pound note will I receive if I spend three pounds and ninety-nine pence?

9. How many 2 p coins are worth the same as twenty 5 p coins?

10. How many centimetres are there in one hundred and five millimetres?

11. Two angles in a triangle are forty-five and sixty-five degrees. What is the third angle?

12. A 'pools' prize of six million pounds is shared equally between one hundred people. How much does each person receive?

13. What is the probability I roll an even number on a fair dice?

14. What is the next prime number after thirteen?

15. How many seconds are there in one hour?

16. I bought a magazine for 79 p and paid with a £1 coin. My change consisted of five coins. What were they?

17. What is the perimeter of a square whose area is nine centimetres squared?

18. What is the name given to a triangle which has two sides the same length and a pair of equal triangles?

19. Write down the number that is halfway between twenty-seven and eighty-three.

20. Answer true or false: 1 km is longer than 1 mile.

Mental Arithmetic Test 6

1. Write ten million pence in pounds.

2. Write down a sensible estimate for eleven multiplied by ninety-nine.

3. Write the number two thousand one hundred and seven in figures.

4. What is nine hundred and fifty-eight to the nearest hundred?

5. In a survey three quarters of people like football. What percentage of people like football?

6. What decimal number is twenty-three divided by one hundred?

7. How many twenty pence coins make three pounds?

8. How many twelve pence pencils can you buy for one pound?

9. One third of a number is eight. What is the number?

10. Write nine tenths as a decimal number.

11. What is the name of the quadrilateral which has only one pair of parallel sides?

12. What number is 10 less than ninety thousand?

13. A sphere is a prism. True or false?

14. What is the probability of scoring less than six on a fair dice?

15. I think of a number, divide it by three and the answer is seven. What number did I think of?

16. What is the area of a rectangle nine metres by seven metres.

17. How many quarters are there in one and a half?

18. How many millimetres are there in one metre?

19. How many hours of recording time are there on a two hundred and forty minute video tape?

20. What number is squared to produce eighty-one?

Test 7	Test 8	Test 9	Test 10
1. $39 + 22$	1. 65×2	1. $7 + 77$	1. 25% of 880
2. $60 - 21$	2. $84 - 7$	2. $330 - 295$	2. $400 \div 20$
3. 20% of 50	3. $0 \cdot 7 + 0 \cdot 3$	3. $(8 - 2)^2$	3. 8×7
4. $0 \cdot 2 + 0 \cdot 62$	4. 23×100	4. $37 + 63$	4. $3 \cdot 5 + 0 \cdot 35$
5. 20×6	5. 7^2	5. 30×7	5. 1% of 20 000
6. $200 - 145$	6. £10 − 50p	6. 25×200	6. $301 - 102$
7. £5 − £1·20	7. 50% of 684	7. 12×7	7. $(3 + 8)^2$
8. 9×7	8. $1 - 0 \cdot 2$	8. $5^2 - 5$	8. Half of 630
9. $14 + 140$	9. 25×12	9. $76 + 14$	9. $1000 \times 0 \cdot 5$
10. 50×22	10. $8 + 9 + 10$	10. 5% of 440	10. $3 \times 4 \times 5$
11. 5% of 300	11. $210 \div 7$	11. $500 - 85$	11. 25×16
12. Half of 330	12. 100×100	12. $0 \cdot 6 + 0 \cdot 4$	12. $54 \div 9$
13. $600 - 245$	13. $5 \cdot 5 + 1 \cdot 5$	13. 10^3	13. 30×60
14. $2 \cdot 4 + 1 \cdot 7$	14. $(2 + 3)^2$	14. $425 - 198$	14. $22 + 23 + 24$
15. $200 \div 5$	15. $240 \div 6$	15. 200×8	15. $6^2 - 2^2$
16. 8×25	16. $8 - 2 \cdot 5$	16. $420 \div 7$	16. $1100 - 999$
17. 60p + £1·50	17. Half of 38·4	17. $4^2 + 7$	17. $11 - 0 \cdot 3$
18. $82 - 63$	18. $400 \div 50$	18. $9 - 0 \cdot 2$	18. $200 \div 200$
19. $7 + 8 + 9$	19. 15% of 300	19. $2 \cdot 6 + 2 \cdot 6$	19. 60×60
20. $2 \times 3 \times 4$	20. $18 + 81$	20. $2600 \div 100$	20. $4 \times 5 \times 6$

2.7 Mathematical problems and puzzles

Largest product

1. Arrange the digits 1, 2, 3 and 4, one into each box, so that the answer is as large as possible. You may use a calculator.

$$\begin{array}{cc} \square\,\square \\ \times\ \square\,\square \\ \hline \\ \hline \end{array} \qquad or \qquad \begin{array}{cc} \square\,\square\,\square \\ \times\qquad \square \\ \hline \\ \hline \end{array}$$

2. Arrange the digits 1, 2, 3, 4 and 5, one into each box, so that the answer is as large as possible.

$$\begin{array}{cc} \square\,\square\,\square \\ \times\ \square\,\square \\ \hline \\ \hline \end{array} \qquad or \qquad \begin{array}{cc} \square\,\square\,\square\,\square \\ \times\qquad\quad \square \\ \hline \\ \hline \end{array}$$

3. What is the largest number which can be found with a single multiplication using each of the digits 1, 2, 3, 4, 5 and 6 once only?

Puzzles

1. The totals for the rows and columns are given. Unfortunately some of the totals are hidden by ink blots. Find the values of the letters.

(a)
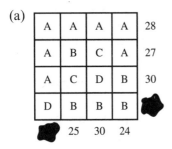

A	A	A	A	28
A	B	C	A	27
A	C	D	B	30
D	B	B	B	●
●	25	30	24	

(b)

A	B	A	B	B	18
B	B	E	C	D	21
A	B	B	A	B	18
C	B	C	B	C	19
E	B	D	E	D	26
27	10	25	23	17	

This one is more difficult

(c)
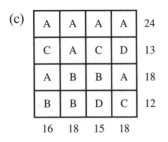

A	A	A	A	24
C	A	C	D	13
A	B	B	A	18
B	B	D	C	12
16	18	15	18	

(d)

A	B	B	A	22
A	A	B	B	22
A	B	A	B	22
B	B	A	B	17
27	17	22	17	

2. Here are some black and white beads in a pattern

(a) What colour is the 20th bead?
(b) What colour is the 71st bead?
(c) What position in the line is the 12th black bead?
(d) What position in the line is the 12th white bead?

3. In these triangle puzzles the numbers
a, b, c, d are connected as follows:

$$a \times b = c$$
$$c \times b = d$$

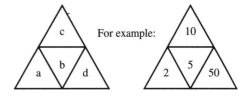

Copy and complete the following triangles:

(a)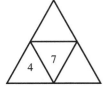

(b)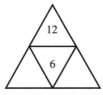

(c)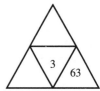

(d)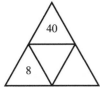

(e)

(f)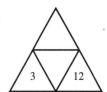

4. What is the largest possible number of people in a room if no
two people have a birthday in the same month?

5. The letters A, B, C, D, E appear once in every
row, every column and each main diagonal of
the square. Copy the square and fill in the
missing letters

				B
D				
				E
A	D			

6. Two different numbers on this section of a till receipt are obscured by food stains. What are the two numbers?

7. Draw four straight lines which pass through all 9 points, without taking your pen from the paper and without going over any line twice. [Hint: Lines can extend beyond the square].

8. King Henry has 9 coins which look identical but in fact one of them is an underweight fake. Describe how he could discover the fake using just *two* weighings on an ordinary balance.

9. Write the digits 1 to 9 so that all the answers are correct.

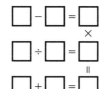

10. Draw six straight lines to pass through all 16 points, subject to the same conditions as in question 7.

Part 3

3.1 Properties of numbers

Prime numbers

A *prime* number is divisible by only two different numbers: by itself and by one. The first six prime numbers are 2, 3, 5, 7, 11, 13. Note that one is *not* a prime number.

Exercise 1

1. Draw a number square like the one shown.
   (a) Cross out in pencil the number 1.
   (b) Cross out in pencil all the even numbers, but leave the number 2.
   (c) Draw a red circle around all the numbers divisible by 3, but leave the number 3.
   (d) Cross out in pencil all the numbers divisible by 5, but leave the number 5.
   (e) Draw a green circle around all the numbers divisible by 7, but leave the number 7.
   (f) Cross out in red all the numbers divisible by 11, but leave the number 11.

1	2	3	4	5	6	7	8	9	10
11	12	13	14	15	16	17	18	19	20
21	22	23	24	25	26	27	28	29	30
31	32	33	34	35	36	37	38	39	40
41	42	43	44	45	46	47	48	49	50
51	52	53	54	55	56	57	58	59	60
61	62	63	64	65	66	67	68	69	70
71	72	73	74	75	76	77	78	79	80
81	82	83	84	85	86	87	88	89	90
91	92	93	94	95	96	97	98	99	100

You should be able to see several patterns in the table.

   (g) The numbers divisible by 3 form diagonals across the table.
   (h) The numbers divisible by 11 form one diagonal across the table.
   (i) The numbers divisible by 7 form a pattern which is not so obvious. Can you describe it?

The numbers which have been left blank are all the prime numbers between 1 and 100. You have drawn a square for finding prime numbers known as the 'sieve of Eratosthenes'. Eratosthenes was a famous Greek mathematician working over 2000 years ago.

2. How many prime numbers are there between 1 and 100?

3. Write down two prime numbers which add up to another prime number. Do this in three ways.

4. How many of the prime numbers are even?

5. How many of the prime numbers between 1 and 100 are odd?

6. Find three prime numbers which add up to another prime number.

7. (Harder) Use a calculator to find which of the following are prime numbers.

(a) 103   (b) 145   (c) 151   (d) 188
(e) 143   (f) 108   (g) 221   (h) 293
(i) 493   (j) 323   (k) 1999   (l) 2639

> Hint: Divide by the prime numbers 2, 3, 5, 7, ...

Factors

- The number 12 can be written as two numbers multiplied together in three different ways

$$\boxed{1 \times 12} \qquad \boxed{2 \times 6} \qquad \boxed{3 \times 4}$$

The numbers 1, 12, 2, 6, 3, 4 are all the *factors* of 12.

- $\boxed{1 \times 8} = 8 \qquad \boxed{2 \times 4} = 8$

The factors of 8 are 1, 2, 4, 8.

Exercise 2

Write down all the factors of the following numbers

1. 6   **2.** 4   **3.** 10   **4.** 7   **5.** 15
6. 18   **7.** 24   **8.** 21   **9.** 36   **10.** 40
11. 32   **12.** 31   **13.** 60   **14.** 63   **15.** 85

16. Factors of a number which are also prime numbers are called prime factors. We can find these prime factors using a 'factor tree'
(a) Here is a factor tree for 60   (b) Here is a factor tree for 24

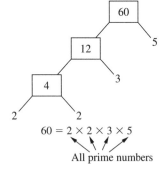

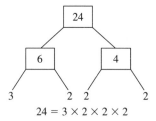

$$24 = 3 \times 2 \times 2 \times 2$$

$$60 = 2 \times 2 \times 3 \times 5$$
All prime numbers

(c) You can turn the diagram upside down and then draw a trunk around the number and branches to give a real 'tree shape'. Some people like to draw the prime factors inside apples, pears, bananas and so on.

(d) Draw a factor tree for 36.

In Questions **17** to **28** draw a factor tree for each number.

17. 28	**18.** 32	**19.** 34	**20.** 81
21. 84	**22.** 216	**23.** 294	**24.** 200
25. 1500	**26.** 2464	**27.** 4620	**28.** 98 175

29. What is the smallest number with exactly 3 factors?

30. What is the smallest number with exactly
   (a) 4 factors
   (b) 5 factors?

Multiples

The *multiples* of 5 divide by 5 with no remainder.
The first four multiples of 5 are 5, 10, 15, 20.
The first four multiples of 6 are 6, 12, 18, 24.

Exercise 3

Write down the first four multiples of:

   1. 3   **2.** 4   **3.** 2   **4.** 7   **5.** 10

Write down the first six multiples of:

   6. 5   **7.** 8   **8.** 9   **9.** 11   **10.** 20

11. Find which numbers the following sets are multiples of
   (a) 8, 12, 20, 28
   (b) 25, 30, 55, 60
   (c) 14, 21, 35, 70

In Questions **12** to **16** find the 'odd one out'. (The number which is not a multiple of the number given.)

12. Multiples of 6:   18, 24, 32, 48, 54.

13. Multiples of 11:   33, 77, 101, 132.

14. Multiples of 10: 5, 10, 20, 30, 60.

15. Multiples of 9: 18, 27, 45, 56, 72.

16. Multiples of 7: 49, 77, 91, 105, 18.

17. Find three numbers that are multiples of both 3 and 4.

18. Find three numbers that are multiples of both 2 and 5.

19. Find three numbers that are multiples of 2, 3 and 5.

20. Find two numbers that are multiples of 2, 4 and 6.

L.C.M. and H.C.F.

(a) The first few multiples of 4 are   4, 8, 12, 16, (20), 24, 28 ...

The first few multiples of 5 are   5, 10, 15, (20), 25, 30, 35 ...

The *Least Common Multiple* (L.C.M.) of 4 and 5 is 20.
It is the lowest number which is in both lists.

(b) The factors of 12 are   1, 2, 3, (4), 6, 12

The factors of 20 are   1, 2, (4), 5, 10, 20

The *Highest Common Factor* (H.C.F.) of 12 and 20 is 4.
It is the highest number which is in both lists.

Exercise 4

1. (a) Write down the first six multiples of 2.
   (b) Write down the first six multiples of 5.
   (c) Write down the L.C.M. of 2 and 5.

2. (a) Write down the first four multiples of 4.
   (b) Write down the first four multiples of 12.
   (c) Write down the L.C.M. of 4 and 12.

3. Find the L.C.M. of
   (a) 6 and 9   (b) 8 and 12   (c) 14 and 35
   (d) 2, 4 and 6   (e) 3, 5 and 10   (f) 4, 7 and 9

4. The table shows the factors and common factors of 24 and 36.

number	factors	common factors
24	1, 2, 3, 4, 6, 8, 12, 24	} 1, 2, 3, 4, 6, 12
36	1, 2, 3, 4, 6, 9, 12, 18, 36	

Write down the H.C.F. of 24 and 36.

5. The table shows the factors and common factors of 18 and 24.

number	factors	common factors
18	1, 2, 3, 6, 9, 18	} 1, 2, 3, 6
24	1, 2, 3, 4, 6, 8, 12, 24	

Write down the H.C.F. of 18 and 24.

6. Find the H.C.F. of
(a) 12 and 18   (b) 22 and 55   (c) 45 and 72
(d) 12, 18 and 30   (e) 36, 60 and 72   (f) 20, 40 and 50

7. Don't confuse you L.C.M.'s with your H.C.F.'s!
(a) Find the H.C.F. of 12 and 30.
(b) Find the L.C.M. of 8 and 20.
(c) Write down two numbers whose H.C.F. is 11.
(d) Write down two numbers whose L.C.M. is 10.

8. Given that $30 = 2 \times 3 \times 5$ and $165 = 3 \times 5 \times 11$, find the highest common factor of 30 and 165. [i.e. The highest number that goes into 30 and 165.]

9. If $315 = 3 \times 3 \times 5 \times 7$ and $273 = 3 \times 7 \times 13$, find the highest common factor of 315 and 273.

Square numbers and cube numbers

Exercise 5

1.

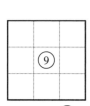
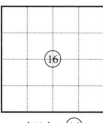

$1 \times 1 = (1)$ $2 \times 2 = (4)$ $3 \times 3 = (9)$ $4 \times 4 = (16)$

(a) The first four *square* numbers are 1, 4, 9, 16.
(b) Draw diagrams with labels to show the next three square numbers.

2. A square number is obtained by multiplying a number by itself.
3×3 is written 3^2 (We say '3 squared...')
4×4 is written 4^2

Work out
(a) 5^2 (b) 8^2 (c) 10^2 (d) 1^2

3. Work out
(a) $3^2 + 4^2$ (b) $1^2 + 2^2 + 3^2$ (c) $9^2 + 10^2$

4. (a) Write down this sentence and fill in the missing numbers

1 $= 1$ $= 1^2$

$1 + 3$ $= 4$ $= 2^2$

$1 + 3 + 5$ $= \boxed{}$ $= \boxed{}^2$

$1 + 3 + 5 + 7$ $= \boxed{}$ $= \boxed{}^2$

(b) Write down the next five lines of the sequence.

5. What number when multiplied by itself gives the following
(a) 49   (b) 81   (c) 144

6. The *square root* of a number is the number which is multiplied by itself to give that number. The symbol for square root is $\sqrt{}$.
So $\sqrt{9} = 3$, $\sqrt{16} = 4$, $\sqrt{100} = 10$
Work out
(a) $\sqrt{25}$ (b) $\sqrt{81}$ (c) $\sqrt{49}$ (d) $\sqrt{1}$

7. Copy the following and fill in the spaces

(a) $7^2 = 49$, $\sqrt{49} = \boxed{}$ (b) $14^2 = 196$, $\sqrt{196} = \boxed{}$

(c) $21^2 = 441$, $\sqrt{\boxed{}} = 21$ (d) $3 \cdot 3^2 = 10 \cdot 89$, $\sqrt{\boxed{}} = 3 \cdot 3$

8. *Lagrange's theorem.* A famous mathematician called Lagrange proved that every whole number could be written as the sum of four or fewer square numbers.

For example: $21 = 16 + 4 + 1$
                       $19 = 16 + 1 + 1 + 1$
                       $35 = 25 + 9 + 1$

Check that the theorem applies to the following numbers.

(a)   10   (b)   24   (c)   47
(d)   66   (e)   98   (f)   63
(g) 120   (h) 141   (i) 423

If you can find a number which needs more than four squares you will have disproved Lagrange's theorem and a new theorem will be named after you.

9. The numbers 1, 8, 27 are the first three *cube* numbers.

$1 \times 1 \times 1 = 1^3 = 1$ (we say '1 cubed')
$2 \times 2 \times 2 = 2^3 = 8$ (we say '2 cubed')
$3 \times 3 \times 3 = 3^3 = 27$ (we say '3 cubed')

The odd numbers can be added in groups to give an interesting sequence:

1 $= 1$ $= 1^3$
$3 + 5$ $= 8$ $= 2^3$
$7 + 9 + 11$ $= 27$ $= 3^3$

Write down the next three rows of the sequence to see if the sum of each row always gives a cube number.

Satisfied numbers

The number 4 is an even number *and* a square number. It *satisfies* both categories.

1. Copy the grid below and use a pencil for your answers (so that you can rub out mistakes.)
   Write the numbers from 1 to 9, one in each box, so that all the numbers satisfy the conditions for both the row and the column.

	Number between 5 and 9	Square number	Prime number
Factor of 6	6	?	?
Even number	?	?	?
Odd number	?	?	?

2. Copy the grid and write the numbers from 1 to 9, one in each box.

	Prime number	Multiple of 3	Factor of 16
Number greater than 5			
Odd number			
Even number			

3. This one is more difficult. Write the numbers from 1 to 16, one in each box. There are several correct solutions. Ask a friend to check yours.

	Prime number	Odd number	Factor of 16	Even number
Numbers less than 7				
Factor of 36				
Numbers less than 12				
Numbers between 11–17				

4. Design a grid with categories of your own and ask a friend to solve it.

Happy numbers

- (a) Take any number, say 23.
  (b) Square the digits and add: $2^2 + 3^2 = 4 + 9 = 13$
  (c) Repeat (b) for the answer: $1^2 + 3^2 = 1 + 9 = 10$
  (d) Repeat (b) for the answer: $1^2 + 0^2 = 1$

  23 is a so-called 'happy' number because it ends in one.

- Take another number, say 7.

  Write 7 as 07 to maintain the pattern of squaring and adding the digits.
  Here is the sequence:

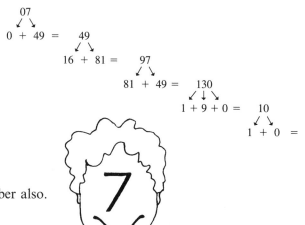

So 7 is a happy number also.

With practice you may be able to do the arithmetic in your head and write: $07 \rightarrow 49 \rightarrow 97 \rightarrow 130 \rightarrow 10 \rightarrow 1$.

You may find it helpful to make a list of the square numbers 1^2, 2^2, 3^2, ... 9^2.

- Your task is to find all the happy numbers from 1 to 100 and to circle them on a grid like the one shown.
  This may appear to be a very time-consuming and rather tedious task!
  But remember: Good mathematicians always look for short cuts and for ways of reducing the working.

  So think about what you are doing and good luck!
  As a final check you should find that there are 20 happy numbers from 1 to 100.

1	2	3	4	5	6	7	8	9	10
11	12	13	14	15	16	17	18	19	20
21	22	23	24	25	26	27	28	29	30
31	32	33	34	35	36	37	38	39	40
41	42	43	44	45	46	47	48	49	50
51	52	53	54	55	56	57	58	59	60
61	62	63	64	65	66	67	68	69	70
71	72	73	74	75	76	77	78	79	80
81	82	83	84	85	86	87	88	89	90
91	92	93	94	95	96	97	98	99	100

3.2 Order of operations

- Mathematicians all over the world regularly exchange their ideas and the results of their theories, even though much of the time they are unable to speak the same language! They can communicate mathematically because it has been agreed that everyone follows certain rules.

- Consider the possible answers to this question:
'What is five add seven multiplied by three?'

By adding first, we obtain: $5 + 7 \times 3$
$$= 12 \times 3$$
$$= 36$$

By multiplying first, we obtain: $5 + 7 \times 3$
$$= 5 + 21$$
$$= 26$$

As it stands both answers make perfect sense, though if we could all come up with different answers to the same mathematical question life would be rather stressful as people would have to argue constantly over who is correct.

- The table below shows the order in which everyone must do the given mathematical operations to ensure we all agree.

B rackets	( )	do first	'B'
I ndices	x^y	do next	'I'
D ivision M ultiplication	$\div$ $\times$	do this pair next	'D' 'M'
A ddition S ubtraction	$+$ $-$	do this pair next	'A' 'S'

Remember the word 'B I D M A S'.

(a) $40 \div 5 \times 2$
$$= 8 \times 2$$
$$= 16$$

(b) $9 + 8 - 7$
$$= 17 - 7$$
$$= 10$$

(c) $5 + 2 \times 3$
$$= 5 + 6$$
$$= 11$$
× before +

(d) $10 - 8 \div 2$
$$= 10 - 4$$
$$= 6$$
÷ before −

Exercise 1

Work out the following. Show every step in your working.

1. $5 + 3 \times 2$	**2.** $4 - 1 \times 3$	**3.** $7 - 4 \times 3$
4. $2 + 2 \times 5$	**5.** $9 + 2 \times 6$	**6.** $13 - 11 \times 1$
7. $7 \times 2 + 3$	**8.** $9 \times 4 - 12$	**9.** $2 \times 8 - 7$
10. $4 \times 7 + 2$	**11.** $13 \times 2 + 4$	**12.** $8 \times 5 - 15$
13. $6 + 10 \div 5$	**14.** $7 - 16 \div 8$	**15.** $8 - 14 \div 7$
16. $5 + 18 \div 6$	**17.** $5 + 18 \div 6$	**18.** $6 - 12 \div 4$
19. $20 \div 4 + 2$	**20.** $15 \div 3 - 7$	**21.** $24 \div 6 - 8$
22. $30 \div 6 + 9$	**23.** $8 \div 2 + 9$	**24.** $28 \div 7 - 4$
25. $13 + 3 \times 13$	**26.** $9 + 26 \div 13$	**27.** $10 \times 8 - 70$
28. $96 \div 4 - 4$	**29.** $36 \div 9 + 1$	**30.** $1 \times 2 + 3$

(a) $8 + 3 \times 4 - 6$
$= 8 + (3 \times 4) - 6$
$= 8 + 12 - 6$
$= 14$

$\times$ and $\div$
before
$+$ and $-$

(b) $3 \times 2 - 8 \div 4$
$= (3 \times 2) - (8 \div 4)$
$= 6 - 2$
$= 4$

(c) $\dfrac{8 + 6}{2} = \dfrac{14}{2}$
$= 7$
A horizontal
line acts as a
bracket.

Notice that we have put brackets in to make the working easier.

Exercise 2

Evaluate the following. Show every step in your working.

1. $2 + 3 \times 4 + 1$	**2.** $4 + 8 \times 2 - 10$	**3.** $7 + 2 \times 2 - 6$
4. $25 - 7 \times 3 + 5$	**5.** $17 - 3 \times 5 + 9$	**6.** $11 - 9 \times 1 - 1$
7. $1 + 6 \div 2 + 3$	**8.** $6 + 28 \div 7 - 2$	**9.** $8 + 15 \div 3 - 5$
10. $5 - 36 \div 9 + 3$	**11.** $6 - 24 \div 4 + 0$	**12.** $8 - 30 \div 6 - 2$
13. $3 \times 4 + 1 \times 6$	**14.** $4 \times 4 + 14 \div 7$	**15.** $2 \times 5 + 8 \div 4$
16. $21 \div 3 + 5 \times 4$	**17.** $10 \div 2 + 1 \times 3$	**18.** $15 \div 5 + 18 \div 6$
19. $5 \times 5 - 6 \times 4$	**20.** $2 \times 12 - 4 \div 2$	**21.** $7 \times 2 - 10 \div 2$
22. $35 \div 7 - 5 \times 1$	**23.** $36 \div 3 - 1 \times 7$	**24.** $42 \div 6 - 56 \div 8$
25. $72 \div 9 + 132 \div 11$	**26.** $19 + 35 \div 5 - 16$	**27.** $50 - 6 \times 7 + 8$
28. $30 - 9 \times 2 + 40$	**29.** $4 \times 11 - 28 \div 7$	**30.** $13 \times 11 - 4 \times 8$

In Questions **31** to **50** remember to perform the operation in the brackets first.

31. $3 + (6 \times 8)$ **32.** $(3 \times 8) + 6$ **33.** $(8 \div 4) + 9$

34. $3 \times (9 \div 3)$ **35.** $(5 \times 9) - 17$ **36.** $10 + (12 \times 8)$

37. $(16 - 7) \times 6$ **38.** $48 \div (14 - 2)$ **39.** $64 \div (4 \times 4)$

40. $81 + (9 \times 8)$ **41.** $67 - (24 \div 3)$ **42.** $(12 \times 8) + 69$

43. $(6 \times 6) + (7 \times 7)$ **44.** $(12 \div 3) \times (18 \div 6)$ **45.** $(5 \times 12) - (3 \times 9)$

46. $(20 - 12) \times (17 - 9)$ **47.** $100 - (99 \div 3)$ **48.** $1001 + (57 \times 3)$

49. $(3 \times 4 \times 5) - (72 \div 9)$ **50.** $(2 \times 5 \times 3) \div (11 - 5)$ **51.** $\dfrac{15 - 7}{2}$

52. $\dfrac{160}{7 + 3}$ **53.** $\dfrac{19 + 13}{6 - 2}$ **54.** $\dfrac{5 \times 7 - 9}{13}$

Indices

Remember BIDMAS: **B** rackets
                    I ndex
                    D ivide
                    M ultiply
                    A dd
                    S ubtract

(a) 5×3^2
$\;\;= 5 \times 9$ ← index before multiplying
$\;\;= 45$

(b) $2 \times (8 - 3)^3$
$\;\;= 2 \times 5^3$
$\;\;= 2 \times 125$ ← bracket then index then multiply
$\;\;= 250$

Exercise 3

Evaluate the following, showing all your working.

1. 2^4 **2.** 3^3 **3.** 0^5

4. $10 + 3^3$ **5.** $4^2 - 8$ **6.** $32 - 5^2$

7. $3 + 3^2$ **8.** 8^2 **9.** 5×4^2

10. $3^2 \times 2$ **11.** 62×2^3 **12.** $5^3 \times 1$

13. $1^4 \times 3^4$ **14.** $(1 + 1)^3$ **15.** $(1 + 2)^3$

16. $(5 - 4)^3$ **17.** $4 \times (3 + 1)^2$ **18.** $(9 - 5)^4 \div 4$

19. $2 \times (3^2 - 1)$ **20.** $(5^2 + 5^2) \div 5$ **21.** $2 \times (6 - 3)^2$

22. $5 \times (2 \times 1)^3$ **23.** 3×2^3 **24.** $20 - 4^2$

Working backwards

Exercise 4

Copy each question and write brackets so that each calculation gives
the correct answer.

1. $3 + 4 \times 5 = 35$
2. $6 + 9 \times 7 = 69$
3. $7 \times 2 + 3 = 17$
4. $9 + 12 \times 5 = 105$
5. $6 \times 8 - 2 = 36$
6. $3 \times 8 - 6 = 18$
7. $19 - 6 \times 3 = 39$
8. $27 - 9 \div 3 = 24$
9. $51 \div 3 + 4 = 21$
10. $7 \times 24 - 5 = 133$
11. $6 + 14 \div 2 = 10$
12. $11 + 6 \times 4 = 68$
13. $12 \times 8 - 9 \times 7 = 33$
14. $8 \times 9 - 4 \times 7 = 44$
15. $5 \times 6 - 4 \div 2 = 13$
16. $81 \div 9 \times 12 - 4 = 72$
17. $3 + 5 \times 9 - 7 = 16$
18. $16 - 10 \div 18 \div 6 = 2$
19. $6 + 7 - 1 \div 2 = 6$
20. $5 + 7 \div 3 \times 0 = 0$

Jumble the numbers

Exercise 5

Using each number once, find the calculation which gives the correct
answer.

For example:

Numbers	Answer	Calculation
5, 3, 6	3	$(6 - 5) \times 3 = 3$

	Numbers			Answer	Calculation		Numbers			Answer	Calculation
1.	2	4	8	6		**2.**	2	3	5	21	
3.	7	2	3	3		**4.**	9	2	4	7	
5.	8	4	5	20		**6.**	20	2	3	6	
7.	7	2	4	30		**8.**	7	22	6	20	
9.	6	4	3	8		**10.**	8	40	3	8	
11.	8	36	4	5		**12.**	7	49	2	14	
13.	21	14	11	24		**14.**	16	3	9	57	
15.	12	4	16	7		**16.**	24	42	6	24	
17.	18	5	13	25		**18.**	40	6	16	4	
19.	7	8	6	50		**20.**	13	8	4	44	
21.	4	3	9	12		**22.**	7	9	3	21	
23.	45	4	3	11		**24.**	121	11	7	77	

25. Make up your own question to try on a friend.
    You may use as many numbers as you like.

3.3 Using a calculator

Money and time on a calculator

- To work out £27·30 ÷ 7, key in
  The answer is 3·9. *Remember* this means £3·90.

- A machine takes 15 minutes to make one toy. How long will it
  take to make 1627 toys?
  15 minutes is one quarter of an hour and $\frac{1}{4} = 0·25$ as a decimal.

  Key in $\boxed{0·25}$ $\boxed{\times}$ $\boxed{1627}$ $\boxed{=}$.

  The answer is 406·75.
  It will take 406·75 hours or 406 hours 45 minutes.

- 6 minutes is $\frac{6}{60}$ of an hour. $\frac{6}{60} = \frac{1}{10} = 0.1$ hours.
  Similarly 27 minutes $= \frac{27}{60}$ of an hour. $\frac{27}{60} = 0·45$ hours.

Exercise 1

1. Work out the following and give your answer in *pounds*.
   (a) £1·22 × 5   (b) £153·60 ÷ 24   (c) £12·35 − £7·65
   (d) 20p × 580   (e) 6p × 2155   (f) £10 ÷ 250

2. Write these time intervals in hours as decimals.
   (a) 2 h 30 min   (b) 4 h 15 min   (c) 3 h 45 min
   (d)   6 min   (e)   12 min   (f)   54 min
   (g) 5 h 24 min   (h) 1 h 20 min   (i) 3 h 40 min

3. Work out the following and give your answer in *hours*.
   (a) 2 h 45 min × 9   (b) 3 h 20 min × 9   (c) 14 h 30 min ÷ 5
   (d) 24 min × 15   (e) 27 min × 22   (f) 18 min × 58

$$6 \text{ min} = \frac{6}{60} \text{ hour}$$
$$= 0·1 \text{ hour}$$
$$15 \text{ min} = \frac{15}{60} \text{ hour}$$
$$= 0·25 \text{ hour}$$

Order of operations

Where there is a mixture of operations to be performed to avoid
uncertainty you must follow these rules:
(a) work out brackets first
(b) work out indices next
(c) work out ÷, × before +, −

Remember: 'BIDMAS' from Section 3.2 in this book.

It is good practice to check your answers by estimation or by
performing the inverse operation.

Exercise 2

Use a calculator and give the answer correct to one decimal place.

1. 2.5×1.67 **2.** $19.6 - 3.7311$ **3.** 0.792^2

4. $0.13 + 8.9 - 3.714$ **5.** $2.4^2 - 1.712$ **6.** $5.3 \times 1.7 + 3.7$

7. $0.71 \times 0.92 - 0.15$ **8.** $9.6 \div 1.72$ **9.** $8.17 - 1.56 + 7.4$

10. $\sqrt{4.52}$ **11.** $\sqrt{198}$ **12.** $\sqrt{\dfrac{2.63}{1.9}}$

In Questions **13** to **30** remember 'B I D M A S'.

13. $2.5 + 3.1 \times 2.4$ **14.** $7.81 + 0.7 \times 1.82$ **15.** $8.73 + 9 \div 11$

16. $11.7 \div 9 - 0.74$ **17.** $7 \div 0.32 + 1.15$ **18.** $2.6 + 5.2 \times 1.7$

19. $2.9 + \dfrac{8.3}{1.83}$ **20.** $1.7^2 + 2.62$ **21.** $5.2 + \dfrac{11.7}{1.85}$

22. $9.64 + 26 \div 12.7$ **23.** $1.27 + 3.1^2$ **24.** $4.2^2 \div 9.4$

25. $0.151 + 1.4 \times 9.2$ **26.** 1.7^3 **27.** $8.2 + 3.2 \times 3.3$

28. $3.2 + \dfrac{1.41}{6.72}$ **29.** $\dfrac{1.9 + 3.71}{2.3}$ **30.** $\dfrac{8.7 - 5.371}{1.14}$

Using brackets

Most calculators (apart from those given away free with a packet of 'Honey Nut Loops') have brackets buttons like these $\boxed{[(\text{---}}$, $\boxed{\text{---})]}$.

When you press the left hand bracket button $\boxed{[(\text{---}}$ you may see

$\boxed{\text{C0I} \qquad \text{0.}}$ ignore this.

When the right hand bracket button is pressed you will see that the calculation inside the brackets has been performed. Try it.

Don't forget to press the $\boxed{=}$ button at the end to give the final answer.

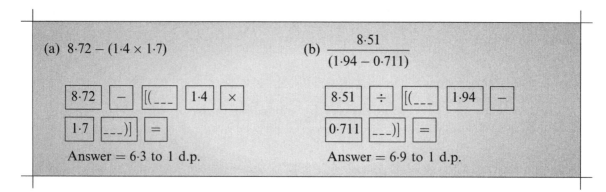

Exercise 3

Work out and give the answer correct to 1 decimal place.

1. $18{\cdot}41 - (7{\cdot}2 \times 1{\cdot}3)$

2. $11{\cdot}01 + (2{\cdot}6 \div 7)$

3. $(1{\cdot}27 + 5{\cdot}6) \div 1{\cdot}4$

4. $9{\cdot}6 + (11{\cdot}2 \div 4)$

5. $(8{\cdot}6 \div 3) - 1{\cdot}4$

6. $11{\cdot}7 - (2{\cdot}6 \times 2{\cdot}7)$

7. $7{\cdot}41 - \left(\dfrac{7{\cdot}3}{1{\cdot}4}\right)$

8. $\left(\dfrac{8{\cdot}91}{1{\cdot}7}\right) - 2{\cdot}63$

9. $\dfrac{1{\cdot}41}{(1{\cdot}7 + 0{\cdot}21)}$

10. $(1{\cdot}56 + 1{\cdot}9) \div 2{\cdot}45$

11. $3{\cdot}2 \times (1{\cdot}9 - 0{\cdot}74)$

12. $8{\cdot}9 \div (1{\cdot}3 - 0{\cdot}711)$

13. $(8{\cdot}72 \div 1{\cdot}4) \times 1{\cdot}49$

14. $(2{\cdot}67 + 1{\cdot}2 + 5) \times 1{\cdot}13$

15. $23 - (9{\cdot}2 \times 1{\cdot}85)$

16. $\dfrac{(8{\cdot}41 + 1{\cdot}73)}{1{\cdot}47}$

17. $\dfrac{7{\cdot}23}{(8{\cdot}2 \times 0{\cdot}91)}$

18. $\dfrac{(11{\cdot}4 - 7{\cdot}87)}{17}$

In Questions **19** to **40** use the $\boxed{x^2}$ button where needed.

19. $2{\cdot}6^2 - 1{\cdot}4$

20. $8{\cdot}3^2 \times 1{\cdot}17$

21. $7{\cdot}2^2 \div 6{\cdot}67$

22. $(1{\cdot}4 + 2{\cdot}67)^2$

23. $(8{\cdot}41 - 5{\cdot}7)^2$

24. $(2{\cdot}7 \times 1{\cdot}31)^2$

25. $8{\cdot}2^2 - (1{\cdot}4 + 1{\cdot}73)$

26. $\dfrac{2{\cdot}6^2}{(1{\cdot}3 + 2{\cdot}99)}$

27. $4{\cdot}1^2 - \left(\dfrac{8{\cdot}7}{3{\cdot}2}\right)$

28. $\dfrac{(2{\cdot}7 + 6{\cdot}04)}{(1{\cdot}4 + 2{\cdot}11)}$

29. $\dfrac{(8{\cdot}71 - 1{\cdot}6)}{(2{\cdot}4 + 9{\cdot}73)}$

30. $\left(\dfrac{2{\cdot}3}{1{\cdot}4}\right)^2$

31. $9{\cdot}72^2 - (2{\cdot}9 \times 2{\cdot}7)$

32. $(3{\cdot}3 + 1{\cdot}3^2) \times 9$

33. $(2{\cdot}7^2 - 2{\cdot}1) \div 5$

34. $\left(\dfrac{2{\cdot}84}{7}\right) + \left(\dfrac{7}{11{\cdot}2}\right)$

35. $\dfrac{(2{\cdot}7 \times 8{\cdot}1)}{(12 - 8{\cdot}51)}$

36. $\left(\dfrac{2{\cdot}3}{1{\cdot}5}\right) - \left(\dfrac{6{\cdot}3}{8{\cdot}9}\right)$

37. $(1{\cdot}31 + 2{\cdot}705) - 1{\cdot}3^2$

38. $(2{\cdot}71 - 0{\cdot}951) \times 5{\cdot}62$

39. $\dfrac{(8{\cdot}5 \times 1{\cdot}952)}{(7{\cdot}2 - 5{\cdot}96)}$

40. $\left(\dfrac{80{\cdot}7}{30{\cdot}3}\right) - \left(\dfrac{11{\cdot}7}{10{\cdot}2}\right)$

Using the memory

We will use the following memory keys: [Min] Puts a number into the memory.

[MR] Recalls a number from the memory.

To *clear* the memory we will press [0] [Min].

Many calculators will keep a number stored in the memory even when they are switched off. A letter 'M' on the display shows that the memory does contain a number.

The [Min] key is very useful because it *automatically* clears any number already in the memory when it puts in the new number.

So if you pressed [13·2] [Min] [6·5] [Min], the number in the memory would be 6·5. The 13·2 is effectively 'lost'.

Work out, correct to 2 decimal places.

(a) $\dfrac{8\cdot97}{1\cdot6 - 0\cdot973}$

Work out the bottom line first.

[1·6] [−] [0·973] [=] [Min]

[8·97] [÷] [MR] [=]

Answer = 14·3 to 1 d.p.

(b) $8\cdot51 - \left(\dfrac{3\cdot24}{1\cdot73}\right)$

Work out the brackets first.

[3·24] [÷] [1·7] [=] [Min]

[8·51] [−] [MR] [=]

Answer = 6·6 to 1 d.p.

A very common error occurs when people forget to press the [=] button at the end of the calculation.

Exercise 4

Work out and give the answer correct to 1 decimal place.

1. $\dfrac{5\cdot63}{2\cdot8 - 1\cdot71}$

2. $\dfrac{11\cdot5}{5\cdot24 + 1\cdot57}$

3. $\dfrac{8\cdot27}{2\cdot9 \times 1\cdot35}$

4. $\dfrac{3\cdot7 - 2\cdot41}{1\cdot9 + 0\cdot72}$

5. $\dfrac{8\cdot5 + 9\cdot3}{12\cdot9 - 8\cdot72}$

6. $\dfrac{0\cdot97 \times 3\cdot85}{1\cdot24 + 4\cdot63}$

7. $14\cdot5 - \left(\dfrac{1\cdot9}{0\cdot7}\right)$

8. $8\cdot41 - 3\cdot2 \times 1\cdot76$

9. $11\cdot62 - \dfrac{6\cdot3}{9\cdot8}$

10. $\dfrac{9\cdot84 \times 0\cdot751}{6\cdot3 \times 0\cdot95}$

11. $5\cdot62 + 1\cdot98 + \dfrac{1\cdot2}{4\cdot5}$

12. $8\cdot5 - \dfrac{8\cdot9}{11\cdot6}$

13. $\dfrac{6\cdot3}{4\cdot2} + \dfrac{8\cdot2}{11\cdot9}$

14. $\dfrac{8\cdot43 + 1\cdot99}{9\cdot6 - 1\cdot73}$

15. $\dfrac{17\cdot6}{8\cdot4} - \dfrac{1\cdot92}{8\cdot41}$

16. $25\cdot1 - 4\cdot2^2$

17. $(9\cdot8 - 4\cdot43)^2$

18. $18\cdot7 - 2\cdot33^2$

19. $8{\cdot}21^2 + 1{\cdot}67^2$

20. $9{\cdot}23^2 - 7{\cdot}42^2$

21. $16{\cdot}1 - 1{\cdot}1^2$

22. $\dfrac{16{\cdot}1}{4{\cdot}7} - 1{\cdot}8^2$

23. $\left(\dfrac{17{\cdot}2}{9{\cdot}8} - 1{\cdot}2\right)^2$

24. $9{\cdot}9 - 8{\cdot}3 \times 0{\cdot}075$

25. $1{\cdot}21 - \dfrac{9}{14^2}$

26. $3{\cdot}7^2 + \dfrac{11{\cdot}4}{1{\cdot}7}$

27. $\dfrac{11{\cdot}7 - 3{\cdot}73}{2{\cdot}45^2}$

28. $\dfrac{8{\cdot}94}{4{\cdot}8 + 1{\cdot}7^2}$

29. $\dfrac{3{\cdot}21^2}{8{\cdot}2 - 4{\cdot}11}$

30. $\dfrac{116{\cdot}7}{8{\cdot}1^2 + 32}$

31. $8{\cdot}7 + \dfrac{8{\cdot}2}{9{\cdot}7} + \dfrac{4{\cdot}1}{5{\cdot}6}$

32. $8{\cdot}5 - (1{\cdot}6^2 + 1{\cdot}9^2)$

33. $8{\cdot}3 + \dfrac{1{\cdot}9}{8{\cdot}4} - \dfrac{1{\cdot}7}{6{\cdot}5}$

34. $3{\cdot}2 + \left(3{\cdot}2 + \dfrac{1{\cdot}4}{5}\right)^2$

35. $\dfrac{3{\cdot}4}{1{\cdot}6} + \left(\dfrac{2{\cdot}1}{1{\cdot}3}\right)^2$

36. $\left(8{\cdot}2 - \dfrac{1}{8{\cdot}2}\right) \times 8{\cdot}2$

3.4 Metric and Imperial units

Originally measurements were made by using appropriately sized bits of human being. The inch was measured using the thumb, (hence we still sometimes say 'rule of thumb' when we mean rough measurement), the foot by using the foot.

After the French Revolution in 1789 the standard unit of length became the metre and the unit of mass became the kilogram. All the smaller and larger units are obtained by dividing or multiplying by ten, a hundred, a thousand and so on.

Here is a table with details of the most commonly used units for length, mass and volume.

Metric units		Imperial units
Length	10 mm = 1 cm	12 inches = 1 foot
	100 cm = 1 m	3 feet = 1 yard
	1000 m = 1 km	1760 yards = 1 mile
Mass	1000 mg = 1 g	16 ounces = 1 pound
	1000 g = 1 kg	14 pounds = 1 stone
	1000 kg = 1 tonne	2240 pounds = 1 ton
Volume	1000 ml = 1 litre	8 pints = 1 gallon
	1 ml = 1 cm^3	

Exercise 1

1. Write each length in cm.
   (a) 3 m   (b) 1·8 m   (c) 20 mm   (d) 0·4 m

2. Write each length in km.
   (a) 5000 m   (b) 2300 m   (c) 650 m   (d) 100 000 m

3. Write each mass in g.
   (a) 2 kg   (b) 1·65 kg   (c) 0·7 kg   (d) 0·085 kg

4. Write each mass in kg.
   (a) 2 tonnes   (b) 50 tonnes   (c) 5500 g   (d) 600 g

Copy and complete.

5. 3 m =   cm   **6.** 1·5 km =   m   **7.** 7 kg =   g   **8.** 500 g =   kg

9. 30 mm =   cm   **10.** 8 cm =   mm   **11.** 60 cm =   m   **12.** 2 m =   mm

13. 0·6 m =   cm   **14.** 1·2 kg =   g   **15.** 800 g =   kg   **16.** 8 tonnes =   kg

17. 2·6 kg =   g   **18.** 3 litres =   ml   **19.** 32 litres =   ml   **20.** 2·5 m =   mm

21. 8·7 m =   cm   **22.** 58 mm =   cm   **23.** 0·45 kg =   g   **24.** 8 g =   kg

25. Write each length in m.
   (a) 5 cm   (b) 0·04 km   (c) 80 mm

26. Write each mass in kg.
   (a) 650 g   (b) 85 tonnes   (c) 40 g

Converting between metric and imperial units

- It is sometimes necessary to convert imperial units into metric units and vice versa.
  Try to remember the following *approximate equivalents*:

> 1 foot ≈ 30 cm
> 8 km   ≈ 5 miles
> 1 kg   ≈ 2·2 pounds
> 1 gallon ≈ 4·5 litres

[The '≈' sign means 'is approximately equal to'.]

- Here are some familiar objects to help you remember.

A one pound coin has a mass of about 10 grams.

A standard bag of sugar has a mass of 1 kg.

A 'tall' adult man is about 6 feet tall. [180 cm]

Exercise 2

Copy and complete using the approximate conversions given above.

1. 2 kg ≈   pounds

2. 6 feet ≈   cm

3. 24 km ≈   miles

4. 10 gallons ≈   litres

5. 16 km ≈   miles

6. 2 feet ≈   cm

7. 90 cm ≈   feet

8. 20 miles ≈   km

9. 9 litres ≈   gallons

10. 22 pounds ≈   kg

11. 3 m ≈   feet

12. 20 gallons ≈   litres

13. The maximum height limit for children on a bouncy castle is four feet. Jason is 150 cm. Is Jason inside the limit?

14. The maximum weight limit for a lift is 2 tonnes. The total mass of a group of people is 6000 pounds. Will all the people be able to go on the lift?

15. Jennie fills up her car with 10 gallons of petrol. Roughly how much will it cost if petrol costs £1 per litre?

16. The maximum range of helicopter is 500 miles from its base. How far is this range in km?

17. The distance from Calais to Paris is about 240 km. How many miles is this?

18. Here are scales for changing:
A kilograms and pounds,
B litres and gallons.
In this question give your answers to the *nearest whole number*.
(a) About how many kilograms are there in 5 pounds?
(b) About how many litres are there in 2·2 gallons?
(c) About how many pounds are there in 1·8 kilograms?

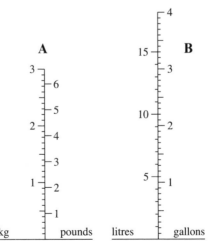

Changing units

When a problem has quantities measured in different units the first
thing you must do is change some of the units so that all quantities
are in the same units.

- Find the area of the rectangular table top shown.

  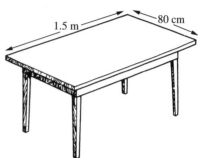

  Write 80 cm as 0·8 m.

  Area of table = 1·5 × 0·8.

  = 1·2 m².

Exercise 3

1. Work out
   (a) 2 m + 55 cm [in cm]
   (b) 3 km + 218 m [in m]
   (c) ·0·3 kg + 700 g [in g]
   (d) 8 cm − 3 mm [in mm]
   (e) 7 cm + 9 mm [in cm]
   (f) 1·2 kg + 805 g [in kg]

2. Work out
   (a) 3 tonnes + 600 kg [in kg]
   (b) 4 litres + 300 ml [in ml]
   (c) 0·5 m + 8 mm [in mm]
   (d) 17 g + 0·2 kg [in g]
   (e) 25 mm + 8·5 cm [in cm]
   (f) 8 kg − 700 g [in g]

3. Find the area of each shape in m².
   (a)
   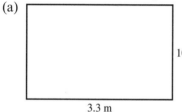
   100 cm
   3.3 m

   (b)
   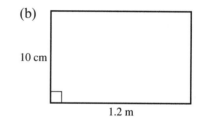
   10 cm
   1.2 m

4. Find the perimeter of each shape in cm.
   (a)

   80 cm
   1.2 m

   (b)
   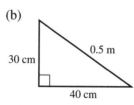
   30 cm   0.5 m
   40 cm

   (c)
   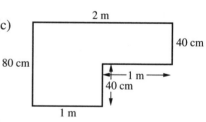
   2 m
   40 cm
   80 cm
   1 m
   40 cm
   1 m

5. A postage stamp measures 22 mm by 2 cm.
   Calculate the area of the stamp in cm².

6. Water flows through a pipe at a rate of 10 ml per second. How
   many litres of water flow through the pipe in 10 minutes?

6.5 Handling data

Bar charts and bar-line graphs

When you do a survey the information you collect is called *data*.
This data is usually easier for someone else to understand if you
display it in some sort of chart or graph.

(a) The scores of 35 golfers competing
in a tournament were

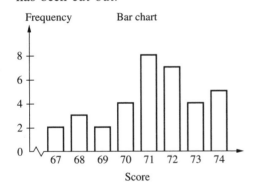

68	74	71	72	71	68	70
74	69	71	70	67	73	71
70	74	69	72	73	74	71
72	74	71	72	72	70	73
67	68	72	73	72	71	71

(b) A tally chart/frequency table is
made for the scores.

score	tally	frequency
67				2
68					3
69				2
70						4
71										8
72									7
73						4
74							5

(c) This data can be displayed on either a bar chart or on a bar-line
graph. The '⌄/\⌄' shows that a section on the horizontal axis
has been cut out.

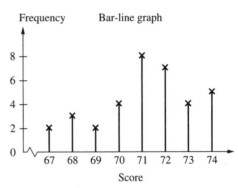

Exercise 1

1. In a survey children were asked to name their
favourite sport.
   (a) What was the most popular sport?
   (b) How many children chose Athletics?
   (c) How many children took part in the survey?

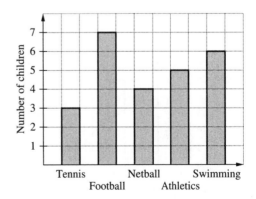

2. Here is a *bar-line graph* showing the number of children in the families of children in a school.
(a) How many families had three children?
(b) How many families were there altogether?

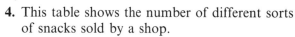

3. Collect your own data for a bar line graph like the one in Question **2**. Ask lots of people to state the number of children in their families.
Draw a graph of the results and use colour to make it more attractive.

4. This table shows the number of different sorts of snacks sold by a shop.

(a) How many snacks were sold on Thursday?
(b) Each Aero costs 22 p. How much was spent on Aeros in the whole week?
(c) Draw a bar chart to show the number of each kind of snack sold in a week.

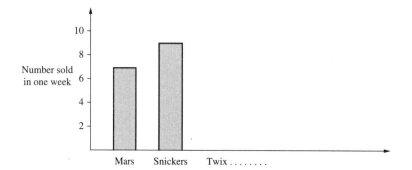

	Mon	Tu	Wed	Th	Fri
Mars	3	1	0	0	3
Snickers	0	4	1	2	2
Twix	2	2	1	3	4
Aero	5	0	0	1	4
Crunchie	2	3	4	1	1
Kit Kat	5	0	2	1	1

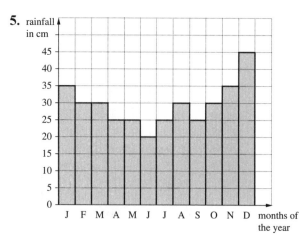

5.

The monthly rainfall in the Lake District is shown left.

(a) How much rain fell in August?
(b) Which was the driest month in the year?
(c) Which was the wettest month in the year?
(d) In which months did 25 cm of rain fall?
(e) In which months did 30 cm of rain fall?

6. The bar charts show the sale of different things over a year but the labels on the charts have been lost. Decide which of the charts A, B, C or D shows sales of:

(a) Christmas trees
(b) Crisps
(c) Flower seeds
(d) Greetings cards [including Christmas, Valentine's Day, etc.]

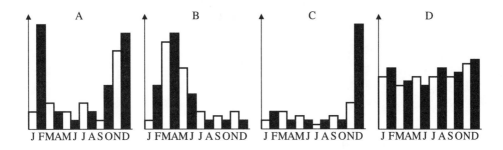

7. The number of people staying in two different hotels in each month of the year is shown below.

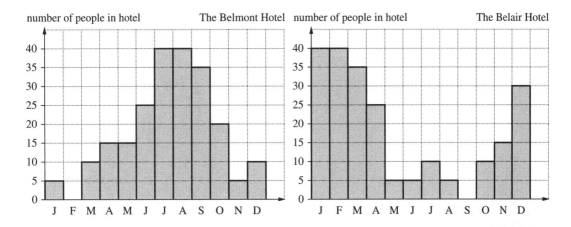

(a) How many people stayed in the 'Belmont' in July?
(b) How many people stayed in the 'Belair' in July?
(c) What was the total number of people staying in the two hotels in April?
(d) One hotel is in a ski resort and the other is by the seaside. Which hotel is in the ski resort?

8.

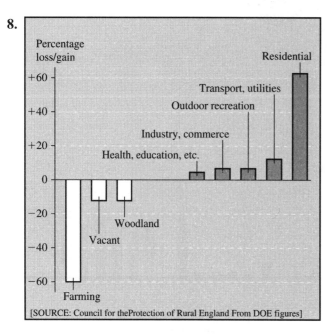

[SOURCE: Council for theProtection of Rural England From DOE figures]

This chart shows changes of land use in rural areas in England between 1960 and 2000.

(a) What was the change in the area of land used for farming?

(b) Write down three activities that would go in the 'outdoor recreation' category.

(c) Describe the main features of the chart.

9. The chart shows the agricultural production figures for four crops in Pakistan. Pakistan has low rainfall but in recent years major irrigation schemes have been introduced. About 50% of the population is employed in agriculture.

Describe how the production of the four crops has changed over the years from 1960 to 2000.

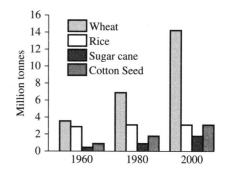

10. Here are details of the official languages spoken in countries around the world.

English	27% of the world population	French	4%
Chinese	19%	Arabic	3%
Hindi	14%	Portuguese	3%
Spanish	6%	Malay	3%
Russian	5%	Bengali	3%
		Japanese	2%

(a) Draw a bar chart to illustrate this data.

(b) England is a fairly small country compared to China. How can you explain the figures given?

11. Some children were asked to state which was their favourite T.V. programme from the list below.

Eastenders	E
Top of the Pops	T
Animal Hospital	A
Neighbours	N
Sister Sister	S

The replies were:

```
S  N  S  A  N  E  T  T  N  A  E  T  A  E  N
A  S  N  A  T  E  S  E  N  S  E  N  N  E  N
N  A  E  N  N  E  A  A  N  S  E  A  N  A  N
```

Make a tally chart and then draw a bar chart to show the results

		Tally	Total
EastEnders	E		
ToTP	T		
Animal Hospital	A		
Neighbours	N		
Sister Sister	S		

Frequency

12. Here are two paragraphs: one in English and one in French. There is the same number of letters in each paragraph.

The England football captain Alan Shearer walks up an ordinary suburban garden path in full kit. He rings the doorbell and asks, "Is Daniel in?", Daniel's mum shouts, "It's Alan", but Daniel is lying on the floor watching Dennis the Menace on the TCC (The Children's Channel) network. "I'm busy," he shouts and his mum shuts the door. Shearer rings the bell again. "He promised he'd come out," he complains, only to have the door shut on him again.

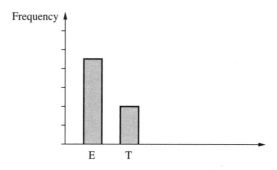

Eurogoals Magazine Les plus beaux buts des championnats européens de football Ce magazine hebdomadaire cinquante-deux minutes présente une sélection des meilleures rencontres du Championnat espagnol, portugais, belge, néerlandais ou français. L'acent est mis sur les buts, et les matchs se soldant par un 0–0 sont systématiquement écartés. Les grandes équipes telles que l'Ajax d'Amsterdam ou le Real

(a) For each paragraph make a tally chart to record how many letters there are in each word.
(b) Draw a bar chart for each language and write a sentence about the main differences in the two charts.

Word length	Tally
1	
2	
3	

Data in groups and line graphs

- Here are the ages of the people at a wedding.

33 11 45 22 50 38 23 54 18 72   5 58
37   3 61 51   7 62 24 57 31 27 66 29
25 39 48 15 52 25 35 18 49 63 13 74

With so many different numbers over a wide range it is helpful to put the ages into *groups*.

- Here is the start of a tally chart

Ages	Tally	Total (Frequency)
0–9	|||	3
10–19	JHT	5
20–29	JHT ||	7
30–39		
40–49		
50–59		
60–69		
70–79		

- Here is the start of a frequency chart

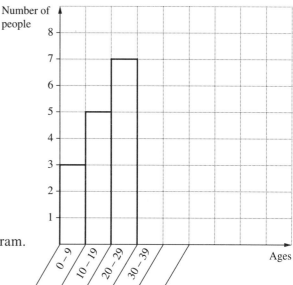

- Finish the tally chart and the frequency diagram. Notice that when the data is in groups the bars are touching.

Exercise 2

1. Shruti started with one frog but it laid eggs and now she has lots! One day she measures all her little pets. Here are the lengths in mm.

82 63 91 78 27 93 87 48 22 15
42 28 84 65 87 55 79 66 85 38

(a) Make a tally chart and then draw the frequency diagram.

Length (mm)	Tally	Frequency
0–20		
21–40		
41–60		
61–80		
81–100		

(b) How many frogs were more than 60 mm long?

2. The heights, in cm, of 30 children are shown below

```
134   146   141   147   151   141   137   159   142   146
151   157   143   154   146   143   149   151   141   148
136   144   147   152   147   137   133   140   139   155
```

(a) Put the heights into groups

class interval	frequency
$130 \leqslant h < 135$	
$135 \leqslant h < 140$	
$140 \leqslant h < 145$	
$145 \leqslant h < 150$	

(b) Draw a frequency diagram

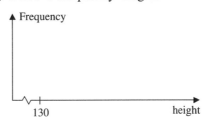

3. Tom has lots of snakes and he likes to weigh them every week. The weights are shown.
  (a) How many snakes weigh between 61 and 80 grams?
  (b) How many snakes weigh less than 41 grams?
  (c) How many snakes does he have altogether?

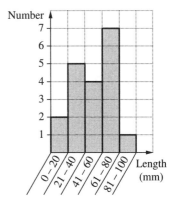

3. Farmer Gray rears pigs. As an experiment, he decided to feed half of his pigs with their normal diet and the other half on a new high fibre diet. The diagrams shows the weight of the pigs in the two groups.

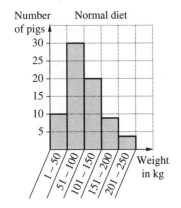

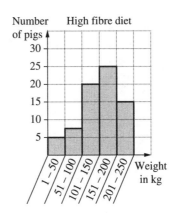

In one sentence describe what effect the new diet had.

5. A teacher has a theory that pupils' test results are affected by the amount of T.V. watched at home.

With the willing cooperation of the children's parents, the pupils were split into two groups:

Group X watched at least two hours of T.V. per day.

Group Y watched a maximum of half an hour per day.

The pupils were given two tests: one at the start of the experiment and another test six months later. Here are the results:

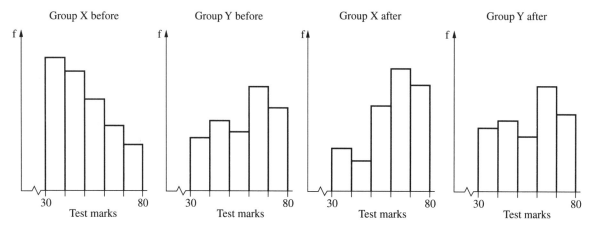

Look carefully at the frequency diagrams.

What conclusions can you draw? Was the teacher's theory correct?

Give details of how the pupils in group X and in group Y performed in the two tests.

6. Here is some information about fireworks.

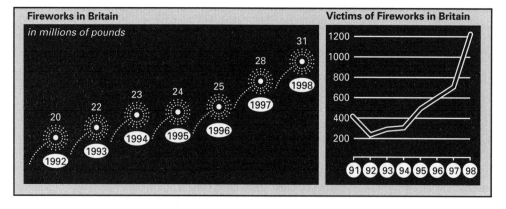

In which year were the lowest number of people injured by fireworks?

7. A car went on a five hour journey starting at 12 00 with a full tank of petrol. The volume of petrol in the tank was measured after every hour; the results are shown below.

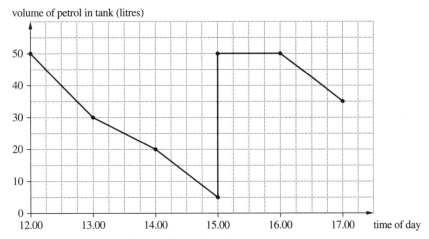

(a) How much petrol was in the tank at 13 00?
(b) At what time was there 5 litres in the tank?
(c) How much petrol was used in the first hour of the journey?
(d) What happened at 15 00?
(e) What do you think happened between 15 00 and 16 00?
(f) How much petrol was used between 12 00 and 17 00?

8. This diagram shows the temperature and rainfall readings in one week.
The rainfall is shown as the bar chart.
The temperature is shown as the line graph.

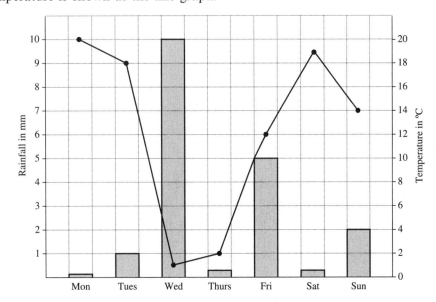

(a) Use both graphs to describe the weather on Monday.
(b) On which day was the weather cold and wet?
(c) Compare the weather on Thursday and Saturday.

Pie charts

In a pie chart a circle is divided into sectors to display information. Pie charts are often used to show the results of a survey. The sectors of the circle show what *fraction* of the total is in each group. Here are two pie charts.

- How children go to a school in the Alps.

- People in a Spanish jail.

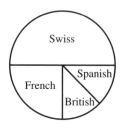

$\frac{1}{2}$ of the children walk to school

$\frac{1}{4}$ of the children swim to school

$\frac{1}{4}$ of the children hang glide to school

$\frac{1}{8}$ of the people were Spanish

$\frac{1}{8}$ of the people were British

$\frac{1}{4}$ of the people were French

$\frac{1}{2}$ of the people were Swiss

Exercise 3

1.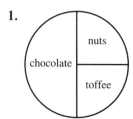

   The pie chart shows the contents of a bar of chocolate.
   (a) What fraction of the contents is chocolate?
   (b) What fraction of the contents is toffee?
   (c) If the total weight of the packet is 400 g, what is the weight of nuts?

2. In a survey children said what pets they had at home.
   (a) What fraction of the children had a hamster?
   (b) What fraction of the children had a dog?
   (c) 40 children took part in the survey.
      How many of these children had a pet spider?

3. In another survey children were asked what *pests* they had at home. $\frac{1}{3}$ of the children said, 'my sister'.
   What angle would you draw for the 'my sister' sector on a pie chart?

4. The pie chart shows the results of a survey in which 80 people were asked how they travelled to work. Copy this table and fill it in.

   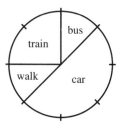

Method	car	walk	train	bus
Number of people				

5. In 1997 and 1998 children were asked in a survey to say which country they would most like to go to for a holiday. The pie charts show the results.

1997

100 children answered in each year

Countries in the 'others' section had only one or two votes each.

1998

(a) Which was the most popular country in the 1997 survey?
(b) Which country was less popular in 1998 than in 1997?
(c) *Roughly* how many children said 'Jamaica' in the 1997 survey?

6. A hidden observer watched Philip in a 40 minute maths lesson.

He spent: 20 minutes talking to a friend,
            10 minutes getting ready to work,
             5 minutes working,
             5 minutes packing up.

Draw and label a pie chart to show Philip's lesson.

7.

Jodie counted the different animals in her pond. Altogether there were 200 animals or fish.
(a) *About* how many frogs were there?
(b) *About* how many goldfish were there?

8. The children at a school were asked to state their favourite colour. Here are the results.

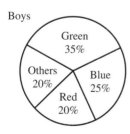

Boys

Girls

There were 40 boys   There were 25 girls

John says 'The same number of boys and girls chose red.'
Tara says 'More boys than girls chose blue.'
(a) Use both charts to explain whether or not John is right.
(b) Use both charts to explain whether or not Tara is right.

Problems answered using statistics

Many problems in mathematics and other subjects, like science or geography can be solved by statistical methods.

The data relevant to such problems might be obtained from:

- a survey of a sample of people;

- an experiment;

- published material, such as tables or charts, from reference books.

Here are two examples of problems which can be answered using statistical methods.

1. Do different newspapers use words of different length or sentences of different length? Why would they do this?

   In this case you could conduct an experiment by choosing a similar page from different newspapers.

   Record your results in a table.

Number of words in a sentence	1–5	6–10	11–15	16–20	21 or more
Times					
Sun					
Mail					

2. What factors are most important to the customers of supermarkets?

   In this case you could conduct a survey asking about price of food, quality of food, speed of checkouts, ease of car parking and so on.
   You would need questions designed so that shoppers could state the importance, or otherwise, of the factors you include.

Reporting on results

Most work of this nature is easier to understand if data is presented in the form of graphs and charts. You should *justify* the choice of the data you present. You might find it helpful to include calculations of mean or range depending on the context.
Your report should highlight the main findings of your work and you shold write a clear *summary* which relates back to the original problem.

3.6 Mid book review

This section contains six review exercises
Review exercises 1 and 2 cover material in part 1
Review exercise 3 covers material in part 2
Review exercise 4 covers material in part 3.

Review exercise 1

Work out

1. 81	**2.** 682	**3.** 599	**4.** 235
-45	$+\ 74$	-315	$+409$

5. $566 + 278$ **6.** $657 - 340$ **7.** $171 + 681$ **8.** $963 - 148$

9. $534 - 208$ **10.** $589 - 99$.

11. There were 122 peaches in a box. 63 were sold. How many peaches were left?

12. There are 763 books in a library. A further 128 books are put on the shelves. How many books does the library now have altogether?

13. 136 paper aeroplanes were entered in a competition. Half of the planes were made by one person and a further 24 were made by his sister. How many planes were made by other people?

14. This is a number triangle. The numbers along each edge add up to 9.

Copy and complete the triangle.

The six numbers are 1, 2, 3, 4, 5, 6.

15. A box has a mass of 230 g when empty.
When it is full of sugar the total mass is 650 g.
What is its mass when it is half full?

16. In a school 316 of the pupils have lunch at the school and 97 go home to lunch. How many pupils have lunch altogether?

17. Work out
    (a) 6×672 (b) $392 \div 7$ (c) $38{\cdot}1 \times 0$
    (d) $5{\cdot}42 + 0{\cdot}9$ (e) $16{\cdot}3 - 4{\cdot}28$ (f) $13 - 5{\cdot}2$

18. This is a number ring.
Start with any number and multiply the units digit
by 4 and then add the tens digit.

For example $(15) \rightarrow 5 \times 4 + 1 \rightarrow (21)$

The rule is then repeated on 21 and so on.

Use the same rule to complete this number ring.

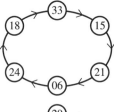

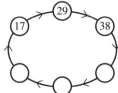

19. Here are three number cards.
One number that can be made with the
three cards is 617.
(a) Use the three cards to make a number which is *more* than 617.
(b) Use the three cards to make the largest possible number.
(c) Use the three cards to make an even number.

20. Here are four number cards.

Use *all four* cards for the following
(a) An add. The answer must be less than 70.

(b) A take away.

The answer must be less than 20.

21. Make a copy of the cross number pattern and complete the
puzzle using the clues given.

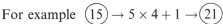

Clues across	**Clues down**
1. $63 + 79$	1. $527 - 418$
3. $71 - 37$	2. $136 + 89$
4. $965 - 668$	3. $241 + 134$
5. $839 + 126$	6. $840 - 211$
7. $100 - 49$	8. $1001 - 815$
9. $17 - 9$	10. $924 - 867$
10. $329 + 267$	11. $25 + 38$
12. $604 - 528$	12. $100 - 27$
13. $1036 - 643$	

Review exercise 2

1. Name the shape whose faces are all squares.

2. Name the shape whose faces are either square or rectangular.

3. What is the name of the family of shapes which have the same cross-section throughout their length?

4. What is the name of the shape formed entirely by triangular faces?

5. What is the name of the shape which has one square face and four triangular faces?

6. Which shape has a circular face at one end and a point at the other?

7. What is the mathematical name for a 'tin can'?

8. What is the mathematical name for a snooker ball?

9. What is the mathematical name for a snooker ball that has been cut in half?

10. A sphere is a prism. True or false?

11. Here is the net for a cube.
(a) When the net is folded up, which edge will be stuck to the edge JI?
(b) Which edge will be stuck to the edge AB?
(c) Which corner will meet corner D?

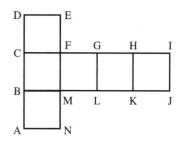

12. Find the number of hours and minutes between:
(a) 15.30 and 18.00
(b) 05.35 and 09.10
(c) 9.30 a.m. and 1.40 p.m.

In Questions **13** to **16** write down the line which is correct.

13. (a) 0·07 is equal to 0·7
(b) 0·07 is greater than 0·7
(c) 0·07 is less than 0·7

14. (a) 0·23 is equal to 0·32
(b) 0·23 is greater than 0·32
(c) 0·23 is less than 0·32

15. (a) 0·03 is equal to 0·030
(b) 0·03 is greater than 0·030
(c) 0·03 is less than 0·030

16. (a) 0·09 is equal to 0·01
(b) 0·09 is greater than 0·1
(c) 0·09 is less than 0·1

In Questions **17** to **22** arrange the numbers in order of size, smallest first.

17. 0·79, 0·791, 0·709, 0·97   **18.** 0·3, 0·33, 0·303, 0·033

19. 1, 0·99, 0·989, 0·09   **20.** 1·2, 0·12, 0·21, 1·12

21. 0·08, 0·096, 1, 0·4   **22.** 0·008, 0·09, 0·091, 0·0075

23. Which list is arranged in ascending order?

  A   0·14, 0·05, 0·062, 0·09
  B   0·14, 0·09, 0·062, 0·05
  C   0·050, 0·062, 0·09, 0·14
  D   0·050, 0·090, 0·14, 0·062

24. (a) Find the area of each shape. All lengths are in cm.
     (b) Find the perimeter of each shape.

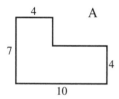 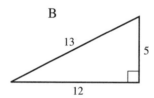 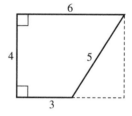

25. There are 5 tyres to each new car. How many tyres are there on 27 new cars?

26. If Jenny has 40 flowers and she puts 8 flowers in each bunch. How many bunches will she have?

27. If your school holiday is for 42 days and there are 7 days to a week, how many weeks holiday is this?

28. Work out the missing digits in each division.

  (a)   ☐☐ 2   (b)   2 9
      4)⎯7⎯2⎯☐   3)⎯☐⎯7

29. A teacher marked 2000 questions. There were 25 pupils in the class. If each pupil did the same number of questions, how many questions did each pupil do?

30. How many hundreds make a million?

31. Choose the correct answer: The number of seconds in a day is *about*:

A 9000   **B** 90 000   **C** 30 000   **D** 300 000

Review exercise 3

1. Draw 3 rectangles like the one shown and label them A, B and C.
   (a) On diagram A shade $\frac{1}{6}$ of the rectangle.
   (b) On diagram B shade $\frac{2}{3}$ of the rectangle.
   (c) On diagram C shade $\frac{5}{12}$ of the rectangle.

2. Write as improper fractions.
   (a) $1\frac{2}{3}$ (b) $2\frac{3}{5}$ (c) $3\frac{1}{2}$

3. Write these fractions in simpler form by cancelling down.
   (a) $\frac{12}{16}$ (b) $\frac{20}{25}$ (c) $\frac{28}{30}$ (d) $\frac{125}{500}$

4. Answer true or false:
   (a) $\frac{3}{4} > \frac{3}{5}$ (b) $\frac{5}{4} = 1\frac{1}{4}$ (c) $\frac{1}{4} + \frac{1}{4} = \frac{2}{8}$
   (d) $20\% = \frac{1}{5}$ (e) $\frac{3}{2} < \frac{2}{3}$ (f) $2\frac{2}{5} > \frac{11}{5}$

5. Work out
   (a) $\frac{3}{7} + \frac{1}{7}$ (b) $\frac{5}{8} - \frac{4}{8}$ (c) $\frac{3}{4} - \frac{1}{2}$
   (d) $\frac{3}{8}$ of 24   (e) $\frac{1}{20}$ of 400   (f) 25% of 200

6. The price of a playstation game was £30 but it is increased by 5%. What is the new price?

7. Write down the co-ordinates of the points which make up the 'S'. You must give the points in the correct order starting at the bottom left.

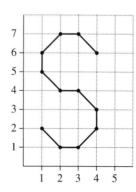

8. Draw a grid with values from 0 to 10. Plot the points below and join them up in order. You should obtain two letters of the alphabet
(a) $(1, 5)$ $(3, 1)$ $(4, 3)$ $(5, 1)$ $(7, 5)$
(b) $(8, 5)$ $(8, 1)$ $(8, 3)$ $(10, 3)$ $(10, 5)$ $(10, 1)$

9.

(a) Points A, D and E are three vertices of a square. Write down the coordinates of the other vertex.
(b) A, B and C are three vertices of a square. Write down the coordinates of the other vertex.

10. Draw a pair of axes with values of x and y from -6 to $+6$. Plot the points given and join them up to make a shape. Write down the name of the shape you have drawn.
(a) $(-6, -5)$ $(-5, -3)$ $(-2, -3)$ $(-3, -5)$ [Join them up *in order*!]
(b) $(2, 0)$ $(3, 2)$ $(4, 2)$ $(6, 0)$
(c) $(2, -2)$ $(5, -4)$ $(2, -6)$ $(1, -4)$
(d) $(-4, 0)$ $(-6, 6)$ $(-2, 6)$
(e) $(1, 5)$ $(4, 6)$ $(5, 3)$ $(2, 2)$

11. Find the expression I am left with.
(a) I start with x, double it and then add 5.
(b) I start with n, treble it and then subtract 7.
(c) I start with p, double it and then add q.

12. Find an expression for the perimeter of each shape

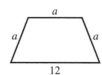 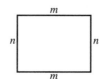

13. (a) Draw a shape with a *perimeter* of $2a + b$.
(b) Draw a shape with *area* $6n$.

14. Simplify the following.
(a) $3a + a + 2b + 2a$ (b) $5n + m - n + 3m$ (c) $4a + 7 - a - 6$

15. Here are five algebra cards.
    (a) Add the expressions on card A and card C.
    (b) Which two cards always have the same value?
    (c) Which card has the largest value when $n = 4$?
    (d) Add the expressions on all five cards.

A $2n$ **B** $n + 1$ **C** $3n - 3$

D $n + n$ **E** $5 - n$

16. Use mental strategies to work out the following *in your head*.
    (a) $44 + 16 + 37$ (b) $99 + 47$ (c) double 74
    (d) 24×50 (e) double 128   (f) $95 - 29$
    (g) 5% of £60   (h) 15% of £80   (i) $300 - 41$

17. Answer true or false:
    (a) $4n = 4 \times n$ (b) $2n + n = 3n$ (c) $n^2 = 2 \times n$
    (d) $3n - 2n = 1$ (e) $n \div 2 = \dfrac{n}{2}$ (f) $m - n + m = 2m - n$
    (g) $p \times 3 = 3p$ (h) $2n \div 2 = n$ (i) $n \times 0 = n$

Review exercise 4 [Topics in part 3]

1. Copy and continue this pattern for multiples of 7.
   7, 14, 21, ?, ?, ? ...

2. List all the factors of each of these numbers
   (a) 18   (b) 27

3. Copy these numbers and circle the numbers that are not prime.
   (a) 7, 19, 13, 27.   (b) 31, 37, 39, 41.

4. Write down the first five multiples of:
   (a) 6   (b) 8

5. There is just one prime number between the numbers given. Copy each question and write the prime number in the box.
   (a) 20, ☐, 26   (b) 44, ☐, 52.

6. (a) List the numbers which are factors of both 18 and 30.
   (b) Write down the H.C.F. of 18 and 30.

7. Find a number which has 8 factors.

8. The numbers 55 and 40 are both multiples of which number?

9. The number in a square is the product of the two numbers on either side of it. Copy and complete the two triangles.

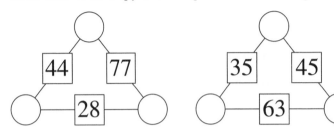

10. Work out
(a) $12 - 6 \div 3$
(b) $18 \div (1 + 5 \times 1)$
(c) $25 + 24 \div 24$
(d) $15 + 2^2$
(e) $5 \times 6 - 3 \times 4$
(f) $10 \times (2^2 - 1) + 4$

11. Use a calculator to work out the following. Give your answers correct to 1 d.p.
(a) $9 \cdot 23 + \dfrac{1 \cdot 7}{0 \cdot 92}$
(b) $\dfrac{3 \cdot 6^2 - 1 \cdot 74}{2 \cdot 2}$
(c) $\sqrt{\dfrac{98 \cdot 2}{1 \cdot 6}}$
(d) $9 \cdot 7 \times (11 \cdot 2 - 8 \cdot 714)$
(e) $\dfrac{9 \cdot 63 - 7 \cdot 291}{1 \cdot 73}$
(f) $\dfrac{32 \cdot 4}{8 \cdot 54 + 1 \cdot 69}$

12. Write the following with the correct signs inside the circles.
(a) $4 \times 3 \times 2 \bigcirc 1 = 25$
(b) $5 \times 2 \times 4 \bigcirc 3 = 37$
(c) $6 + 5 \bigcirc 4 \bigcirc 1 = 8$

13 A man's heart beats at 70 beats/min. How many times will his heart beat between 03.30 and 23.30 on the same day?

14. In one million seconds which of these would you be able to do?
(a) Take a term off school.
(b) Go without sleep for two whole days.
(c) Spend ten days on the beach in France.
(d) Go to Africa for a year.

Explain your working.

Part 4

4.1 Calculating angles

Angles on a straight line

The angles on a straight line add up to 180°

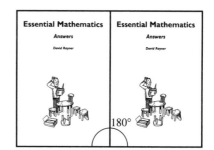

Find the angles marked with letters.

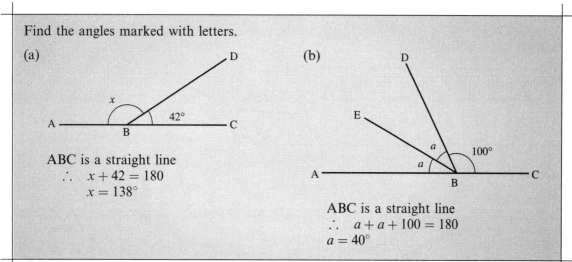

(a)

x

$42°$

A —— B —— C

D

ABC is a straight line

∴ $x + 42 = 180$

$x = 138°$

(b)

D

E

a

$100°$

a

A —— B —— C

ABC is a straight line

∴ $a + a + 100 = 180$

$a = 40°$

Exercise 1

Find the angles marked with letters.

1.
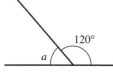
$120°$
a

2.

c $70°$

3.
$63°$
i

4.
$132°$
j

5.
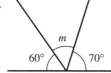
m
$60°$ $70°$

6.

n $50°$

7.

p $18°$

8.
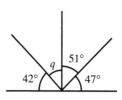
q $51°$
$42°$ $47°$

9.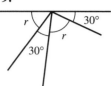

10.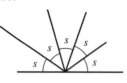

11.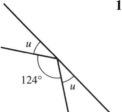

12.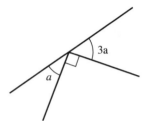

13.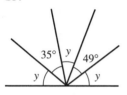

14.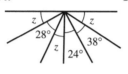

15.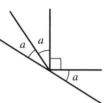

16.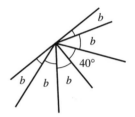

Angles at a point

The angles at a point add up to $360°$

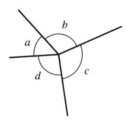

$$a + b + c + d = 360°$$

Exercise 2

Find the angles marked with letters.

1.

2.

3.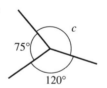

4.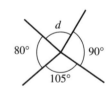

5.

6.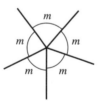

7.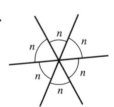

8.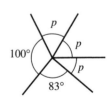

9.

10.

11.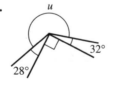

12.

Angles in a triangle

Draw a triangle of any shape on a piece of card and cut it out accurately. Now tear off the three corners as shown.

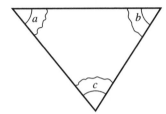

When the angles a, b and c are placed together they form a straight line.

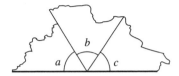

We see that:

> The angles in a triangle add up to 180°

Isosceles and equilateral triangles

An *isosceles* triangle has two equal sides and two equal angles.

The sides AB and AC are equal (marked with a dash) so angles B̂ and Ĉ are also equal.

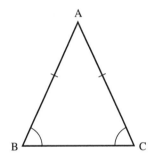

An *equilateral* triangle has three equal sides and three equal angles (all 60°).

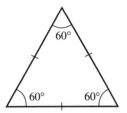

Intersecting lines

When two lines intersect, the opposite angles are equal. In the diagram, $a = 36°$ and $b = 144°$.

The angles are called *vertically opposite* angles.

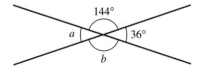

Find the angles marked with letters

(a)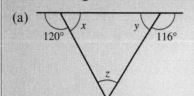

$x = 60°$ (angles on a straight line)
$y = 64°$ (angles on a straight line)
$z + 60 + 64 = 180$
$\quad z = 56°$

(b)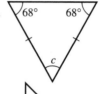

$a = 71°$ (isosceles triangle)
$b + 71 + 71 = 180°$
$\quad b = 38°$

Exercise 3

Find the angles marked with letters.

1.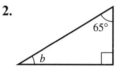

2.

3.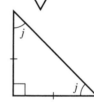

4.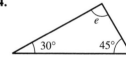

5.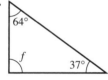

6.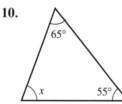

7.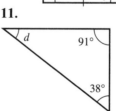

8.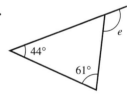

9.

10.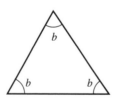

11.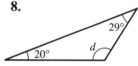

12.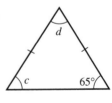

13.

14.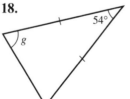

15.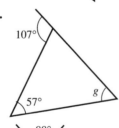

16.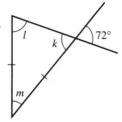

17.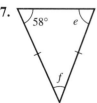

18.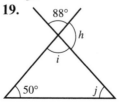

19.

20.

4.2 Proportion and ratio

Proportion

- We use proportion to compare part of something to the whole. We usually express a proportion as a fraction, decimal or percentage.
  For example:

  (a) In a class of 17 children, there are 7 boys and 10 girls. The proportion of boys in the class is $\frac{7}{17}$.
  (b) Clothes may be made from material in which the proportion which is cotton is 90%.

Exercise 1

1. The chart shows how people in a survey travel to work.
   (a) What proportion travel by train?
   (b) What proportion travel by car?

2. What proportion of the rectangle is shaded?

3. In a class of 30 children, 7 are left-handed. What proportion of the class is left-handed?

4. Count the children in your class. What proportion of the class went to the same junior school as you?

5. The diagram shows how the government spends money on transport. Estimate, as a percentage, what proportion is spent on roads.

6. A soup contains 200 g of water and 50 g of vegetables. What proportion of the soup is vegetables?

- If 4 litres of oil costs £12, find the cost of 3 litres. The cost of oil is directly proportional to the quantity bought.

  $$4 \text{ litres costs } £12$$
  $$\therefore \quad 1 \text{ litre costs } £12 \div 4 = £3$$
  $$\therefore \quad 3 \text{ litres costs } £3 \times 3 = £9$$

- If 4 bottles of cider contain 10 litres, find how much cider there is in 7 bottles.

  $$4 \text{ bottles contain } 10 \text{ litres.}$$
  $$\therefore \quad 1 \text{ bottle contains } 10 \div 4 \text{ litres}$$
  $$1 \text{ bottle contains } 2\tfrac{1}{2} \text{ litres}$$
  $$\therefore \quad 7 \text{ bottles contain } 2\tfrac{1}{2} \times 7 \text{ litres} = 17\tfrac{1}{2} \text{ litres.}$$

Exercise 2

1. If 5 books cost £20, find the cost of 10 books.

2. Magazines cost £16 for 8. Find the cost of 4 magazines.

3. Find the cost of 12 cakes, if 3 cakes cost £15.

4. A machine fills 1000 bottles in 5 minutes. How many bottles will it fill in 20 minutes?

5. A train travels 100 km in 20 minutes. How long will it take to travel 50 km?

6. 5 tea pots cost £7·50. Find the cost of 50 tea pots.

7. Telephone wire costs £2·50 for 50 m. Find the cost of 3000 m.

8. £1 is worth 10·30 francs. How many francs will I get for £20?

9. £1 is worth 1·65 dollars. How many dollars will I get for £100?

10. The total weight of 8 CDs is 96 grams. How much do 11 CDs weigh?

11. If 8 bottles of coke hold 12 litres, find how much coke there is in 6 bottles.

12. £20 can be exchanged for 210 francs. How many francs can be exchanged for £60?

13. £15 can be exchanged for 24 dollars. How many dollars can be exchanged for £75?

14. Usually it takes 10 hours for 4 men to build a wall. How many men are needed to build a wall twice as big in 10 hours?

15. A car travels 280 km on 35 litres of petrol. How much petrol is needed for a journey of 840 km?

Ratio

- We use ratio to compare parts of a whole.

  For example:
  In an office of 18 people there are 12 men and 6 women.
  The ratio of men:women is 12:6.
  This is the same as 2:1.   [divide both numbers by 6]

- Ratios can often be written in a simpler form.

  For example:
  The ratios 4:16 and 1:4 are equivalent.   [divide by 4]
  The ratio 3:6:15 and 1:2:5 are equivalent.
  The ratios 0·5:3 and 1:6 are equivalent.   [multiply by 2]

- Split up £25 in the ratio 3:2

  We divide £25 into 3 + 2 'parts'.
  So there are 5 'parts'.
  Each part is £5.
  So 3 parts is £15 and 2 parts is £10.

Exercise 3

1. In a mixed class of 18 children, 11 are girls. Write down the ratio girls:boys.

2. In a cupboard there are 4 rulers and 20 pens. Find the ratio of pens:rulers.

3. In an evening, a vet sees 12 dogs and 8 cats. Find the ratio of dogs:cats.

4. Write these ratios in a more simple form.
    (a) 5:15   (b) 6:10   (c) 3:33
    (d) 4:6:8   (e) 14:35   (f) 12:18:60

5. On a farm, the ratio of cows to sheep is 5:8. If there are 25 cows, how many sheep are there?

6. In a crowd, the ratio of men to women is 3:5. If there are 12 men, how many women are there?

7. In a wood, the ratio of yew trees to ash trees is 2:3. If there are 30 ash trees, how many yew trees are there?

8. In a hall, the ratio of chairs to tables is 7:2. If there are 10 tables, how many chairs are there?

9. In a kitchen drawer, the ratio of knives to forks to spoons is 4:3:5. If there are 9 forks, how many knives are there and how many spoons are there?

10. Share these quantities in the ratios given.

    (a) 12 apples between Sam and Joe, ratio 2:1
    (b) 15 bananas between Emi and Maya, ratio 3:2
    (c) 35 chocolates between Rahul and Joel, ratio 1:6

11. Split up the quantity given in the ratio given.

    (a) split 35 kg in the ratio 2:3
    (b) split £99 in the ratio 4:7
    (c) split £39 in the ratio 4:9
    (d) split 44 kg in the ratio 6:2:3
    (e) split £80 in the ratio 4:1:5
    (f) split 56 m in the ratio 4:3:1

12. Andy, Ben and Chris did some work on a farm. They were paid in the ratio 4:2:1. Andy got £28, which was the most. What did Ben and Chris get paid?

13. Jim and Dave have a total of £60 between them. Jim has three times as much money as Dave. How much does Jim have?

14. Will says 'A ratio of 1 to 4 means the same as a proportion of 1 in 4.' Explain why Will is wrong.

15. On a bus, the ratio of children to adults is 4:1. What proportion of the people are adults?

4.3 Construction

Estimating angles

- When angles are measured accurately they are usually in *degrees*.

  A full turn $= 360°$
  A half turn $= 180°$
  A quarter turn $= 90°$

- Any angle between $0°$ and $90°$ is called an *acute* angle.

- Any angle between $90°$ and $180°$ is called an *obtuse* angle.

- Any angle bigger than $180°$ is called a *reflex* angle.

Exercise 1

State whether these angles are correctly or incorrectly labelled. Do *not* measure the angles, estimate! Where the angles are clearly incorrect, write down an estimate for the correct angle.

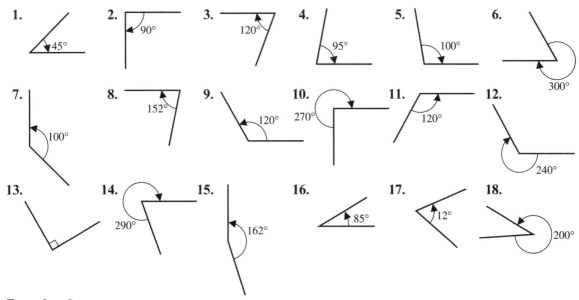

Exercise 2

For each angle in Exercise 1 above, state whether the angle *marked* is acute, obtuse or reflex.

Labelling angles

- The angle shown is $\widehat{ABC}$ (or $\widehat{CBA}$).

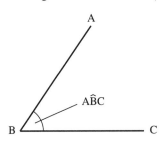

The 'B' must be in the middle.

- This angle is $\widehat{POR}$ (or $\widehat{ROP}$).

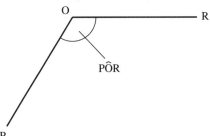

The 'O' must be in the middle.

- Angles are labelled with capital letters and the middle letter wears a 'hat' to indicate an angle.

Exercise 3

Copy each diagram and write down the size of each angle requested.

1.

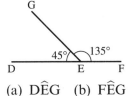

(a) $\widehat{DEG}$ (b) $\widehat{FEG}$

2.

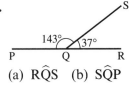

(a) $\widehat{RQS}$ (b) $\widehat{SQP}$

3.

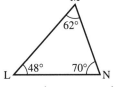

(a) $\widehat{MNL}$ (b) $\widehat{NLM}$ (c) $\widehat{LMN}$

4.

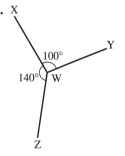

(a) $\widehat{KJL}$ (b) $\widehat{JLK}$
(c) $\widehat{JKL}$

5.

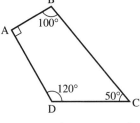

(a) $\widehat{ZWX}$ (b) $\widehat{XWY}$

6.

(a) $\widehat{DCB}$ (b) $\widehat{DAB}$
(c) $\widehat{CDA}$ (d) $\widehat{ABC}$

Using a protractor

A *protractor* is an instrument used to measure angles accurately.

Remember: When measuring an acute angle the answer must be less than 90°.
When measuring an obtuse angle the answer must be more than 90°.

Exercise 4

Give the measurement of each angle listed below.
Remember to read the correct scale. Some questions are done for you, to remind you of this.

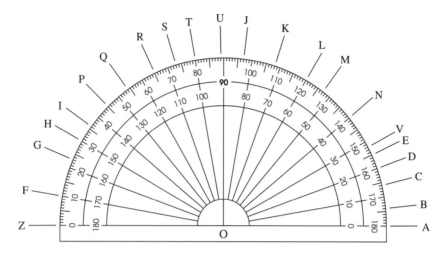

1. AÔD = 20°   **2.** AÔN =   **3.** AÔL = 60°   **4.** AÔK =

5. ZÔF =   **6.** ZÔP = 45°   **7.** ZÔR =   **8.** ZÔT = 80°

9. ZÔI =   **10.** ZÔG =   **11.** AÔC =   **12.** AÔV =

13. AÔQ = 126°   **14.** AÔP =   **15.** AÔF =   **16.** AÔB =

17. ZÔH =   **18.** ZÔB =   **19.** ZÔC =   **20.** ZÔD =

21. AÔG =   **22.** AÔH =   **23.** AÔI =   **24.** AÔM =

25. AÔR =   **26.** ZÔE =   **27.** ZÔJ =   **28.** ZÔK =

29. ZÔL =   **30.** ZÔM =   **31.** AÔE =   **32.** AÔJ =

33. AÔU =   **34.** AÔS =   **35.** ZÔN =   **36.** ZÔQ =

37. ZÔS =   **38.** ZÔU =   **39.** ZÔV =   **40.** AÔT =

Exercise 5

Measure these angles.

1.

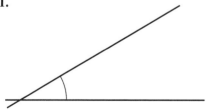

2.

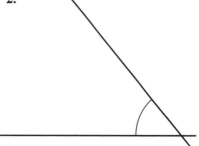

3. 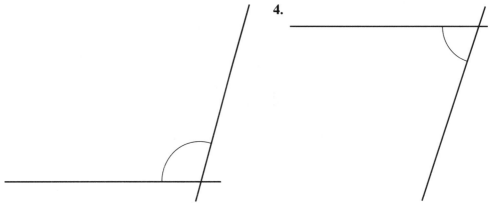   **4.**

In Questions **5**, **6**, **7**, **8** measure all the angles in each triangle.

5. 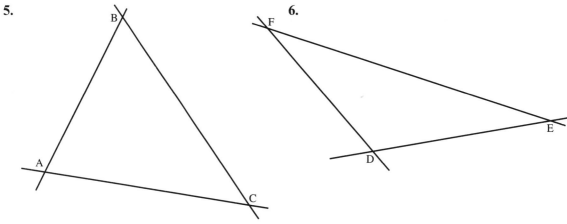   **6.**

7. 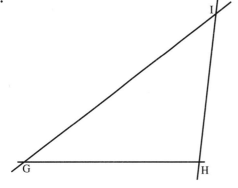   **8.**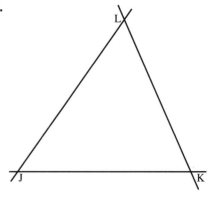

Exercise 6

Draw the following angles accurately.

   1. 35°   **2.** 68°   **3.** 140°   **4.** 85°   **5.** 210°   **6.** 300°

Constructing triangles

A triangle is an extremely rigid structure. It is used extensively in the real world to support many objects. These objects can range from large structures, such as the roof on your house, to smaller structures, such as the brackets holding up your bookshelf.

Draw the triangle ABC full size and measure the length x.
(a) Draw a base line *longer than* 8·5 cm
(b) Put the centre of the protractor on A and measure an angle 64°. Draw line AP.
(c) Similarly draw line BQ at an angle 40° to AB.
(d) The triangle is formed.
    Measure $x = 5.6$ cm.

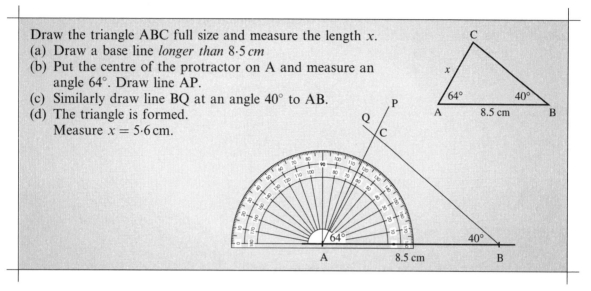

Exercise 7

Construct the triangles and measure the lengths of the sides marked x.

1.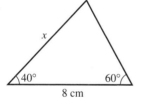

2.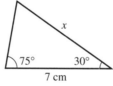

3.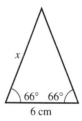

4.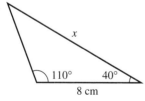

5.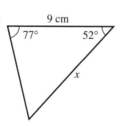

6.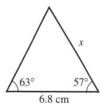

7.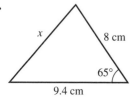

8.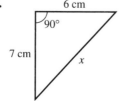

9.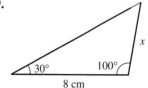

4.4 Decimals 2

Multiplying decimals by whole numbers

Method 1

• $7\cdot93 \times 4 \approx 8 \times 4 = 32$
  (Estimate first)
  $7\cdot93 \times 4 \quad 7\cdot00 \times 4 = 28\cdot00$
  $ 0\cdot90 \times 4 = 3\cdot60$
  $ 0\cdot03 \times 4 = \underline{0\cdot12} \; +$
  $ \underline{31\cdot72}$

• $3\cdot16 \times 6 \approx 3 \times 6 = 18$
  (Estimate first)
  $3\cdot16 \times 6 \quad 3\cdot00 \times 6 = 18\cdot00$
  $ 0\cdot10 \times 6 = 0\cdot60$
  $ 0\cdot06 \times 6 = \underline{0\cdot36} \; +$
  $ \underline{18\cdot96}$

Method 2

• $7\cdot24 \times 4 \approx 7 \times 4 = 28$
  (Estimate first)
  $7\cdot24$
  $\underline{\times 4}$
  $\underline{28\cdot96}$
  1

• $0\cdot096 \times 9 \approx 0\cdot1 \times 9 = 0\cdot9$
  (Estimate first)
  $0\cdot096$
  $\underline{\times 9}$
  $\underline{0\cdot864}$
  $8\,5$

> The answer has the same number of figures after the point as there are in the numbers being multiplied.

Exercise 1

Work out the following. Find an estimate first.

1. $5\cdot1$	**2.** $2\cdot3$	**3.** $3\cdot7$	**4.** $5\cdot6$
$\underline{\times 2}$	$\underline{\times 3}$	$\underline{\times 4}$	$\underline{\times 5}$

5. $6\cdot13$	**6.** $10\cdot22$	**7.** $5\cdot34$	**8.** $1\cdot29$
$\underline{\times 6}$	$\underline{\times 7}$	$\underline{\times 8}$	$\underline{\times 9}$

9. $7 \times 0\cdot63$ **10.** $1\cdot452 \times 6$ **11.** $9 \times 0\cdot074$ **12.** $11\cdot3 \times 5$

13. $13\cdot6 \times 5$ **14.** $0\cdot074 \times 5$ **15.** $6 \times 2\cdot22$ **16.** $8\cdot4 \times 11$

17. Copy and complete with the missing numbers.

(a) $0\cdot3 \times 4 = \boxed{}$

(b) $0\cdot6 \times \boxed{} = 4\cdot2$

(c) $\boxed{} \times 5 = 2\cdot0$

(d) $1\cdot5 = 6 \times \boxed{} + 0\cdot3$

(e) $\boxed{} \times 7 - 2 = 1\cdot5$

(f) $8 \times \boxed{} = 0\cdot16$

18. Find the cost of 4 calculators at £6.95 each.

19. What is the cost of 2 CDs at £10.95 each?

20. If one brick weighs $1\cdot35\,kg$, how much do 5 weigh?

21. What is the total cost of 6 books at £2·13 each?

22. A new car tyre costs £29·99.
What is the total cost of 4 new tyres?

23. Find the total cost of 8 batteries at £1·19 each.

24. If 1 kg of cheese costs £4·59, find the cost of 3 kg.

25. Ink cartridges cost £1·25 a packet. What is the cost of 10 packets?

26. A sack of coal costs £6·90. Find the total cost of 9 sacks.

27. If 1 litre equals 1·76 pints, how many pints is 8 litres?

In Questions **28** to **31** find the total cost.

28. 2 jars at £1·75 each
4 boxes at £0·40 each
1 bottle at £1·25

29. 3 tins at £0·51 each
5 packets at £1·10 each
2 pints of milk at 22p per pint.

30. 4 litres of oil at 97p per litre
6 bags at £0·33 each
3 lb of meat at £2·12 per lb
1 cauliflower at 42p

31. 18 eggs at 50p per dozen
$\frac{1}{2}$ lb of cheese at £1·30 per lb
3 lb of leeks at 18p per lb
2 packets at £2·30 each

Multiplying by 10, 100, 1000

• Using a calculator, $3·24 \times 10 = 32·4$
$16·17 \times 10 = 161·7$
$0·53 \times 10 = 5·3$
$1·414 \times 10 = 14·14$

'When you multiply by 10 you move the digits one place to the left.'

• What do you notice in these calculations?
$4·235 \times 100 = 423·5$
$1·138 \times 100 = 113·8$
$0·258 \times 100 = 25·8$

• Without a calculator, write down the answer to the following:
$1·174 \times 100$
$32·56 \times 10$
$1·2\,359 \times 1000$

Exercise 2

Do the following calculations

1. $4·23 \times 10$ **2.** $5·63 \times 10$ **3.** $0·427 \times 100$ **4.** $4·63 \times 100$
5. $0·075 \times 10$ **6.** $0·0063 \times 100$ **7.** $1·147 \times 1000$ **8.** $10·7 \times 1000$
9. $6·33 \times 100$ **10.** $0·007\,14 \times 10\,000$ **11.** $6·36 \times 100$ **12.** $8·142 \times 10$
13. $0·71 \times 10\,000$ **14.** $8·9 \times 1000$ **15.** 12×100 **16.** 13×10
17. 7×1000 **18.** $9·2 \times 10\,000$ **19.** $0·7 \times 100$ **20.** $0·5 \times 100\,000$

21. 0.01×10 **22.** 5.2×100 **23.** 14×1000

24. 0.1×10 **25.** $0.2 \times 10\,000$ **26.** $8.31 \times 100\,000$

27. 9.2×1 million   **28.** 8.34×1 million   **29.** 0.71×1 million

30. 8.6×100 **31.** 27×1000 **32.** 53×100

33. 0.0084×10 **34.** $0.74 \times 10\,000$ **35.** 91×100

36. 0×1000 **37.** $5.6 \times 10 \times 10$ **38.** $2.14 \times 10 \times 10$

39. $0.0634 \times 10 \times 100$ **40.** $0.1111 \times 100 \times 100$ **41.** $8 \times 100 \times 10$

42. $7.24 \times 100 \times 100$ **43.** $0.12 \times 1000 \times 10$ **44.** $0.1434 \times 100 \times 10$

Division of decimals by whole numbers

(a) $9.6 \div 3$

$$\begin{array}{r} 3.2 \\ 3\overline{)9.6} \end{array}$$

(b) $22.48 \div 4$

$$\begin{array}{r} 5.62 \\ 3\overline{)22.^248} \end{array}$$

(c) $7.3 \div 4$

$$\begin{array}{r} 1.825 \\ 4\overline{)7.^33^10^20} \end{array}$$

↑ ↑
Note the extra zeros.

(d) $21.28 \div 7$

$$\begin{array}{r} 3.04 \\ 7\overline{)21.2^28} \end{array}$$

(e) $3.12 \div 4$

$$\begin{array}{r} 0.78 \\ 4\overline{)3.^31^22} \end{array}$$

Exercise 3

1. $8.42 \div 2$ **2.** $205.2 \div 6$ **3.** $18.52 \div 4$

4. $4.984 \div 7$ **5.** $236.0 \div 5$ **6.** $18.93 \div 3$

7. $49.92 \div 8$ **8.** $487.26 \div 9$ **9.** $6.7 \div 5$

10. A father shares £4.56 between his three children. How much does each receive?

11. A length of wood measuring 39.41 cm has to be cut into seven equal lengths. How long is each piece?

12. The total bill for a meal for nine people is £76.23. How much does each person pay if they each paid the same?

13. Work out

    (a) $11.2 \div 5$ (b) $9.01 \div 4$ (c) $12.1 \div 8$

    (d) $0.82 \div 4$ (e) $17 \div 5$ (f) $22 \div 8$

14. If 5 bricks weigh 4.64 kg, find the weight of one brick.

15. Five people share the fuel cost of a car journey which amounts to £18.65. How much does each person pay?

16. Six cows produce 33.84 litres of milk each day. What is the average milk production of each cow?

17. How many times will a 9 litre bucket have to be filled and emptied to completely empty a water drum containing 139·5 litres?

18. Barbecued sausages cost £5·94 for six. How much does each one cost?

19. A steel rod of length 2·86 m is divided into 11 equal pieces. How long is each piece?

20. Ten ball bearings weigh 2·5 kg. What is the weight of one?

Dividing by 10, 100, 1000 etc

The rules for dividing decimals are very similar to the rules for multiplying decimals.

● To divide by 10 move the digits one place to the right.

● To divide by 100 move the digits two places to the right.

● To divide by 1000 move the digits three places to the right.

    (a) $56 \div 10 = 5 \cdot 6$ (b) $6 \cdot 24 \div 100 = 0 \cdot 0624$

    (c) $3 \cdot 14 \div 10 = 0 \cdot 314$ (d) $57 \div 1000 = 0 \cdot 057$

Exercise 4

Do the following calculations. (They are not all dividing!.)

1. $57 \cdot 2 \div 10$	**2.** $89 \cdot 2 \div 10$	**3.** $5 \cdot 3 \div 10$	**4.** $47 \cdot 1 \div 100$
5. $141 \cdot 2 \div 100$	**6.** $19 \cdot 3 \div 10$	**7.** $1518 \div 100$	**8.** $4 \cdot 7 \div 100$
9. $25 \cdot 2 \div 1000$	**10.** $0 \cdot 63 \div 10$	**11.** $47 \cdot 2 \div 100$	**12.** $27 \cdot 9 \div 1000$
13. $6 \cdot 2 \div 1000$	**14.** $198 \cdot 7 \div 100$	**15.** $47 \div 10$	**16.** $416 \div 1000$
17. $2400 \div 10\,000$	**18.** $89 \div 100$	**19.** $63 \div 100$	**20.** $7 \div 1000$
21. $0 \cdot 86 \div 10$	**22.** $516 \div 10\,000$	**23.** $0 \cdot 077 \div 100$	**24.** $21 \cdot 9 \div 1000$
25. $500 \div 10\,000$	**26.** $260 \div 100\,000$	**27.** $0 \cdot 051 \div 100$	**28.** $890 \cdot 4 \div 10$
29. $4007 \div 100$	**30.** $20 \div 1000$	**31.** $5 \cdot 14 \times 10$	**32.** $6 \cdot 26 \times 100$
33. $0 \cdot 414 \times 100$	**34.** $0 \cdot 0631 \times 1000$	**35.** $0 \cdot 005 \times 100$	**36.** $0 \cdot 0063 \times 10\,000$
37. $47 \cdot 4 \div 10$	**38.** $8 \cdot 97 \div 100$	**39.** $54 \cdot 2 \div 1000$	**40.** 63×100
41. 47×10	**42.** $0 \cdot 84 \times 10\,000$	**43.** $0 \cdot 7 \div 100$	**44.** $6 \cdot 2 \div 10$
45. $4 \cdot 73 \times 10$	**46.** $0 \cdot 001 \times 1000$	**47.** $47 \div 100$	**48.** 47×100

Operator squares

Each empty square contains either a number or an operation ($+$, $-$, $\times$, $\div$). Copy each square and fill in the missing details. The arrows are equals signs.

1.

15	÷	3	→	
+		×		
		5	→	110
↓		↓		
37	−		→	

2.

14	+		→	31
×		+		
4		23	→	92
↓		↓		
	−		→	

3.

13	×		→	52
−		+		
	÷		→	
↓		↓		
8	÷		→	1

4.

17	×		→	170
−		÷		
	×		→	
↓		↓		
8	−	0.1	→	

5.

38	×	8	→	
÷		×		
2	×		→	
↓		↓		
	+	112	→	

6.

		574	→	1532
÷		+		
9	×	25	→	
↓		↓		
234	+		→	

7.

10	×		→	1
÷		×		
	÷		→	
↓		↓		
2.5	+	1.6	→	

8.

19.6	÷	7	→	
×		+		
0.1	×		→	1
↓		↓		
	+		→	

9.

8.42	−	0.2	→	
×		×		
100	×		→	1200
↓		↓		
	+		→	

10.

20	÷	100	→	
×		÷		
	×	200	→	
↓		↓		
440	×		→	

11.

1.22	×	3	→	
+		−		
	+		→	
↓		↓		
5	+		→	7.8

12.

	+		→	902
÷		−		
9	×	52	→	
↓		↓		
	+	526	→	

4.5 Solving equations

- Annie is thinking of a
  mystery number

  We could write | ? | for the

  mystery number.

  So Annie said $2 \times$ | ? | $+ 7 = 15$

  This is an *equation*. There is
  one unknown number shown
  by the question mark.

If I double the
number and then add
seven, the answer is
fifteen.

- Mathematicians all over the world prefer to use *letters* to stand
  for unknowns when they write equations.

  For Annie's problem a mathematician might write
  $2 \times n + 7 = 15$, where n is the mystery number.
  or $2n + 7 = 15$
  What *is* Annie's mystery number?

- Equations are like weighing scales which are balanced. The scales
  remain balanced if the same weight is added or taken away from
  both sides.

  On the left pan is an unknown
  weight x plus a 2 kg weight. On the
  right pan there is a 2 kg weight and a
  3 kg weight

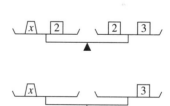

  If the two 2 kg weights are taken
  from each pan the scales are still
  balanced. So the weight x is 3 kg.

Exercise 1

Find the weight x by removing weights from both pans.
Weights are in kg.

1.

2.
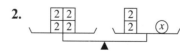

3.
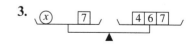

4.

5.
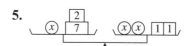

6.
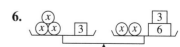

7.    **8.**

9.    **10.**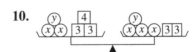

11. 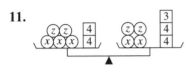   **12.**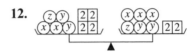

Rules for solving equations

Equations are solved in the same way as we solve the weighing scale problems.

The main rule when solving equations is

'Do the same thing to both sides'

You may *add* the same thing to both sides.
You may *subtract* the same thing from both sides.
You may *multiply* both sides by the same thing.
You may *divide* both sides by the same thing.

Solve the equations. The operations circled are performed on both sides

(a) $x + 7 = 12$
$\quad\quad \ominus 7 \quad \ominus 7$
$\quad\quad x = 5$

(b) $x - 3 = 11$
$\quad\quad \oplus 3 \quad \oplus 3$
$\quad\quad x = 14$

(c) $2x = 12$
$\quad\quad \oslash 2 \quad \oslash 2$
$\quad\quad x = 6$

(d) $\dfrac{x}{5} = 7$
$\quad\quad \otimes 5 \quad \otimes 5$
$\quad\quad x = 35$

Exercise 2

Solve the equations.

1. $x + 7 = 10$	**2.** $x + 3 = 20$	**3.** $x - 7 = 7$
4. $x - 5 = 11$	**5.** $6 + x = 13$	**6.** $8 + x = 15$
7. $7 = x + 4$	**8.** $7 = x - 6$	**9.** $1 = x - 3$
10. $7 + x = 7$	**11.** $x - 11 = 20$	**12.** $14 = 6 + x$

$7 = x + 4$
is the same as
$x + 4 = 7$

Questions **13** to **24** involve different operations.

13. $3n = 15$	**14.** $2n = 30$	**15.** $5n = 35$
16. $8 = 2n$	**17.** $6 = 6n$	**18.** $2n = 1$
19. $3n = 2$	**20.** $4n = 1000$	**21.** $7n = 0$
22. $60 = 6n$	**23.** $2n = 10\,000$	**24.** $3x = 1$

In Questions **25** to **42** find a.

25. $7 + a = 100$	**26.** $a - 13 = 13$	**27.** $5a = 1000$
28. $10a = 20$	**29.** $2 = a + 2$	**30.** $54 = 9a$
31. $a - \frac{1}{2} = \frac{1}{2}$	**32.** $11a = 1$	**33.** $a + 58 = 110$
34. $3a = 333$	**35.** $25 = a - 35$	**36.** $120 = a - 10$
37. $206 = a - 205$	**38.** $7a = 2$	**39.** $\frac{1}{2}a = 10$
40. $\frac{1}{4}a = 100$	**41.** $0 = 17a$	**42.** $a + 17 = 17$

Equations with two operations

(a) $4n - 1 = 11$
  $(+1)$ $(+1)$
  $4n = 12$
  $(\div 4)$ $(\div 4)$
  $n = 3$
  Check: $4 \times 3 - 1 = 11$ ✓

(b) $2n + 3 = 4$
  (-3) (-3)
  $2n = 1$
  $(\div 2)$ $(\div 2)$
  $n = \frac{1}{2}$
  Check: $2 \times \frac{1}{2} + 3 = 4$ ✓

Exercise 3

Solve the equations. Check solutions by substituting back in the equation.

1. $2n - 3 = 1$	**2.** $3n + 4 = 16$	**3.** $5n - 4 = 6$
4. $3n + 1 = 13$	**5.** $2n - 7 = 3$	**6.** $6n + 1 = 37$
7. $10n + 5 = 35$	**8.** $8n + 3 = 67$	**9.** $7n - 7 = 7$

In Questions **10** to **21** solve the equations to find *a*.

10. $3a - 1 = 2$ **11.** $5a + 7 = 17$ **12.** $8a - 5 = 11$

13. $10a + 20 = 100$ **14.** $3 + 2a = 9$ **15.** $8 + 3a = 14$

16. $6a - 5 = 19$ **17.** $7a - 11 = 24$ **18.** $3 + 2a = 4$

19. $5 + 7a = 705$ **20.** $5 + 3a = 6$ **21.** $18a - 3 = 33$

Solve the equations where the '*n*' terms are on the right hand side.

(a) $25 = 7n - 10$ (b) $8 = 6 + 3n$

                         $\boxed{-6}$ $\boxed{-6}$

        $35 = 7n$ $2 = 3n$

      $\boxed{\div 7}$ $\boxed{\div 7}$ $\boxed{\div 3}$ $\boxed{\div 3}$

          $5 = n$ $\frac{2}{3} = n$

Exercise 4

Solve the equations to find *n*. Check your solutions by substituting back in the equation.

1. $4 = 3n + 1$ **2.** $9 = 5n - 1$ **3.** $15 = 6n - 3$

4. $20 = 4n - 8$ **5.** $0 = 5n - 20$ **6.** $16 = 13 + 3n$

7. $25 = 5 + 2n$ **8.** $36 = 11n + 3$ **9.** $90 = 3n + 60$

In Questions **10** to **18** find the value of the letter in each question.

10. $3y - 7 = 8$ **11.** $20 = 4c + 4$ **12.** $5 = 4 + 5t$

13. $6p + 10 = 58$ **14.** $8 + 5m = 908$ **15.** $0 = 2x - 30$

16. $2u - 1 = 51$ **17.** $1 + 6n = 55$ **18.** $5p + 111 = 136$

Use mental methods to find the missing number.

19. $\boxed{} + 20 = 30$ **20.** $15 - \boxed{} = 9$ **21.** $\boxed{} \times 3 = 66$

22. $\boxed{} - 18 = 21$ **23.** $\boxed{} \div 2 = 40$ **24.** $\boxed{} \times 2 = 18$

25. $2 \times \boxed{} - 11 = 5$ **26.** $3 \times \boxed{} + 4 = 19$ **27.** $5 \times \boxed{} - 7 = 28$

28. $\boxed{} \div 2 + 10 = 20$ **29.** $\boxed{} \div 5 - 1 = 2$ **30.** $45 = 6 \times \boxed{} + 3$

Using equations to solve problems

Philip is thinking of a number. He tells us that when he doubles it and adds 7, the answer is 18. What number is Philip thinking of?

Suppose that Philip is thinking of the number x

He tells us that $\qquad\qquad\qquad 2x + 7 = 18$

Subtract 7 from both sides: $\qquad\qquad 2x = 11$

Divide both sides by 2 $\qquad\qquad\qquad x = \frac{11}{2}$

$$x = 5\tfrac{1}{2}$$

So Philip is thinking of the number $5\tfrac{1}{2}$

Exercise 5

In each question I am thinking of a number. Use the information to form an equation and then solve it to find the number.

1. If we multiply the number by 3 and then add 2, the answer is 20.

2. If we multiply the number by 5 and then subtract 3, the answer is 12.

3. If we multiply the number by 6 and then add 11, the answer is 47.

4. If we multiply the number by 11 and then subtract 4, the answer is 51.

5. If we double the number and add 10, the answer is 30.

6. If we multiply the number by 9 and then subtract 15, the answer is 30.

7. If we treble the number and then add 1000, the answer is 4000.

8. If we multiply the number by 20 and then subtract 2, the answer is 3.

9. Form equations to find x.

   (a) 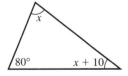   (b)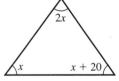

10. The angles of a triangle are A, B and C. Angle B is twice as big as angle A. Angle C is 8° bigger than angle A. Find the size of angle A.
    [Hint let the size of angle A be $x°$.]

11. The length of a rectangle is twice its width. If the perimeter is 54 cm, find its width.

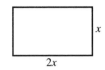

12. The length of a rectangle is three times its width. If the perimeter of the rectangle is 20 cm, find its width.

13. The length of a rectangle is 3 cm more than its width. If the perimeter of the rectangle is 30 cm, find its width.

14. Number walls are formed by adding adjacent numbers to get the number above. Find n in these walls.

(a) 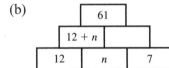 (b)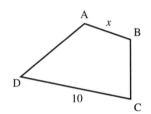

15. In a quadrilateral ABCD, BC is twice as long as AB and AD is three times as long as AB. Side DC is 10 cm long. The perimeter of ABCD is 31 cm.
Write an equation and solve it to find the length of AB.

16. An equilateral triangle has sides of length $(3x - 2)$, $(2x + 3)$ and 13. Find x.

4.6 Straight line graphs

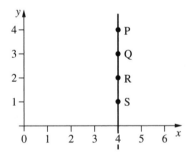

- The points P, Q, R and S have coordinates (4, 4), (4, 3), (4, 2) and (4, 1) and they all lie on a straight line. Since the x-coordinate of all the points is 4, we say the *equation* of the line is $x = 4$.

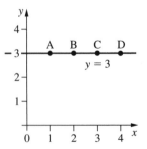

- The points A, B, C and D have coordinates (1, 3), (2, 3), (3, 3) and (4, 3) and they all lie on a straight line. Since the y-coordinate of all the points is 3, we say the *equation* of the line is $y = 3$.

Exercise 1

1. Write down the equations for the lines marked A, B and C.

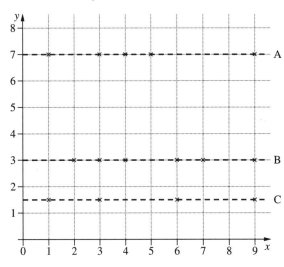

2. Write down the equations for the lines marked P, Q and R.

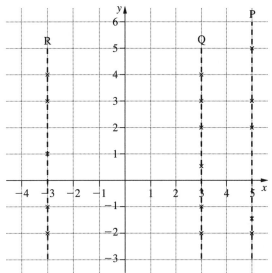

In Questions **3** and **4** there is a line of dots A, a line of crosses B and a line of circles C.

Write down the equations of the lines in each question.

3.

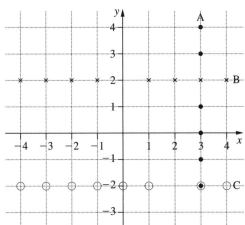

4.

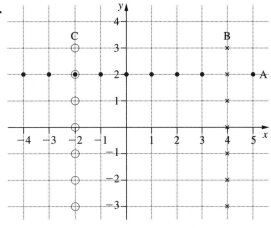

5. On squared paper
(a) Draw the lines $y = 2$ and $x = 3$. At what point do they meet?
(b) Draw the lines $y = 5$ and $x = 1$. At what point do they meet?
(c) Draw the lines $x = 7$ and $y = 3$. At what point do they meet?

6. In the diagram, E and N lie on the line with equation $y = 1$. B and K lie on the line $x = 5$. In parts (a) to (h) find the equation of the line passing through the points given:

(a) A and D   (e) L and E
(b) A, B and I   (f) D, K and G
(c) M and P   (g) C, M, L and H
(d) I and H   (h) P and F

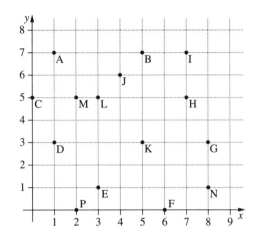

Relating *x* and *y*

- The sloping line passes through the following points:
  (1, 1), (2, 2), (3, 3), (4, 4), (5, 5).

  For each point, the *y*-coordinate is equal to the *x*-coordinate.

  The equation of the line is $y = x$ (or $x = y$).

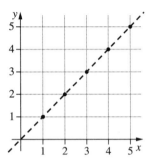

- This line passes through:
  (0, 1), (1, 2), (2, 3), (3, 4), (4, 5).

  For each point the *y*-coordinate is one more than the *x*-coordinate. The equation of the line is $y = x + 1$.

  We could also say that the *x* coordinate is always one less than the *y* coordinate. The equation of the line could then be written as $x = y - 1$.
  [Most mathematicians use the equation beginning '$y =$'].

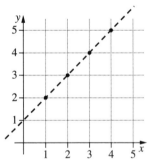

- This line slopes the other way and passes through:
  (0, 5), (1, 4), (2, 3), (3, 2), (4, 1), (5, 0).

  The sum of the *x* coordinate and the *y* coordinate is always 5. The equation of the line is $x + y = 5$.

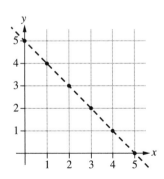

Exercise 2

For each question write down the coordinates of the points marked.
Find the equation of the line through the points.

1.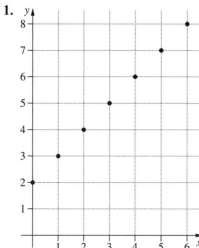

2.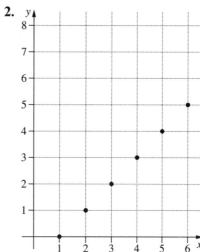

3.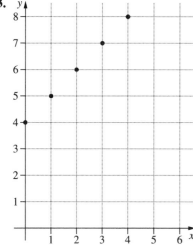

4.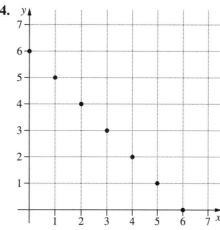

5.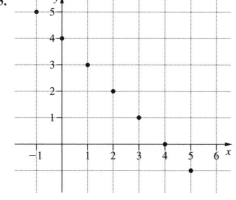

6.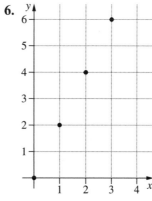

Drawing graphs

- The equation of a line is $y = x + 2$. Here is a list of five points on the line: (0, 2), (1, 3), (2, 4), (3, 5), (4, 6)

  The points are plotted on a graph and the line $y = x + 2$ is drawn.

  Notice that the line extends beyond (0, 2) and (4, 6).

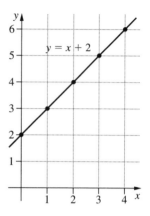

Exercise 3

1. The equation of a line is $y = x + 3$. Copy and complete a list of points on the line:

   (0, 3) (1, 4) (2, ☐) (3, ☐) (4, ☐)

   Draw the graph of $y = x + 3$

2. The equation of a line is $y = x + 5$. Copy and complete a list of points on the line:

   (0, 5) (1, 6) (2, ☐) (3, ☐) (4, ☐)

In Questions **3** to **10** you are given the equation of a line and a list of points on the line. Fill in the missing numbers and then draw the graph.

3. $y = x - 2$; (0, −2), (1, −1), (2, ☐), (3, ☐), (4, ☐)

4. $y = x - 4$; (0, −4), (1, −3), (2, ☐), (3, ☐), (4, ☐)

5. $y = 2x$; (0, 0), (1, 2), (2, ☐), (3, ☐), (4, ☐)

6. $y = 2x + 1$; (0, ☐), (2, ☐), (4, ☐)

7. $y = 2x - 2$; (0, ☐), (2, ☐), (4, ☐)

8. $y = 6 - x$; (1, ☐), (3, ☐), (5, ☐), (6, ☐)

9. $y = 4 - x$; (0, ☐), (2, ☐), (4, ☐)

10. $y = 3x + 2$; (0, ☐), (1, ☐), (2, ☐)

11. Draw the lines $y = 5 - x$ and $y = 2x - 1$ on the same graph. Write down the co-ordinates of the point where the lines meet.

4.7 Solving problems (no calculators)

Exercise 1

1. Work out
   (a) 4×808 (b) $370 - 25$ (c) 8×0
   (d) $348 \div 6$ (e) $8279 + 182$ (f) $2314 - 276$

2. Write the number 'three thousand and fourteen' in figures.

3. (a) Copy and shade one quarter
   of this shape:
   (b) What percentage of the shape
   is left unshaded?

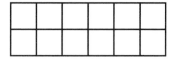

4. Steve has read 97 of the 448 pages in his book. How many more pages must be read to reach the middle?

5. There are 15 piles of magazines. Eight piles have 20 magazines each, of the other piles each have 25 magazines. How many magazines are there altogether?

6. There are 127 youngsters playing football.
   How many teams of five can be formed?
   How many will be left over?

7. It cost 6 children a total of £12.90 to watch a film. What did it cost each child?

8. Copy and complete this multiplication square

$\times$	2	5		
		40		72
			18	
7	14			
			24	36

9. Write 10 million pence in pounds and pence.

10. The area of the 'Z' shape is $20 \, \text{cm}^2$.
    (a) Write down the area of each small square.
    (b) Work out the length of the perimeter of the shape.

Exercise 2

1. In a 'magic square' all rows (←——→) columns

$\left(\updownarrow\right)$ and main diagonals $\left(\times\right)$ add up

to the same 'magic number'. Copy and
complete this magic square.

6		12	7
	4		
	16	13	2
10			11

2. (a) What is the length of this line in millimetres?
 (b) What is this length in centimetres?

├───────────────────────────┤

3. In a new airport terminal, 25 new doors are
 required.
 (a) If each door is fastened by 3 hinges, how
 many hinges are needed altogether?
 (b) If each hinge requires 6 screws, what is
 the total number of screws required to fit
 all the doors?

4. A multi-storey office block has 104 offices altogether. If there
 are 8 offices on each floor, how many storeys does the building
 have?

5. Numbers are missing on four of these calculator buttons. Copy
 the diagram and write in numbers to make the answer 25.

[2] [8] [+] [ ] [ ] [−] [ ] [ ] [=] [2] [5]

6. Here are some number cards. [3] [4] [7] [2] [9]

 (a) Use two cards to make a
 fraction which is equal to $\frac{1}{2}$.

 $\dfrac{\Box}{\Box}$

 (b) Use three of the cards to make
 the smallest possible fraction.

 $\dfrac{\Box}{\Box\Box}$

7. (a) How many 12 centimetre pieces of string can be cut from a
 piece of string which is 1 metre in length?
 (b) How much string is left over?

8. Look at this group of numbers ...

                15, 9, 27, 24, 7

 (a) Which of the numbers is a multiple of both 3 and 4?
 (b) Which of the numbers is a prime number?
 (c) Which of the numbers is a square number?

9. Write down these calculations and find the missing digits.

(a)   3 ☐ 4
     + 2 6 ☐
        6 3 9

(b)   5 ☐ 9
     + 3 8 ☐
     ☐ 2 5

(c)   ☐ 2 ☐
     + 3 ☐ 4
        8 0 0

10. The rule for the number sequences below is '*double and add 2*'.
    Write down each sequence and fill in the missing numbers.

(a) 1 → 4 → 10 → 22 → ☐

(b) ☐ → 6 → 14 → 30

(c) ☐ → 8 → ☐ → ☐

Exercise 3

1. How many grams of sugar must be added to 1·3 kg to make 3 kg altogether?

2. Serena bought a packet of 100 raspberries.
   She ate a quarter of them on Monday.
   She ate a fifth of the remaining
   raspberries on Tuesday.
   How many raspberries
   did she have left?

3. For sports day a school has 40 litres of drink. One cup of drink is 200 ml. How many cups of drink can be provided?

4. Change this cake recipe for 4 people to a recipe for 6 people.

   320 g   mixed fruit
    90 g   butter
   200 ml milk
      4   eggs

5. Stainless steel contains Iron, Chromium and Nickel. 74·2% of stainless steel is Iron, 8·3% is Nickel. What percentage is Chromium?

6. Work out
   (a) $114 \times 0·4$ (b) $18 - 5·7$ (c) $211 + 57·3 + 5·42$

7. Write the number 'two and a half million' in figures.

8. How many minutes are there from 07·20 to 09·15?

9. Measure the sides of the rectangle
   and work out
   (a) the area
   (b) the perimeter

10. Work out the missing numbers

   (a) $310 + 560 = \boxed{}$ (b) $530 + \boxed{} = 700$ (c) $734 + \boxed{} = 780$

   (d) $\boxed{} + 210 = 500$ (e) $338 + \boxed{} = 558$ (f) $\boxed{} - 420 = 535$

11. Work out the missing numbers

   (a) $5 \cdot 6 + \boxed{} = 6$ (b) $3 \cdot 7 - \boxed{} = 2$ (c) $0 \cdot 54 + \boxed{} = 0 \cdot 74$

   (d) $0 \cdot 4 - \boxed{} = 0 \cdot 15$ (e) $\boxed{} - 0 \cdot 7 = 1 \cdot 4$ (f) $0 \cdot 86 - \boxed{} = 0 \cdot 5$

12. Jesper has the same number of 20p and 50p coins. The total
   value is £7. How many of each coin does he have?

Exercise 4

1. There are 35 rows of chairs and there are 20 chairs in each row.
   (a) How many chairs are there altogether?
   (b) How many rows of chairs are needed for 300 people?

2. I think of a number, add $2 \cdot 3$ and then multiply by 4. The answer
   is $23 \cdot 4$. What is the number I am thinking of?

3. How many roses, costing 42p each, can
   be bought for £20? How much change will
   there be?

4. Use each of the digits 1 to 6. $\boxed{5}\ \boxed{} \times \boxed{} = \boxed{1}\ \boxed{}\ \boxed{}$
   Put one digit in each box to
   make the statement true.

5. A restaurant has 5000 litres of milk. It sells
   350 litres per day on average. How many days
   will the milk last?

6. Julie runs across the playground, which is
   90 m wide, in 15 seconds. What was her
   average speed in metres per second?

7. This is a number triangle. The numbers along each edge add up to 9.

Copy and complete the triangle.

The six numbers are 1, 2, 3, 4, 5, 6.

8. A box has a mass of 230 g when empty.
When it is full of sugar the total mass is 650 g.
What is its mass when it is half full?

9. This is a number ring.
Start with any number and multiply the units digit by 4 and then add the tens digit.

For example $(14) \rightarrow 4 \times 4 + 1 \rightarrow (17)$

The rule is then repeated on 21 and so on.

Use the same rule to complete this number ring.

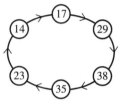

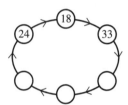

10. A piece of A4 size paper measures 297 mm by 210 mm.
  (a) A money spider starts at a corner and decides to walk around all sides of the paper.
     How far will the spider walk in millimetres?
  (b) Change your answer in part (a) into centimetres.
  (c) Has the spider travelled more or less than one metre?

11. A birthday card rests on a horizontal table.
Copy these sentences and fill the space with one of the words:

'vertical;   horizontal;   parallel;   perpendicular'

  (a) The edge BC is _____ .

  (b) The edge AB is _____ to edge AD.

  (c) Edges DE and DC are _____ .

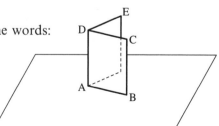

Part 5

5.1 Rotation

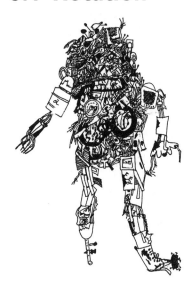

Professor M. Adman has designed a robot called 'The Rubbish Man' entirely from waste materials.

The robot is still in the early stages of development and is only able to move in four directions.

The 'Rubbish Man's' options are:-

1. Turn left (causing a change in direction of 90°).
2. Turn right (causing a change in direction of 90°).
3. Go straight on (meaning no change in direction).
4. About turn (causing a change in direction of 180°).

A *quarter turn* is a turn of **90°**, called *1 right angle*.
A *half turn* is a turn of **180°**, called *2 right angles*.
A *three-quarter* turn is a turn of **270°**, called *3 right angles*.
A *full turn* is a turn of **360°**, called *4 right angles*.

- When turning through right angles we have two options, we can turn clockwise (⌒) or anti-clockwise (⌒).

- Here are two example of rotations.

(a)

(b)

90° turn, clockwise

90° turn, anti-clockwise

Exercise 1

1. These pictures have been hung incorrectly. Give instructions to turn them the right way round. Remember to give both the angle and the direction.

(a) 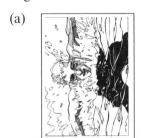   (b) 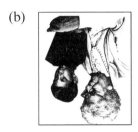   (c)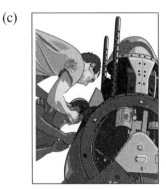

(d)    (e)    (f)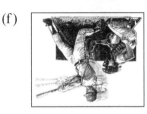

In Questions **2** to **10** copy each diagram and then draw its new position after it has been turned. You can use tracing paper if you wish.

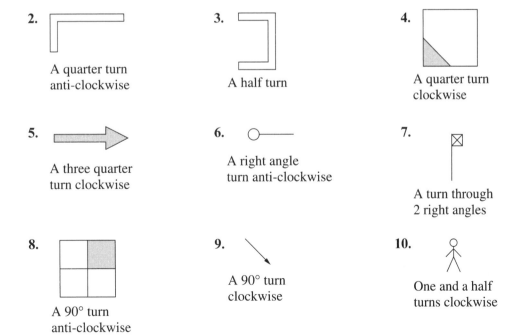

2.

A quarter turn
anti-clockwise

3.

A half turn

4.

A quarter turn
clockwise

5.

A three quarter
turn clockwise

6.

A right angle
turn anti-clockwise

7.

A turn through
2 right angles

8.

A 90° turn
anti-clockwise

9.

A 90° turn
clockwise

10.

One and a half
turns clockwise

In Questions **11** to **16** describe the rotation. Give the angle and the direction.

11.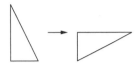

12.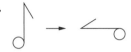

13.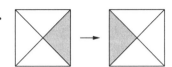

14.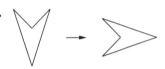

15.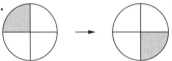

16.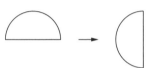

17. (a) This shape is going
to be turned 90°
clockwise around
the point A

Here is
the result.

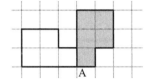

(b) Turn this shape
90° clockwise around
the point B

Copy the shape and shade in the new
position of the shape

In Questions **18** to **20** copy the shape on squared paper and then draw and shade its new position.

18.

Half turn around
the point C

19.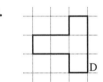

Quarter turn clockwise
around the point D

20.

Turn 90° anti-clockwise
around the point E

LOGO

LOGO is used to give commands to move a turtle on a computer.
Here is a list of the main commands.

FD 20   Go **F**orwar**D** 20 spaces
BK 30   Go **B**ac**K** 30 spaces

RT 90   **R**ight **T**urn 90 degrees
RT 45   **R**ight **T**urn 45 degrees
LT 90   **L**eft **T**urn 90 degrees

PU   **P**en **U**p   ⎫ These are used to move across the
PD   **P**en **D**own   ⎬ screen without drawing a line.

Here are two examples in which the turtle goes from A to B.

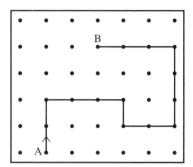

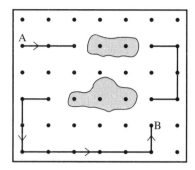

FD 20, RT 90, FD 30, RT 90,
FD 10, LT 90, FD 20, LT 90,
FD 30, LT 90, FD 30

In this one the turtle has to
'fly over' the obstacles shown.
FD 20, PU, FD 30, PD, FD 10,
RT 90, FD 20, RT 90, FD 10,
PU, FD 40, PD, FD 10, LT 90,
FD 20, LT 90, FD 50, LT 90,
FD 10

Exercise 2

1. Write down the commands that would move the turtle from A to B. The dots are 10 spaces apart

(a) 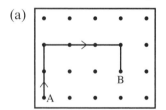   (b)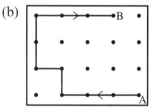

2. Write the commands that would move the turtle from A to B. In this question the turtle has to 'jump over' the obstacles shown by shaded areas.

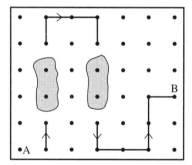

3. Write the commands that would move the turtle along the route given.
   (a) A → E → D → C → F → A
   (b) A → B → D → H → G → I → J → A
   (c) A → B → A → F → C

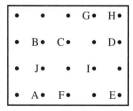

4. Leslie Smith wants to write her
  initials. Write down the LOGO
  commands.
  Start at the top of the 'L'.

5. Write down the LOGO commands for *your* own initials.

6. Draw the patterns given by the commands below.
  (a) FD 50, RT 90, FD 50, RT 90, FD 40, RT 90, FD 40, RT 90,
      FD 30, RT 90, FD 30, RT 90, FD 20, RT 90, FD 20, RT 90,
      FD 10, RT 90, FD 10.
  (b) FD 40, RT 90, FD 20, RT 90, FD 20, RT 90, FD 20, LT 90,
      FD 20, LT 90, PU, FD 30, PD, FD 20, LT 90, FD 20, LT 90,
      FD 20, BK 20, RT 90, FD 20, LT 90, FD 20.

7. Design your own pattern and write down the LOGO commands
  for it. Ask a friend to test your commands.

8. Investigate the patterns you can obtain using the 'Repeat'
  command. Start with REPEAT 4 [FD 20, LT 90].

Compass directions

Another way of describing a direction is provided by the *points* of
the *compass*.

There are four major directions (called cardinal points) on a
compass:

N represents north.
E represents east.
S represents south.
W represents west.

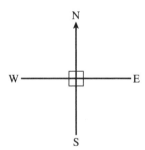

The directions between the four cardinal points are:

NE representing North-East.
SE representing South-East.
SW representing South-West.
NW representing North-West.

Exercise 3

Copy and complete this table.

	You are facing	Movement (Angle and Direction)	Direction you are now facing
1.	N	180°	?
2.	E	360°	?
3.	S	90° clockwise	?
4.	W	90° clockwise	?
5.	NW	180°	?
6.	SE	90° anti-clockwise	?
7.	NE	270° clockwise	?
8.	SW	270° anti-clockwise	?
9.	S	90° anti-clockwise	?
10.	E	?	W
11.	NW	?	SW
12.	NE	?	E
13.	W	?	S
14.	?	90° clockwise	W
15.	?	90° anti-clockwise	S
16.	?	180°	NE
17.	?	90° clockwise	E
18.	SW	?	S
19.	N	?	SW
20.	S	?	NE

21. The points A, B, C, D, E, F, G, H, I are places on a map.
    Work out where I am in the following:

    (a) I am North of G and West of C
    (b) I am South of A and West of E
    (c) I am West of D and North of F
    (d) I am East of H and South of B
    (e) I am South-East of G and South of I
    (f) I am East of A and South of C
    (g) I am South-West of C and East of H
    (h) I am North-West of G and South-West of B.

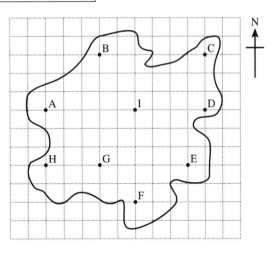

Rotational symmetry

The shape B fits onto itself three times when rotated through a complete turn. It has *rotational symmetry of order three*.

The shape C fits onto itself six times when rotated through a complete turn. It has rotational symmetry of order six.

Exercise 4

For each diagram decide whether or not the shape has rotational symmetry. For those diagrams that do have rotational symmetry state the order.

1.

2.

3.

4.

5.

6.

7.

8.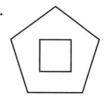

9.

10.

11.

12.

13.

14.

15.

16.

5.2 Reflection

Paper folding activities

1. Take a piece of paper, fold it once and then cut out a shape across the fold. This will produce a shape with one line of symmetry, which is a mirror line.

cut along the broken line →

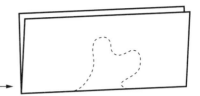

2. Fold another piece of paper twice so that the second fold is at right angles to the first fold. Again cut along the fold to see what shapes you can make.
This will produce a shape with two lines of symmetry. [i.e. two mirror lines]

3. Fold the paper three times and cut.

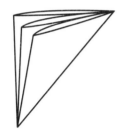 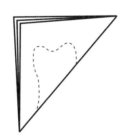

This will produce a shape with four lines of symmetry.

Below are three shapes obtained by folding and cutting as above.
Try to make similar shapes yourself.
Stick the best shapes into your exercise book.

1.

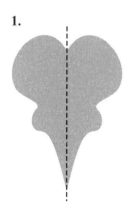

one line of symmetry
(or one mirror line)

2.

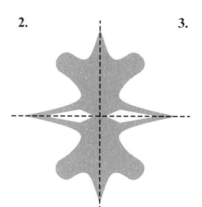

two lines of symmetry
(or two mirror lines)

3.

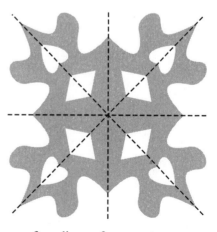

four lines of symmetry
(or four mirror lines)

Exercise 1

Copy each of the following shapes and mark on the diagram all lines of symmetry.

1. 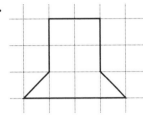   **2.** 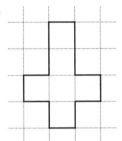   **3.**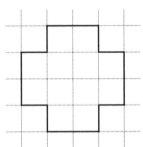

4. 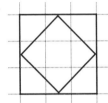   **5.** 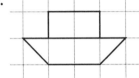   **6.**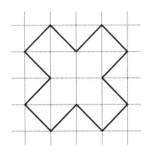

Reflection

A reflection is a transformation in which points are mapped to images by folding along a mirror line.

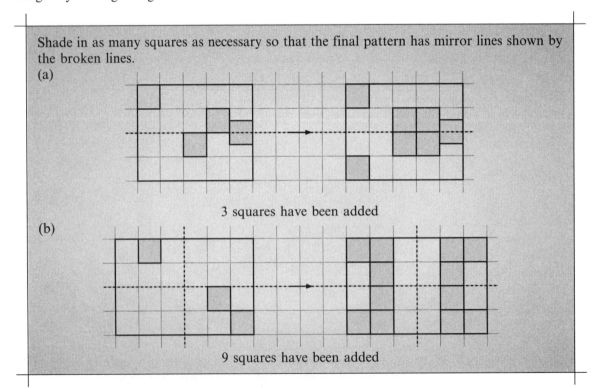

Shade in as many squares as necessary so that the final pattern has mirror lines shown by the broken lines.

(a)

3 squares have been added

(b)

9 squares have been added

Exercise 2

Copy each diagram and, using a different colour, shade in as many squares as necessary so that the final pattern has mirror lines shown by the broken lines. For each question write down how many new squares were shaded in.

1. 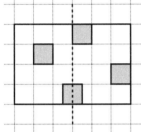   **2.** 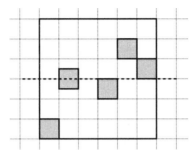   **3.**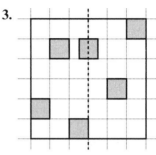

4. 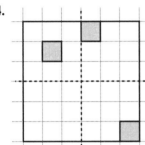   **5.** 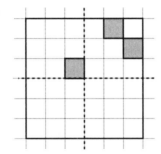   **6.**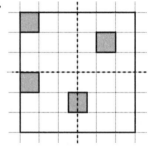

Be careful when the mirror line is a diagonal line. You can check your diagram by folding along the mirror line.

7. 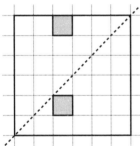   **8.** 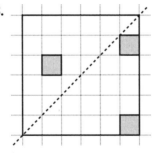   **9.**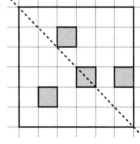

10. 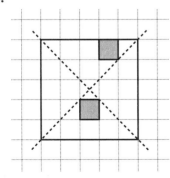   **11.** 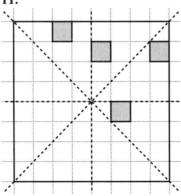   **12.**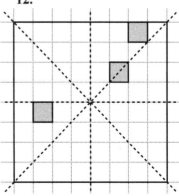

Investigating line symmetry

Exercise 3

1. You have 3 square black tiles and 2 square white tiles, which can be joined together along whole sides.

   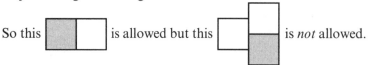

   So this [ ] is allowed but this [ ] is *not* allowed.

   Draw as many diagrams as possible with the 5 tiles joined together so that the diagram has line symmetry.

   For example fig. 1 and fig. 2 have line symmetry but fig. 3 does not have line symmetry so fig. 3 is not acceptable.

   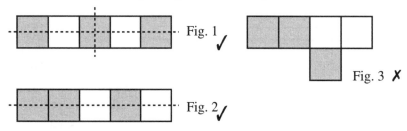

2. Now you have 2 black tiles and 2 white tiles. Draw as many diagrams as possible with these tiles joined together so that the diagram has line symmetry.

3. Finally with 3 black tiles and 3 white tiles draw as many diagrams as possible which have line symmetry.

   Here is one diagram which has line symmetry

   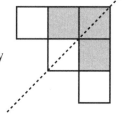

4. Shape A is a single square. [ ] A Shape B consists of four squares.  B

   Draw three diagrams in which shapes A and B are joined together along a whole edge so that the final shape has line symmetry.

5. Shape C is a single square. [ ] C Shape D consists of five squares. [ ] D

   Draw four diagrams in which shapes C and D are joined together along a whole edge so that the final shape has line symmetry.

The tile factory: an activity

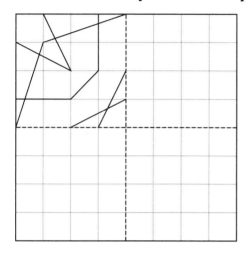

1. Copy this square and pattern onto the top left hand corner of a piece of A4 centimetre squared paper.

2. Lightly mark the reflection lines on the diagram as shown.

3 Use these lines to help you reflect the pattern across ...

... and then down.

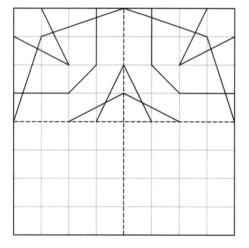

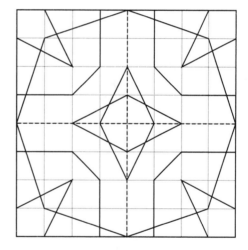

4. Repeat the process with the same tile so that your tile neatly covers the piece of paper →.

5. Now colour or shade in your work as neatly and symmetrically as you can.

5.3　Translation

A translation is a transformation in which every point of the object moves the same distance in a parallel direction.

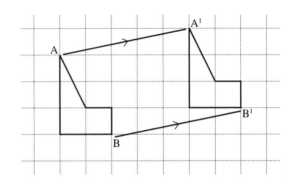

A translation can be described by two instructions, the move parallel to the *x*-axis and the move parallel to the *y*-axis.

In the example shown, the translation is 5 units to the right and 1 unit up.

Exercise 1　Use squared paper

1. (a) Draw the object triangle A on squared paper.
   (b) Draw the image of A after a translation of 4 units to the right and 1 unit up. Label the image B.
   (c) Draw the image of A after a translation of 2 units to the right and 2 units down. Label the image C.

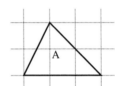

2.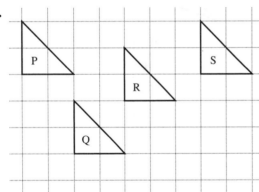

   Describe the following translations.
   (a) P → Q
   (b) Q → S
   (c) R → P
   (d) S → P

3. (a) Draw shape A as shown.
   (b) Translate shape A 5 units right and label the image B.
   (c) Translate shape B 3 units down and label the image C.
   (d) Translate shape C 3 units left and 1 unit down and label the image D.
   (e) What is the single translation which would move shape A onto shape D?

4.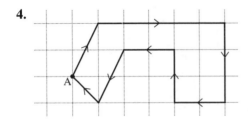

   A computer controls a pen which starts at A. Describe the 8 translations required to draw the shape given.

5.4 Long multiplication and division

Long multiplication

- Seventeen 23s is the same as ten 23s plus seven 23s
  17×23 is the same as $10 \times 23 + 7 \times 23$

(a) $\begin{array}{r} 23 \\ \times 10 \\ \hline 230 \end{array}$ (b) $\begin{array}{r} 23 \\ \times\ 7 \\ \hline 161 \end{array}$ (c) $\begin{array}{r} 230 \\ +161 \\ \hline 391 \end{array}$

Quick method $\begin{array}{r} 23 \\ \times 17 \\ \hline 230 \\ 161 \\ \hline 391 \end{array}$ $\begin{array}{l} \longleftarrow 10 \times 23 \\ \longleftarrow 7 \times 23 \end{array}$

- $16 \times 35 = 10 \times 35 + 6 \times 35$

(a) $\begin{array}{r} 35 \\ \times 10 \\ \hline 350 \end{array}$ (b) $\begin{array}{r} 35 \\ \times\ 6 \\ \hline 210 \\ {\scriptstyle 3} \end{array}$ (c) $\begin{array}{r} 350 \\ +210 \\ \hline 560 \end{array}$

Quick method $\begin{array}{r} 35 \\ \times 16 \\ \hline 350 \\ 210 \\ \hline 560 \end{array}$ $\begin{array}{l} \longleftarrow 10 \times 35 \\ \longleftarrow 6 \times 35 \end{array}$

- Begin by working out an approximate answer.

  (a) $17 \times 33 \approx 20 \times 30$
  $\qquad = 600$

  (b) $24 \times 56 \approx 20 \times 60$
  $\qquad = 1200$

Exercise 1

Do the following, after working out an approximate answer first.

1. 15×23 2. 14×31 3. 16×32 4. 17×14

5. 18×33 6. 19×24 7. 17×31 8. 13×52

9. 21×24 10. 27×32 11. 26×28 12. 27×21

13. 32×25 14. 33×27 15. 36×14 16. 35×27

17. 234×41 18. 142×61 19. 331×47 20. 453×21

21. 123×32 22. 291×42 23. 804×61 24. 74×243

In Questions **25** to **28**, find the missing digits.

25. $26 \times 33 = 85\boxed{}$ 26. $132 \times 55 = 726\boxed{}$

27. $\boxed{}\boxed{}\boxed{} \div 37 = 25$ 28. $10\boxed{}\boxed{}\boxed{} \div 84 = 124$

Long division

Here are two examples of division.

- 3480 ÷ 8 is approximately 3200 ÷ 8 = 400

$$8 \overline{)3480}$$
$$\underline{-3200} \quad 8 \times 400$$
$$280$$
$$\underline{-240} \quad 8 \times 30$$
$$40$$
$$\underline{-40} \quad 8 \times 5$$
$$0$$

Answer: 435

- 390 ÷ 15 is approximately 300 ÷ 15 = 20

$$15 \overline{)390}$$
$$\underline{-300} \quad 15 \times 20$$
$$90$$
$$\underline{-90} \quad 15 \times 6$$
$$0$$

Answer: 26

Exercise 2

1. Copy and complete

(a)
$$7 \overline{)3374}$$
$$\underline{-2800} \quad 7 \times 400$$
$$574$$
$$\underline{-560} \quad 7 \times 80$$
$$14$$
$$\underline{-14} \quad 7 \times 2$$
$$0$$

Answer: 4 ☐☐

(b)
$$13 \overline{)702}$$
$$\underline{-650} \quad 13 \times 50$$
$$52$$
$$\underline{-52} \quad 13 \times 4$$
$$0$$

Answer: ☐☐

Do the following, after working out an approximate answer first.

2. $8 \overline{)272}$ **3.** $7 \overline{)2464}$ **4.** $6 \overline{)2142}$

5. $12 \overline{)420}$ **6.** $13 \overline{)494}$ **7.** $15 \overline{)930}$

8. $13 \overline{)275}$ **9.** $16 \overline{)498}$ **10.** $17 \overline{)544}$

11. $459 \div 17$ **12.** $735 \div 21$ **13.** $858 \div 33$

14. $669 \div 19$ **15.** $900 \div 25$ **16.** $814 \div 22$

Exercise 3

To do these questions you have to multiply or divide. Do not use a calculator. Begin by finding an approximate answer.

1. Work out the total cost of 45 pens at 22p each. Give your answer in pounds.

2. A box of 15 golf balls costs 975 pence. How much does each ball cost?

3. There are 23 rooms in a school and each room has 33 chairs. How many chairs are there altogether?

4. A shop owner buys 52 tins of
   paint at 84p each. How much
   does he spend altogether?

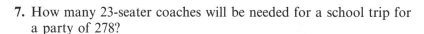
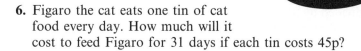
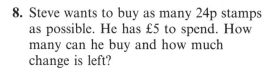

5. Eggs are packed twelve to a box.
   How many boxes are needed for
   444 eggs?

6. Figaro the cat eats one tin of cat
   food every day. How much will it
   cost to feed Figaro for 31 days if each tin costs 45p?

7. How many 23-seater coaches will be needed for a school trip for
   a party of 278?

8. Steve wants to buy as many 24p stamps
   as possible. He has £5 to spend. How
   many can he buy and how much
   change is left?

9. It costs £972 to hire a boat for a day. A trip is organised for 36
   people. How much does each person pay?

10. Tins of spaghetti are packed 24 to a box. How many boxes are
    needed for 868 tins?

11. On average a school needs 87 exercise books a week. How many
    books are needed for 38 weeks?

12. A prize of 470 chocolate bars is shared equally between 18
    winners. How many bars does each winner get and how many
    are left over?

13. Each class of a school has 31 pupils plus one teacher and there
    are 15 classes in the school.
    The school hall can take 26 rows of chairs with 18 chairs in a
    row. Is that enough chairs for all the pupils and teachers?

14. When Philip was digging a hole in
    his garden he struck oil! The oil
    came out at a rate of £17 for
    every minute of the day and
    night. How much does Philip
    receive in a 24-hour day?

5.5 Averages and range

If you have a set of data, like exam marks or heights, and are asked to find the 'average', just what are you trying to find? The answer is: a single number which can be used to represent the entire set of data. This could be done in three different ways.

- **The mean**
  All the data is added and the total is divided by the number of items.
  In everyday language the word 'average' usually stands for the mean.

- **The median**
  When the data is arranged in order of size, the median is the one in the middle. If there are two 'middle' numbers, the median is in the middle of these two numbers.

- **The mode** is the number which occurs most often. The mode is the most popular value and comes from the french 'a la mode' meaning 'fashionable'. A set of data may have more than one mode.

- **Range**
  The range is not an average but is the difference between the largest value and the smallest value. The range is a measure of how spread out the data is.

The marks achieved by 10 pupils in a test were:

8, 5, 7, 4, 5, 6, 9, 7, 5, 10.

(a) Mean mark $= \dfrac{8+5+7+4+5+6+9+7+5+10}{10} = \dfrac{66}{10} = 6.6$

(b) Arrange the marks in order: 4 5 5 5 6 7 7 8 9 10

$\uparrow$

the median is here

Median $= \dfrac{6+7}{2} = 65$

(c) Mode $= 5$, since there are more fives than any other number.
(d) Range $= 10 - 4 = 6$

Exercise 1

1. A fisherman caught five fish. Their masses were 200g, 300g, 220g, 190g and 90g. What is the mean mass of the fish?

2. In four different shops the price of one litre of lemonade is 43p, 37p, 41p, 35p. What is the mean price of the lemonade?

3. In a test the marks were 9, 3, 4, 7, 7. Calculate the mean mark.

4. For each set of numbers find (i) the mean
                                (ii) the median
   (a) 8, 5, 9, 8, 7
   (b) 1, 5, 6, 11, 3, 4, 5
   (c) 4, 9, 2, 5.

5. The marks awarded to a skater were
      58, 60, 57, 59, 56.
   Find the mean mark.

6. The shoe sizes of the children in a Year 6 class were
      3, 2, 3, 4, 3, 2, 3, 4, 3, 2, 3, 3
      3, 3, 4, 5, 3, 4, 3, 3, 3, 5, 2, 3.
   What shoe size is the mode?

7. The temperature in a garden was measured at midnight every day for a week. The results (in °C) were
      −3, 0, 1, 7, −5, 3, 0.
   What was the range of the temperatures?

8. There were 9 people in the Oxford rowing boat. The mean age of the people was 22 and the range of their ages was 6.
   Write each sentence below and write next to it whether it is *True, Possible* or *Impossible*.
   (a) Every person was 22 years old.
   (b) All the people were at least 20 years old
   (c) The oldest person was 6 years older than the youngest person.
   (d) The youngest person on the boat was 14 years old.

9. The total mass of seven cows is 3570 kg.
   Calculate the mean mass of the cows.

10. The total height of 6 children is 930 cm.
    Calculate the mean height of the children.

11. There were 5 people living in a house. The *median* age of the people was 21 and the range of their ages was 3.
Write each sentence below and write next to it whether it is *True, Possible* or *False*.
(a) Every person was either 20 or 21 years old.
(b) The oldest person in the house was 24 years old.
(c) The mean age of the people was less than 21 years.

12. Think of five numbers which have a mean of 6 and a median of 4. Ask a friend to check your answer.

Exercise 2

1. The temperature was recorded at 0400 in seven towns across the U.K. The readings were $0°$, $1°$, $-4°$, $1°$, $-2°$, $-5°$, $-4°$.
What was the median temperature.

2. The number of occupants in the 33 houses in a street is as follows:

    2   4   3   4   1   4   2   4   1   5   2
    3   0   5   3   4   3   6   7   3   3   6
    4   1   4   2   0   1   4   3   2   5   0

What is the modal number of occupants in the houses?

3. The test results for a class of 30 pupils were as follows:

Mark	3	4	5	6	7	8
Frequency	2	5	4	7	6	6

What was the modal mark?

4. (a) Calculate the mean of the numbers 3, 2, 5, 11, 9, 6
(b) Calculate the new mean when the lowest number is removed.

5. In a maths test the marks for the boys were 9, 3, 5, 7, 4, 8 and the marks for the girls were 10, 6, 7, 3.
(a) Find the mean mark for the boys.
(b) Find the mean mark for the girls.
(c) Find the mean mark for the whole class.

6. (a) Copy and complete: 'For the set of numbers
5, 5, 6, 8, 9, 10, 10, 11, there are ☐ modes. The modes
are ☐ and ☐.'

(b) Find the mode or modes for this set of numbers
1, 2, 2, 2, 3, 3, 5, 6, 7, 7, 7, 9.

7. The range for nine numbers on a card is 60. One number is covered by a piece of blu-tac. What could that number be?

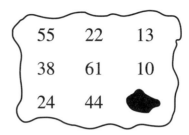

55 22 13
38 61 10
24 44 ▮

8. The total weight of seven cars on a transporter is 3360 kg. What is the mean weight of the cars.

9. Sally throws a dice eight times and wins 20p if the median score is more than 3. The dice shows 6, 1, 2, 6, 4, 1, 3, 6. Find the median score. Does she win 20p?

10. Lynn has 3 cards. Find the mean.
She takes another card and the mean goes up by 3. What number is on the new card?

| 6 | 2 | 7 |

| 6 | 2 | 7 | ? |

11. Make a list of 9 numbers (not all the same!) so that the mode, the median and the mean are all the same value.
For example: The set of numbers 5, 6, 7, 7, 10 have mode, median and mean equal to 7.
Ask a friend to check your list.

12. Serena has 5 cards.
The mean of the five cards is 8.
The range of the five cards is 6.
What numbers are on the two other cards?

| 8 | 8 | 8 | | |

13.* I can dial a computer helpline at either AOL or COMPI. For my last five calls to each company, this is how long I had to wait.

| AOL | 7 min | 8 min | 5 min | 7 min | 8 min |
| COMPI | 2 min | 14 min | 8 min | 1 min | 5 min |

Calculate the mean and the range for the waiting time for each company. Using the mean and the range, decide which company gives the better service. Explain why.

14.* A dice was thrown 20 times. Here are the results.

Score on dice	1	2	3	4	5	6
Number of throws	2	4	5	1	5	3

Copy and complete: mean score $= \dfrac{(1 \times 2) + (2 \times 4) + (3 \times 5) + \ldots}{20}$

$$= \boxed{}$$

15.* Work out the mean score in these two dice rolling experiments.

(a)

Score on dice	1 2 3 4 5 6
Number of throws	4 5 3 2 6 5

(b)

Score on dice	1 2 3 4 5 6
Number of throws	7 6 9 5 6 7

5.6 Negative numbers

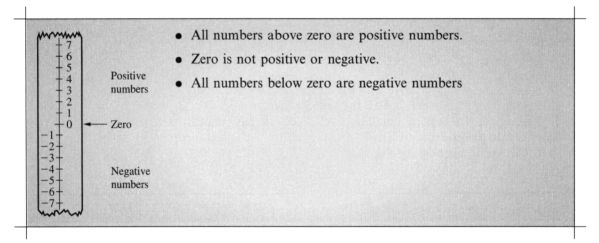

- All numbers above zero are positive numbers.
- Zero is not positive or negative.
- All numbers below zero are negative numbers

- The most common application of negative numbers is in illustrating temperature.

  This is a weather map showing temperatures across the United Kingdom and Ireland on a day in Winter.

  The temperatures are given in degrees Celsius (°C).

  Water freezes at 0°C.

  The weather map shows lower temperatures in the north than in the south.

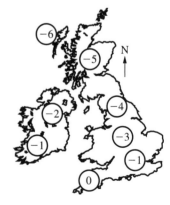

Exercise 1

1. What temperature is shown at each arrow?

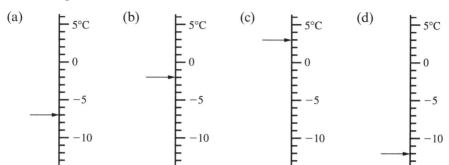

(a)   (b)   (c)   (d)

2.

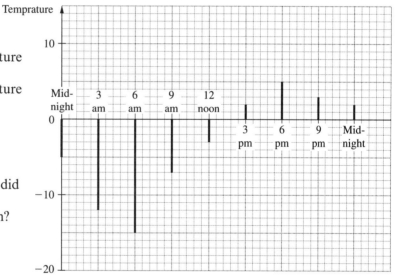

-2°C   -1°C

0°C   5°C   -8°C

(a) Which of these temperatures is the coldest?
(b) Which of these temperatures is the hottest?
(c) Which temperatures are below freezing?

3. The graph shows the temperatures for one day in Greenland.
  (a) What was the temperature at 6 pm?
  (b) What was the temperature at 9 am?
  (c) What was the lowest temperature recorded?
  (d) At what time was it −12°C?
  (e) By how many degrees did the temperature go up between 6 am and 6 pm?

4. Find the new temperature in the following problems.
  (a) The temperature is 5°C and falls by 9°C.
  (b) The temperature is −7°C and falls by 4°C.
  (c) The temperature is −6°C and rises by 13°C.
  (d) The temperature is −9°C and rises by 11°C.
  (e) The temperature is 13°C and falls 17°C.

5. State in the following questions whether the temperature has risen or fallen and by how many degrees.
  (a) It was −3°C and it is now −7°C.
  (b) It was 6°C and is now −2°C.
  (c) It was −11°C and is now −5°C.
  (d) It was −9°C and is now 1°C.
  (e) It was 12°C and is now −23°C.

Exercise 2

1. The *range* is the difference between the highest and the lowest. The scale shows the highest and lowest temperatures one day in Paris.
The range of the temperatures is 10°C.

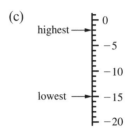

Find the range in these temperatures

(a) 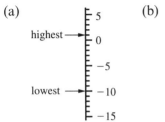   (b) 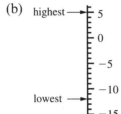   (c)

(d) 5°C and −3°C   (e) 0°C and −11°C   (f) 12°C and −10°C.

2. Write down each statement with either > or < in place of the box.

   (a) −3 ☐ −2   (b) −1·5 ☐ −5   (c) 0 ☐ −3

3. Give a possible value for x and y.

   (a) $-10\cdot5 < x < -9$ (b) $-2\cdot5 < y < 0$

4. In a test there are +2 marks for a correct answer and −1 marks for an incorrect answer. Find the total marks in the tests below:

   Test A   ✓, ✓, ✗, ✗, ✗, ✓, ✓, ✗, ✓, ✗.

   Test B   ✗, ✗, ✓, ✓, ✗, ✓, ✗, ✗, ✗, ✗.

5. Here is a number line from −10 to +10

   Find the difference between
   (a) −7 and 2   (b) −6 and −1   (c) 8 and −3
   (d) −5 and 0   (e) −8 and 8   (f) −3 and −10.

6. Write down these temperatures in order, coldest first.
   (a)   7°,   −2°,   −7°,   0°,   8°,   −5°
   (b) −6°,   3°,   −15°,   21°,   −7°   2°
   (c) −8°,   11°,   0°,   −5°,   −10°,   2°

7. Write down each sequence and fill in the missing number.

(a) 6   4   2   0   −2   ☐

(b) 10   6   2   −2   ☐

(c) 10   7   4   1   −2   ☐

(d) 9   5   1   ☐   −7

(e) −12   −9   −6   −3   ☐

(f) ☐   −1   4   9   14

8. The heights of places on a map are always measured in relation to sea level. For example a hill marked 510 m is 510 m above sea level.
(a) Think of something which could be at a height of −20 m.
(b) Some places in Holland are at a height of −3 m. What problems does this cause and what do the people do about it?

9. A diver is below the surface of the water at −20 m. She dives a further 8 m, then rises 5 m. At what depth is she now?

Adding and subtracting

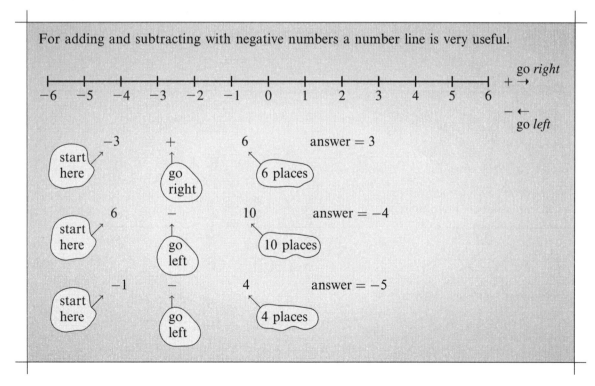

For adding and subtracting with negative numbers a number line is very useful.

Exercise 3

1. Use a number line to work out

2. Use a number line to work out

3. Use a number line to work out
   (a) $3 - 6$ (b) $-2 + 4$ (c) $-3 - 2$
   (d) $-6 + 9$ (e) $5 - 8$ (f) $-8 + 2$
   (g) $5 - 10$ (h) $-8 + 3$ (i) $-3 - 4$
   (j) $-3 + 7$ (k) $-10 + 10$ (l) $8 - 12$

4. Work out
   (a) $-7 + 4$ (b) $6 - 11$ (c) $-3 - 3$
   (d) $8 - 20$ (e) $-4 + 8$ (f) $9 - 2$
   (g) $-8 - 3$ (h) $-12 + 5$ (i) $-2 + 2$
   (j) $4 - 10$ (k) $-6 + 1$ (l) $-6 - 5$

5. Now work out these
   (a) $-5 + 5$ (b) $6 - 9$ (c) $-4 - 1$
   (d) $8 - 7$ (e) $-2 + 2$ (f) $-6 - 2$
   (g) $2 - 10$ (h) $-5 + 6$ (i) $8 - 13$
   (j) $-50 + 10$ (k) $-4 - 14$ (l) $20 - 100$

Two signs together

The calculation $8 - (+3)$ can be read as
   '8 take away positive 3'.

Similarly $6 - (-4)$ can be read as
   '6 take away negative 4'.

In the sequence of subtractions on
the right the numbers in column A
go down by one each time.
The numbers in column B
increase by one each time.

$$
\begin{array}{ccc}
A & & B \\
\downarrow & & \downarrow \\
8 - (+3) & = & 5 \\
8 - (+2) & = & 6 \\
8 - (+1) & = & 7 \\
8 - (0) & = & 8
\end{array}
$$

Continuing the sequence downwards:

We see that $8 - (-3)$ becomes $8 + 3$.

$$
\begin{array}{rl}
8 - (-1) = & 9 \\
8 - (-2) = & 10 \\
8 - (-3) = & 11
\end{array}
$$

This always applies when subtracting negative numbers. It is possible to replace *two* signs next to each other by *one* sign as follows:

$$+ + = +$$
$$- - = +$$
$$- + = -$$
$$+ - = -$$

Remember: 'same signs: +'
          'different signs: −'

When two adjacent signs have been replaced by one sign in this way, the calculation is completed using the number line as before.

● Work out the following

(a) $-7 + (-4)$
$= -7 - 4$
$= -11$

(b) $8 + (-14)$
$= 8 - 14$
$= -6$

(c) $5 - (+9)$
$= 5 - 9$
$= -4$

(d) $6 - (-2) + (-8)$
$= 6 + 2 - 8$
$= 0$

Exercise 4

1. Work out
(a) $6 + (-4)$
(b) $5 - (+7)$
(c) $8 - (-4)$
(d) $-3 + (+2)$
(e) $-3 + (-6)$
(f) $-9 + (-1)$
(g) $7 - (+10)$
(h) $8 - (-2)$
(i) $10 - (-3)$
(j) $-8 + (-2)$
(k) $-6 - (-6)$
(l) $-7 + (-2)$

2. Work out
(a) $-3 - (-2)$
(b) $7 + (-8)$
(c) $-6 + (-2)$
(d) $8 + (-11)$
(e) $-4 - (-4)$
(f) $7 - (+10)$
(g) $-6 - (-2)$
(h) $9 + (-9)$
(i) $-3 - (+4)$
(j) $5 + (-9)$
(k) $-3 - (-8)$
(l) $4 + (-8)$

3. Now do these
(a) $8 + (-6)$
(b) $-7 - (+3)$
(c) $16 - (-2)$
(d) $-9 - (-3)$
(e) $11 + (-20)$
(f) $-17 - (-3)$
(g) $12 + (-9)$
(h) $3 - (+8)$
(i) $100 + (-99)$
(j) $-17 - (+4)$
(k) $-5 - (-5)$
(l) $6 - (+11)$

4. Decide whether each statement is true or false.
(a) $7 + (-9) = -2$
(b) $5 - 13 = 8$
(c) $12 - (-2) = 10$
(d) $-2 + (-8) = -10$
(e) $9 + (-29) = -20$
(f) $7 - (-7) = 12$
(g) $3 - (-3) = 6$
(h) $9 - (-9) = 0$
(i) $12 + (-15) = -3$

5.7 Mathematical reasoning

This section contains a wide variety of activities. There is no standard method for most of these problems. You need to think logically and should avoid guessing.

Cross numbers without clues

Here are cross number puzzles with a difference. There are no clues, only answers, and you have to find where the answers go.
(a) Copy out the cross number pattern.
(b) Fit all the given numbers into the correct spaces. Work logically and tick off the numbers from lists as you write them in the squares.

1. Ask your teacher if you do not know how to start.

2 digits	3 digits	4 digits	5 digits	6 digits
18	375	1274	37 125	308 513
37	692	1625		
53	828	3742		
74		5181		
87				

2.

2 digits	3 digits	4 digits	5 digits	6 digits
13	382	2630	12 785	375 041
21	582	2725		
45	178	5104		
47		7963		
72				

3.

2 digits	3 digits	4 digits	6 digits
53	182	4483	375 615
63	324	4488	
64	327	6515	*7 digits*
	337		3 745 124
	436		4 253 464
	573		8 253 364
	683		8 764 364
	875		

4.

2 digits	3 digits	4 digits	5 digits	6 digits
27	161	1127	34 462	455 185
36	285	2024	74 562	
54	297	3473	81 072	
63	311	5304	84 762	
64	412	5360		
69	483	5370		
	535	5380		
	536			
	636			
	714			

5.

2 digits	3 digits	4 digits	5 digits	6 digits
21	121	1349	24 561	215 613
22	136	2457	24 681	246 391
22	146	2458	34 581	246 813
23	165	3864		
36	216	4351		
53	217	4462		
55	285	5321		
56	335	5351		
58	473	5557		
61	563	8241		
82	917	8251		
83		9512		
91				

6. *This one is more difficult.*

2 digits	3 digits	4 digits	5 digits	6 digits
16	288	2831	47 185	321 802
37	322	2846	52 314	
56	607	2856	56 324	
69	627	2873	56 337	
72	761	4359		
98	762	5647		
	768	7441		
	769			
	902			
	952			

General statements, counter examples

- Consider the statement: 'If n is a positive, integer (whole number), then n^2 is never equal to $2n + 8$.'

  For $n = 1$, 2 and 3 the statement is true.
  But when $n = 4$, the statement is not true because 4^2 does equal $2 \times 4 = 8$.

  This is a *counter example* which shows the statement is false.

- Consider the statement: 'The sum of any five consecutive numbers is five times the middle number.'

  This statement is always true. Here are two examples:
  $$1 + 2 + ③ + 4 + 5 = 15 \quad \text{and} \quad 5 \times 3 = 15$$
  $$6 + 7 + ⑧ + 9 + 10 = 40 \quad \text{and} \quad 5 \times 8 = 40.$$

Exercise 1

In each question there is a general statement. Some statements are true and some are not true.
If you think the statement is true, write 'true' and give two examples to illustrate it. Otherwise write down a counter example which shows the statement is not true.

1. The sum of three consecutive numbers is three times the middle number.

2. The product of two consecutive numbers is even.

3. All prime numbers are odd numbers.

4. The product of three consecutive numbers is a multiple of 6.

5. Except for 1, no square number is also a cube number.

6. The sum of four even numbers is always divisible by four.

7. For any two rectangles, the rectangle with the larger perimeter has the larger area.

8. If the product of two numbers is zero, then one of the numbers must be zero.

9. Dividing a number by 0·1 makes the answer ten times as big as the original number.

10. Every positive integer greater than 10 has an even number of factors.

Part 6

6.1 Probability

In probability we ask questions like ...

'How likely is it?'

'What are the chances of ... ?'

Here are some questions where we do not know the answer ...

'Will my parachute open?'

'Will I live to be over 100 years old?'

'Who will win the F.A. cup?'

Some events are certain. Some events are impossible.

Some events are in between certain and impossible.

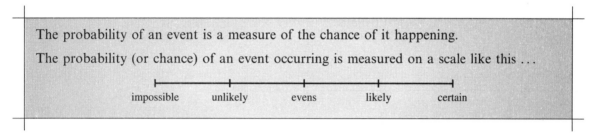

The probability of an event is a measure of the chance of it happening.

The probability (or chance) of an event occurring is measured on a scale like this ...

impossible   unlikely   evens   likely   certain

Exercise 1

Draw a probability scale like this ...

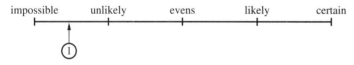

impossible   unlikely   evens   likely   certain

Draw an arrow to show the chance of the events below happening.

[The arrow for question ① has been done for you.]

1. When a card is selected from a pack it will be an 'ace'.

2. When a coin is tossed it will show a 'head'.

3. The letter 'a' appears somewhere on the next page of this book.

4. When a drawing pin is dropped it will land 'point up'.

5. There will be at least one baby born somewhere in Great Britain on the first day of next month.

6. Your local vicar will win the national lottery next week.

7. The day after Monday will be Tuesday.

8. There will be a burst pipe in the school heating system next week and the school will have to close for 3 days.

9. You will blink your eyes in the next minute.

10. You will be asked to tidy your room this week.

11. When a slice of toast is dropped, it will land on the floor buttered side down.

12. You will get maths homework this week.

13. England will win the next World Cup at football.

14. Your maths teacher has a black belt in Judo.

15. You will be captured by aliens tonight.

Probability as a number

Different countries have different words for saying how likely or unlikely any particular event is.
All over the world people use probability as a way of doing this, using numbers on a scale instead of words.
The scale looks like this . . .

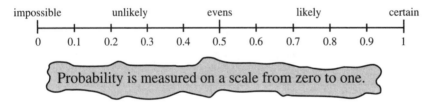

Probability is measured on a scale from zero to one.

Exercise 2

Look at the events in the last exercise and for each one estimate the probability of it occurring using a probability from 0 to 1.

As an example in question ① you might write 'about 0·1'. Copy each question and write your estimate of its probability at the end.

Experimental probability

The chance of certain events occurring can easily be predicted. For example the chance of tossing a head with an ordinary coin. Many events, however, cannot be so easily predicted.

Experiment: To find the experimental probability that the third word in the third line on any page in this book contains the letter 'a' (You could use a non-mathematical book if you prefer)

Step 1. We will do 50 *trials*. Write down at random 50 page numbers between 1 and 180 (say 3, 15, 16, 21, 27, etc.).

Step 2. For each page look at the third word in the third line. This is a *trial*.
If there is not a third word on the third line it still counts as a trial. (The third line might be all numbers.)

Step 3. If the word contains the letter 'a' this is a *success*.

Step 4. Make a tally chart like this ...

Number of trials	Number of successes
ⲓⲏⲧ ⲓⲏⲧ ‖	ⲓⲏⲧ ‖

> **37**
>
> ## Angles in triangles
> Draw a triangle of any shape on a piece of card (and) cut it out accurately. Now tear off the three corners as shown.
>
> (third line, third word.)

$$\text{Experimental probability} = \frac{\text{Number of trials in which a success occurs}}{\text{Total number of trials made}}$$

Exercise 3

Carry out experiments to work out the experimental probability of some of the following events.
Use a tally chart to record your results. Don't forget to record how many times you do the experiment (the number of 'trials').

1. Roll a dice. What is the chance of rolling a six? Perform 100 trials.

2. Toss two coins. What is the chance of tossing two tails? Perform 100 trials.

3. Pick a counter from a bag containing counters of different colours. What is the chance of picking a red counter? Perform 100 trials.

4. Roll a pair of dice. What is the chance of rolling a double? Perform 100 trials.

5. Butter a piece of toast and drop it on the floor. What is the chance of it landing buttered side down? Would you expect to get the same result with margarine? How about butter and jam? Suppose you don't toast the bread?
If you run into difficulties at home, blame your maths teacher, not the authors of this book.

Expected probability

For simple events, like throwing a dice or tossing a coin, we can work out the expected probability of an event occurring.

For a fair dice the *expected probability* of throwing a '3' is $\frac{1}{6}$.

For a normal coin the expected probability of tossing a 'head' is $\frac{1}{2}$

$$\text{Expected probability} = \frac{\text{the number of ways the event can happen}}{\text{the number of possible outcomes}}$$

Random choice: If a card is chosen at random from a pack it means that every card has an equal chance of being chosen.

Nine identical discs numbered 1, 2, 3, 4, 5, 6, 7, 8, 9 are put into a bag. One disc is selected at random.

In this example there are 9 possible equally likely outcomes of a trial.

(a) The probability of selecting a '4' = $\frac{1}{9}$

This may be written p (selecting a '4') = $\frac{1}{9}$

(b) p (selecting an odd number) = $\frac{5}{9}$

(c) p (selecting a number greater than 5) = $\frac{4}{9}$

Exercise 4

1. A bag contains a red ball, a blue ball and a yellow ball. One ball is chosen at random. Copy and complete these sentences.

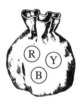

(a) The probability that the red ball is chosen is ... $\dfrac{\square}{3}$

(b) The probability that the blue ball is chosen is ... $\dfrac{\square}{\square}$

(c) The probability that the yellow ball is chosen is ... $\dfrac{\square}{\square}$

2. One ball is chosen at random from a bag which contains a red ball, a blue ball, a yellow ball and a white ball. Write down the probability that the chosen ball will be

(a) red   (b) blue   (c) yellow.

3. One ball is chosen at random from a box which contains 2 red balls and 2 blue balls. Write down the probability that the chosen ball will be
   (a) red.
   (b) blue.
   (c) yellow.

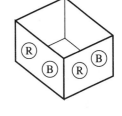

4. A hat contains 2 white balls and 1 black ball. One ball is chosen at random. Find the probability that it is
   (a) white.
   (b) black.

5. A pencil case contains pencils of the following colours:- 6 red, 3 black, 1 green and 1 blue. One pencil is selected without looking. Find the probability that the pencil is
   (a) red.
   (b) black.
   (c) green.

6. I roll an ordinary dice.
   Find the probability that I score
   (a) 3
   (b) 1
   (c) less than 5

7. Eight identical discs numbered 1, 2, 3, 4, 5, 6, 7, 8 are put into a bag. One disc is selected at random. Find the probability of selecting
   (a) a '5'. (b) an odd number. (c) a number less than 6.

8. Nine identical discs numbered 1, 3, 4, 5, 7, 8, 10, 11, 15 are put into a bag. One disc is selected at random. Find the probability of selecting.
   (a) a '10'. (b) an even number. (c) a number more than 6.

9. A bag contains 4 red balls and 7 white balls. One ball is selected at random. Find the probability that it is
   (a) red.   (b) white.

10. One card is selected at random from the ten cards shown . . .
    Find the probability of selecting
    (a) the King of spades   (b) a heart
    (c) a diamond   (d) a 3

11. A bag contains 2 red balls, 4 white balls and 5 blue balls. One ball is selected at random. Find the probability of selecting.
    (a) a red ball   (b) a white ball   (c) a blue ball

12. I buy a fish at random from a pond containing 3 piranhas, 2 baby sharks and 7 goldfish. Find the probability that the fish I choose is
    (a) a goldfish.   (b) a baby shark
    (c) dangerous   (d) glad I rescued it!
    (e) able to play the piano.

Probability Problems

A pack of playing cards, without Jokers, contains 52 cards.
There is Ace, King, Queen, Jack, 10, 9, 8, 7, 6, 5, 4, 3, 2 of four suits.
The suits are . . .

<table>
<tr><td>spades</td><td>hearts</td><td>diamonds</td><td>clubs</td></tr>
</table>

A pack of cards is shuffled and then one card is chosen at random.
(a) The probability that it is a King of hearts is $\frac{1}{52}$
(b) The probability that it is an ace is $\frac{4}{52}\left(=\frac{1}{13}\right)$
(c) The probability that it is a spade is $\frac{13}{52}\left(=\frac{1}{4}\right)$

Exercise 5

1. One card is picked at random from a pack of 52.
Find the probability that it is
(a) a Queen
(b) the King of diamonds
(c) a spade

2. One card is selected at random from a full pack of 52 playing
cards. Find the probability of selecting
(a) a heart
(b) a red card
(c) a '2'
(d) any King, Queen or Jack
(e) the ace of spades

3. A small pack of twenty cards consists of the Ace, King, Queen,
Jack and 10 of spades, hearts, diamonds and clubs. One card is
selected at random. Find the probability of selecting
(a) the ace of hearts
(b) a King
(c) a '10'
(d) a black card
(e) a heart

4. A bag contains 3 black balls, 2 green balls, 1 white ball and 5
orange balls. Find the probability of selecting
(a) a black ball
(b) an orange ball
(c) a white ball

5. A bag contains the balls shown. One ball is
taken out at random. Find the probability
that it is

(a) yellow   (b) blue   (c) red

One more blue ball and one more red ball are added to the bag.

(d) Find the new probability of selecting a yellow ball from the bag.

Y = yellow
B = blue
R = Red

6. If Jake throws a 1 or a 4 on his next throw of a dice when
playing 'Snakes and Ladders' he will climb up a ladder on the
board. What is the probability that he will *miss* a ladder on his
next throw?

7. A box contains 11 balls: 3 green, 2 white, 4 red and 2 blue
(a) Find the probability of selecting
   (i) a blue ball
   (ii) a green ball
(b) The 3 green balls are replaced by 3 blue balls.
   Find the probability of selecting
   (i) a blue ball
   (ii) a white ball.

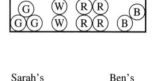

8. Here are two spinners.
Say whether the following statements are true or false.
Explain why in each case.
(a) 'Sarah is more likely to spin a 6 than Ben'.
(b) 'Sarah and Ben are equally likely to spin an
   even number.'
(c) 'If Sarah spins her spinner six times,
   she is bound to get at least one 6.'

Sarah's spinner   Ben's spinner

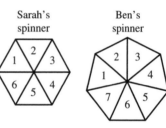

In Questions **9**, **10**, **11**, **12** a bag contains a certain number of red
balls and a certain number of white balls. The tally charts show the
number of times a ball was selected from the bag and then
replaced. Look at the results and say what you think was in the
bag each time.

9. 2 balls in the bag →

| red | JHT JHT | 10 |
| white | JHT JHT | 10 |

10. 3 balls in the bag →

| red | JHT | 5 |
| white | JHT JHT | 10 |

11. 3 balls in the bag →

| red | JHT JHT JHT JHT I | 21 |
| white | JHT JHT | 9 |

12. 4 balls in the bag →

| red | JHT IIII | 9 |
| white | JHT JHT JHT JHT JHT JHT I | 31 |

13. A bag contains 9 balls, all of which are black or white. Jane selects a ball and then replaces it. She repeats this several times. Here are her results (B = black, W= white):

B W B W B B B W B B W B B W B
B B W W B B B B W B W B B W B

How many balls of each colour do you think there were in the bag?

14. Cards with numbers 1, 2, 3, 4, 5, 6, 7, 8, 9, 10 are shuffled and then placed face down in a line. The cards are then turned over one at a time from the left. In this example the first card is a '4'.

Find the probability that the next card turned over will be
(a) 7
(b) a number higher than 4.

15. Suppose the second card is a 1

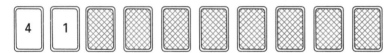

Find the probability that the next card will be
(a) the 6
(b) an even number
(c) higher than 1.

16. Suppose the first three cards are [4] [1] [8] ...

Find the probability that the next card will be
(a) less than 8
(b) the 4
(c) an odd number.

17. Three friends Aljit, Ben and Curtis sit next to each other on a bench.
    (a) Make a list of all the different ways in which they can sit.
        (Use A = Aljit, B = Ben and C = Curtis).
    Find the probability that
    (b) Aljit sits in the middle.
    (c) Aljit sits next to Curtis.
    (d) Ben sits at one end of the bench.

18. Debbie, Alan and Nicky were asked to toss a fair coin 16 times. Here are the results they wrote down.

Debbie   H T H T H T H T H T H T H T H T
Alan   H H T H T T H T T H H T H H T
Nicky   H H H H H H H H T T T T T T T T

One of the three did the experiment properly while the other two just made up results. Explain what you think each person did.

6.2 Fractions, decimals, percentages

Changing fractions to decimals

- Many fractions can be converted to decimals by using known equivalent fractions. You should *learn* the following:

  $\frac{1}{4} = 0.25$, $\frac{1}{2} = 0.5$, $\frac{3}{4} = 0.75$, $\frac{1}{10} = 0.1$, $\frac{2}{10} = 0.2$, $\frac{7}{100} = 0.07$ etc

- Here are some examples:

  $\frac{6}{8} = \frac{3}{4} = 0.75$ $\frac{1}{25} = \frac{4}{100} = 0.04$

  $\frac{1}{5} = \frac{2}{10} = 0.2$ $\frac{30}{120} = \frac{1}{4} = 0.25$

  $\frac{7}{20} = \frac{35}{100} = 0.35$ $\frac{11}{50} = \frac{22}{100} = 0.22$

Exercise 1

Convert the fractions to decimals. These are fractions where you should *know* the decimal equivalent.

1. $\frac{1}{4}$ **2.** $\frac{7}{10}$ **3.** $\frac{99}{100}$ **4.** $\frac{1}{2}$

5. $\frac{9}{10}$ **6.** $\frac{8}{100}$ **7.** $\frac{3}{4}$ **8.** $\frac{1}{100}$

Copy and complete the working.

9. $\frac{2}{8} = \frac{1}{4} = 0.\boxed{}\boxed{}$ **10.** $\frac{3}{5} = \frac{6}{10} = 0.\boxed{}$

11. $\frac{3}{20} = \frac{15}{100} = 0.\boxed{}\boxed{}$ **12.** $\frac{11}{20} = \frac{\boxed{}}{100} = \boxed{}$

13. $\frac{4}{5} = \frac{\boxed{}}{10} = \boxed{}$ **14.** $\frac{2}{25} = \frac{\boxed{}}{100} = \boxed{}$

Use the method above to convert these fractions to decimals

15. $\frac{2}{5}$ **16.** $\frac{1}{20}$ **17.** $\frac{3}{20}$ **18.** $\frac{1}{25}$

19. $\frac{9}{20}$ **20.** $\frac{21}{25}$ **21.** $\frac{140}{200}$ **22.** $\frac{150}{200}$

Convert the fractions to decimals and then write the numbers in order of size, smallest first.

23. $\frac{3}{4}, \frac{3}{5}, 0\cdot7$ **24.** $\frac{8}{20}, 0\cdot3, \frac{9}{25}$

25. $\frac{1}{5}, 0\cdot15, \frac{1}{20}$ **26.** $\frac{12}{16}, 0\cdot75, \frac{4}{5}$

Changing decimals to fractions

• $0\cdot8 = \frac{8}{10} = \frac{4}{5}$ $0\cdot21 = \frac{21}{100}$

  $0\cdot35 = \frac{35}{100} = \frac{7}{20}$ $0\cdot08 = \frac{8}{100} = \frac{2}{25}$

Simplify the answer if possible

Exercise 2

Change the decimals to fractions in their most simple form.

  1. $0\cdot6$ **2.** $0\cdot9$ **3.** $0\cdot05$ **4.** $0\cdot55$ **5.** $0\cdot07$

  6. $0\cdot11$ **7.** $0\cdot48$ **8.** $0\cdot25$ **9.** $0\cdot04$ **10.** $0\cdot95$

11. $0\cdot06$ **12.** $0\cdot44$ **13.** $0\cdot37$ **14.** $1\cdot1$ **15.** $2\cdot5$

16. $4\cdot01$ **17.** $0\cdot96$ **18.** $3\cdot75$ **19.** $0\cdot88$ **20.** $3\cdot05$

Changing to a percentage and vice versa

• Fraction to percentage   • Percentage to fraction

  (a) $\frac{2}{5} = \frac{40}{100} = 40\%$ $40\% = \frac{40}{100} = \frac{2}{5}$

    $\frac{1}{20} = \frac{5}{100} = 5\%$ $22\% = \frac{22}{100} = \frac{11}{50}$

    $2\frac{1}{2} = \frac{250}{100} = 250\%$ $8\% = \frac{8}{100} = \frac{2}{25}$

• You should learn the following:

    $\frac{1}{4} = 25\%$ $\frac{1}{8} = 12\frac{1}{2}\%$ $\frac{1}{3} = 33\frac{1}{3}\%$ $\frac{2}{3} = 66\frac{2}{3}\%$

Exercise 3

Convert these percentages to fractions. Cancel down where possible.

  1. 60%   **2.** 75%   **3.** 80%   **4.** 44%

  5. 10%   **6.** 99%   **7.** 2%   **8.** 9%

Copy and complete the following

9. $\frac{3}{5} = \frac{60}{100} = \boxed{} \%$

10. $\frac{11}{25} = \frac{44}{100} = \boxed{} \%$

11. $\frac{3}{20} = \frac{15}{100} = \boxed{} \%$

12. $\frac{7}{25} = \frac{\boxed{}}{100} = \boxed{} \%$

13. $\frac{7}{10} = \frac{\boxed{}}{100} = \boxed{} \%$

14. $\frac{7}{50} = \frac{\boxed{}}{100} = \boxed{} \%$

Write down each fraction with its equivalent percentage.

15. $\frac{3}{4}$ **16.** $\frac{1}{8}$ **17.** $\frac{1}{3}$ **18.** $\frac{2}{3}$

19. The chart shows the kinds of trees in a wood.
What percentage of the trees are:
(a) oak
(b) beech
(c) birch?

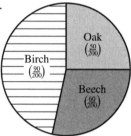

20. Here are some test results. Change them to percentages.
  (a) $\frac{19}{25}$ (b) $\frac{13}{20}$ (c) $\frac{32}{40}$

21. Rewrite these sentences using percentages.
  (a) One quarter of the meat sold in Britain is beef.
  (b) One in five cars have at least one fault.
  (c) Seven out of twenty people in a train were reading a paper.

22. Draw three lines 10 cm long and fill in the missing numbers.

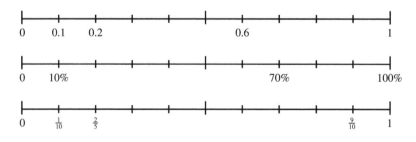

23. Change these decimals to percentages.
  (a) 0·27   (b) 0·19   (c) 0·09   (d) 0·6

24. Change these percentages to decimals.

    (a) 37%   (b) 42%   (c) 90%   (d) 8%

    (e) 6%   (f) 11%   (g) 12·5%   (h) 120%

25. Copy and complete the table.

	fraction	decimal	percentage
(a)		0·4	
(b)			35%
(c)	$\frac{3}{5}$		

Exercise 4

Each fraction, decimal or percentage has an equivalent in the list
with letters. Find the letters to make a sentence.

A. $\boxed{50\%,\ \frac{1}{4},\ 10\%,\ 0·2,\ 0·11}$ $\boxed{17\%,\ 11\%}$ $\boxed{0·75,\ 99\%,\ \frac{1}{10}}$ $\boxed{20\%,\ \frac{1}{4},\ \frac{1}{8},\ 0·7}$

B. $\boxed{\frac{7}{10},\ 0·8,\ 45\%,\ \frac{17}{100},\ 0·5,\ \frac{1}{4},\ \frac{10}{25},\ 0·11}$ $\boxed{\frac{3}{6},\ \frac{4}{16},\ 0·05,\ 80\%}$ $\boxed{\frac{22}{200},\ 0·8,\ 75\%,\ 11\%,\ \frac{8}{10}}$

C. $\boxed{17\%}$ $\boxed{45\%,\ 0·25,\ 75\%,\ 10\%}$ $\boxed{0·11,\ \frac{99}{100},\ \frac{4}{10},\ \frac{41}{50},\ \frac{400}{500}}$

   $\boxed{0·8,\ \frac{3}{20},\ \frac{1}{3},\ 0·25,\ \frac{1}{10},\ \frac{17}{100},\ \frac{198}{200},\ \frac{15}{20},\ \frac{110}{1000}}$

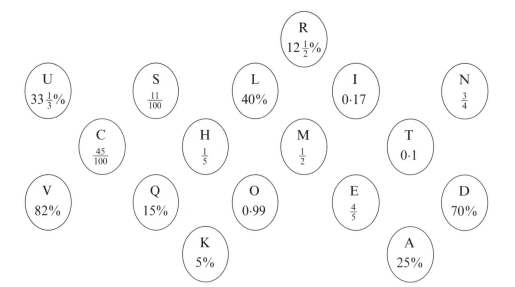

6.3 Formulas

Finding a rule

- Here is a sequence of shapes made from sticks

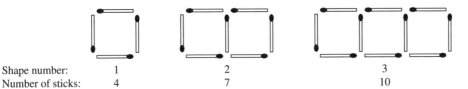

Shape number: 1   2   3
Number of sticks: 4   7   10

- There is a *rule* or *formula* which we can use to calculate the number of sticks for any shape number.

  'The number of sticks is three times the shape number add one'.

  Check that this rule works for all the shapes above and also for shape number 4 which you can draw.

- We could also write the rule using symbols. Let *n* stand for the diagram number and let *s* stand for the number of sticks.

  The rule (or formula) is '$s = 3n + 1$'.

Here is a sequence of boxes with three spaces.

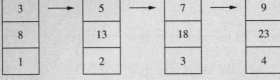

We can write letters in the spaces like this

In words the rule is: 'To find *n* you multiply *x* by 3 and then subtract *y*.'

Using algebra the rule is: $n = 3x - y$

Exercise 1

1. Here is a sequence of triangles made from sticks.

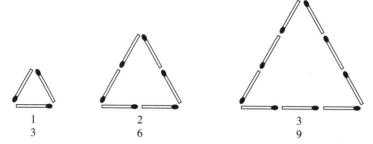

Shape number: 1   2   3
Number of sticks: 3   6   9

    (a) Draw shape number 4 and count the number of sticks.
    (b) Write down and complete the rule for the number of sticks
        in a shape: 'The number of sticks is ____ times the shape
        number'.

2. Here is a sequence of 'steps' made from sticks

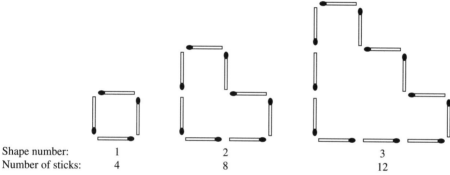

Shape number: 1   2   3
Number of sticks: 4   8   12

    (a) Draw shape number 4 and count the number of sticks.
    (b) Write down the rule for the number of sticks in a shape.
        'The number of sticks is ____ times the shape number'.

3. Louise makes a pattern of triangles from sticks.

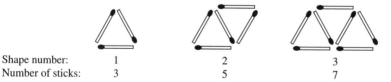

Shape number: 1   2   3
Number of sticks: 3   5   7

(a) Draw shape number 4 and shape number 5

(b) Make a table:

shape number	1	2	3	4	5
number of sticks	3	5	7		

(c) Write down the rule for the number of sticks in a shape.
    'The number of sticks is ____ times the shape number and
    then add ____ .'

4. Crosses are drawn on 'dotty' paper to make a sequence.

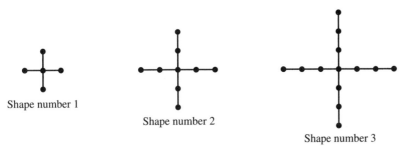

Shape number 1

Shape number 2

Shape number 3

(a) Draw shape number 4

(b) Make a table:

shape number	1	2	3	4
number of dots	5	9	13	

(c) Write down the rule.
'The number of dots is _____ times the shape number and then add _____.'

5. In these diagrams black squares are surrounded on three sides by white squares. Let the number of black squares be b and let the number of white squares be w.

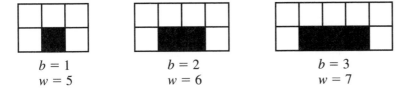

$b = 1$
$w = 5$

$b = 2$
$w = 6$

$b = 3$
$w = 7$

(a) Draw the next diagram which has 4 black squares.
(b) Write down the rule.
'The number of white squares is . . . .'

6. Look again at Questions **1**, **2**, **3**, and **4**. Use n for the shape number and s for the number of sticks or dots. For each question write the rule connecting n and s without using words. In each question write '$s =$.'

Sequences

- Here is a sequence 5, 10, 15, 20, ...

  The first term is 5×1, the second term is 5×2, the third term is 5×3 ......
  the 30th term is 5×30.
  The *general term*, or the *n*th term, is $5 \times n$.

  We can use the *n*th term to write down any term of the sequence.
  E.g. 14th term $= 5 \times 14$, 100th term $= 5 \times 100$.

- In another sequence the nth term is $5n + 3$

1st term $= 5 \times 1 + 3$	2nd term $= 5 \times 2 + 3$	3rd term $= 5 \times 3 + 3$
$(n = 1)$ $\quad = 8$	$(n = 2)$ $\quad = 13$	$(n = 3)$ $\quad = 18$

Exercise 2

1. The *n*th term of a sequence is $3n$. Write down:

    (a) the first term   (put $n = 1$)
    (b) the second term   (put $n = 2$)
    (c) the tenth term   (put $n = 10$)

2. The *n*th term of a sequence is $7n$. Write down:

    (a) the first term   (put $n = 1$)
    (a) the fifth term
    (a) the one hundredth term

In Questions **3** to **7** you are given the *n*th term of a sequence.
Write down the first four terms of each sequence.

3. $5n$ **4.** $11n$ **5.** $n + 2$ **6.** $20 - n$ **7.** $2n + 10$

8. Write down each sequence and select the correct formula for the
    *n*th term from the list given.

    (a) 2, 4, 6, 8, ...
    (b) 10, 20, 30, 40, ...
    (c) 4, 8, 12, 16, 20, ...
    (d) 11, 22, 33, 44, ...
    (e) 100, 200, 300, 400, ...
    (f) 6, 12, 18, 24, ...
    (g) $1^2, 2^2, 3^2, 4^2, ...$
    (h) 3, 5, 7, 9, 11, ...

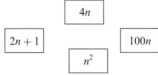

9.

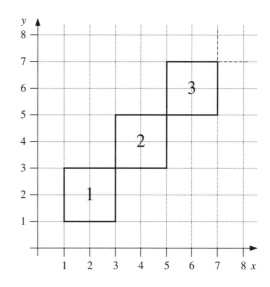

The numbers N1, N2, N3, N4 and M1, M2, M3, M4 form two sequences.
(a) Find M5, M6, N5, N6.
(b) Think of rules and use them to find M15 and N20.

10. Here is a sequence of touching squares.
Copy and complete the table.

Square number	Coordinates of centre
1	(2, 2)
2	(4, 4)
3	
5	
40	
45	

Find the coordinates of:
(a) the top of triangle 5
(b) the top of triangle 50
(c) the bottom right corner of triangle 50
(d) the bottom right corner of triangle 100.

11. Here is a sequence of touching triangles.

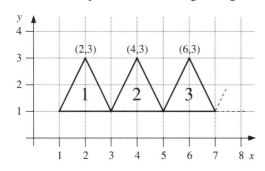

12.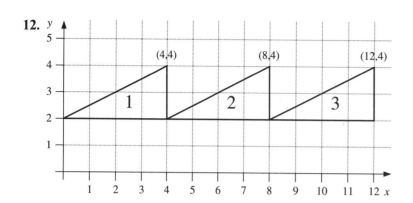

Find the coordinates of the top vertex of:
(a) triangle 4
(b) triangle 20
(c) triangle 2000.

13. Write down the coordinates of the centres of squares 1, 2 and 3.
Find the coordinates of:
(a) the centre of square 4
(b) the centre of square 10
(c) the top vertex of square 70.

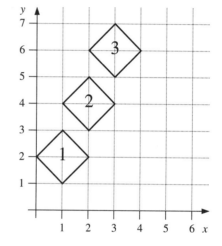

14. Write down the coordinates of the centres of the first six squares.
Find the coordinates of:
(a) the centre of square 60
(b) the centre of square 73
(c) the top left corner of square 90   [Hint: Find the centre of the square 90]
(d) the top left corner of square 101.

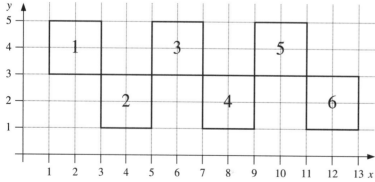

15. Now design some patterns of your own.

Count the crossovers: an investigation

Two straight lines have a maximum of one crossover

Three straight lines have a maximum of three crossovers.

Notice that you can have less than three crossovers if the lines all go through one point. Or the lines could be parallel.
In this work we are interested only in the *maximum* number of crossovers.

Four lines have a maximum of six crossovers.

☑ Draw five lines and find the maximum number of crossovers.

☑ Does there appear to be any sort of sequence in your results?
If you can find a sequence, use it to *predict* the maximum number of crossovers with six lines.

☑ Now draw six lines and count the crossovers to see if your prediction was correct.
(Remember not to draw three lines through one point.)

☑ Predict the number of crossovers for seven lines and then check if your prediction is correct by drawing a diagram.

☑ Write your results in a table:

Number of lines	Number of crossovers
2	1
3	3
4	6
5	
6	

(a) Predict the number of crossovers for 20 lines.

(b) (Harder) Predict the number of crossovers for 2000 lines.

Substituting into a formula

The perimeter, P, of the shape is
given by the formula

$P = 5a + b$

Find P when $a = 4$ and $b = 3$.

$P = 5a + b$
$P = 5 \times 4 + 3$ Work *down* the page.
$P = 23$

Exercise 3

1. A formula to give the perimeter P of a
   square is $P = 4l$.
   Find P, when $l = 11$.

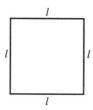

2. The cost in pounds, C, for hiring a car is given by the formula
   $C = 2m + 30$, where m is the number of miles travelled.
   Find C, when $m = 200$.

3. For a rectangle with sides l and b the perimeter is given by the
   formula $P = 2(l + b)$.
   Find P, when $l = 7$ and $b = 5$.

4. A formula for the perimeter of the
   trapezium shown is $P = 3a + b$.
   Find P, when $a = 12$ and $b = 15$.

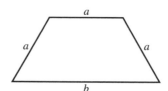

5. A formula for calculating the speed of an accelerating object is
   $v = u + at$.
   Calculate the value of v when, $u = 3$, $a = 10$ and $t = 2$.

In Questions **6** to **24** you are given a formula. Find the value of the letter required in each case.

6. $p = 4a + 10$

Find p, when $a = 8$.

7. $t = 5m - 7$

Find t, when $m = 5$.

8. $x = \dfrac{a}{4} + 5$

Find x, when $a = 20$.

9. $y = \dfrac{b}{3} - 2$

Find y, when $b = 27$.

10. $h = 3(p + 4)$

Find h, when $p = 6$.

11. $h = 5(m - 7)$

Find h, when $m = 10$.

12. $r = \dfrac{s}{10} + 6$

Find r, when $s = 1000$.

13. $m = \dfrac{2n + 1}{3}$

Find m, when $n = 7$.

14. $e = ab + 5$

Find e, when $a = 3$, $b = 5$.

15. $B = ut - 6$

Find B, when $u = 9$, $t = 8$.

Remember:
'ab' means $a \times b$
'ut' means $u \times t$

16. $w = 2x + xy$

Find w, when $x = 4$, $y = 5$.

17. $k = 3(a + a^2)$

Find k, when $a = 5$.

18. $g = u^2 - v^2$

Find g, when $u = 9$, $v = 1$.

19. $f = x(y + 2)$

Find f, when $x = 2$, $y = 5$.

20. $y = ab + b^2$

Find y, when $a = 5$, $b = 3$.

21. $t = 3mp + 1$

Find t, when $m = 10$, $p = 5$.

22. $h = \dfrac{m}{n} + m^2$

Find h, when $m = 6$, $n = 2$.

23. $c = \dfrac{x + x^2}{6}$

Find c, when $x = 5$.

24. p and q are connected by the formula $p = 2(4q + q^2)$
Find p, when $q = 3$.

6.4 Interpreting graphs

Information is sometimes given in the form of a *line graph*. Line graphs are particularly useful when quantities vary continuously over a period of time.

Exercise 1

1. The temperature in a centrally heated house is recorded every hour from 12.00 till 24.00; the results are shown below.

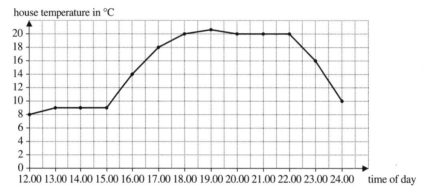

(a)   What was the temperature at 20.00?

(b)   Estimate the temperature at 16.30.

(c)   Estimate the two times when the temperature was 18°C.

(d)   When do you think the central heating was switched on?

(e)   When do you think the central heating was switched off?

2. A man climbing a mountain measures his height above sea level after every 30 minutes; the results are shown below.

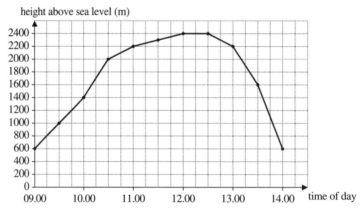

(a)   At what height was he at 10.00?

(b)   At what height was he at 13.30?

(c)   Estimate his height above sea level at 09 45.

(d)   At what two times was he 2200 m above sea level?

(e)   How high was the mountain? (He got to the top!)

(f)   How long did he rest at the summit?

(g)   How long did he take to reach the summit?

3. The cost of making a telephone call depends on the duration of the call as shown below.

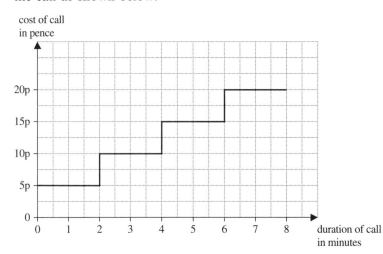

(a) How much is a call lasting 1 minute?
(b) How much is a call lasting 1 minute 30 seconds?
(c) How much is a call lasting 6 minutes 30 seconds?
(d) How much is a call lasting 4 minutes 27 seconds?
(e) What is the minimum charge for a call?
(f) A call costing 15p is between ___ minutes and ___ minutes in length. Fill in the spaces.

4. A car went on a five hour journey starting at 12.00 with a full tank of petrol. The volume of petrol in the tank was measured after every hour; the results are shown below.

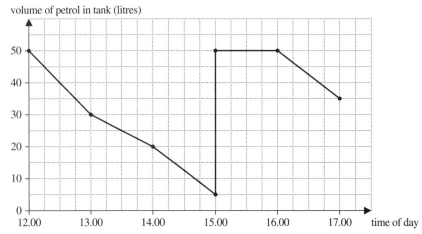

(a) How much petrol was in the tank at 13.00?
(b) At what time was there 5 litres in the tank?
(c) How much petrol was used in the first hour of the journey?
(d) What happened at 15.00?
(e) What do you think happened between 15.00 and 16.00?
(f) How much petrol was used between 12.00 and 17.00?

Exercise 2

1. Draw a graph to convert kilometres into miles.
Draw a line through the point where 80 km is
equivalent to 50 miles. Use a scale of 1 cm to 10 units.
Use the graph to convert:
(a) 60 km into miles   (b) 20 miles into km.

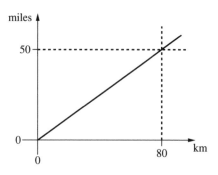

2.

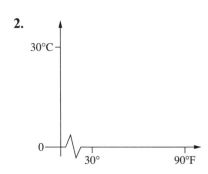

Draw a graph to convert temperatures from °F to °C.
Draw a line through the points 50°F = 10°C.
and 86°F = 30°C.

Use the graph to convert:
(a) 77°F into °C   (b) 15°C into °F

3. A mobile phone company charges £10 a month rental
plus 20p per minute for calls.

minutes of calls	0	20	40	60	80
cost in £	10	14	18	22	26

Draw a graph to show this information.

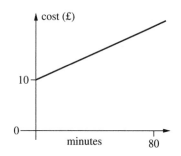

Travel graphs

• This graph shows the details of a cycle ride
that Jim took starting from his home.

(a) In the first hour Jim went 30 km so his
speed was 30 km/h.

(b) He stopped for ½ hour at a place 30 km
from his home.

(c) From 0930 until 1100 he cycled back
home. We know that he cycled back home
because the distance from his home at
1100 is 0 km.

(d) The speed at which he cycled home was
20 km/h.

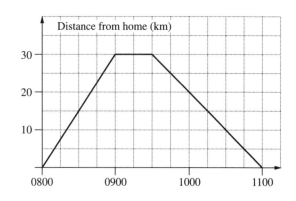

Exercise 3

1. The graph shows a car journey from
   A to C via B.
   (a) How far is it from A to C?
   (b) For how long does the car stop
       at B?
   (c) When is the car half way
       between B and C?
   (d) What is the speed of the car
       (i) between A and B?
       (ii) between B and C?

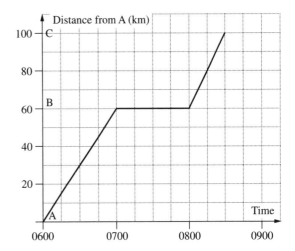

2. The graph shows the motion of a
   train as it accelerates away from
   Troon.
   (a) How far from Troon is the train
       at 0845?
   (b) When is the train half way
       between R and S?
   (c) Find the speed of the train
       (i) from R to S
       (ii) from Q to R
   (d) How long does it take the train
       to travel 100 km?

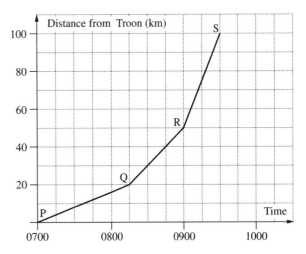

3. The graph shows a car journey from
   Lemsford.
   (a) For how long did the car stop at
       Mabley?
   (b) When did the car arrive back at
       Lemsford?
   (c) When did the car leave Mabley
       after stopping?
   (d) Find the speed of the car
       (i) from Mabley to Nixon
       (ii) from Nixon back to
            Lemsford.

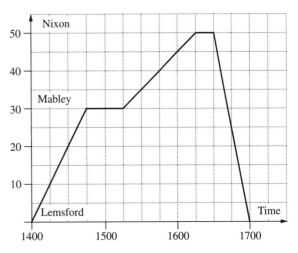

6.5 Mixed problems

Exercise 1

1. Mark is paid a basic weekly wage of £65 and then a further 30p for each item completed. How many items must be completed in a week when he earns a total of £185?

2. What number, when divided by 7 and then multiplied by 12, gives an answer of 144?

3. A 10p coin is 2 mm thick. Alex has a pile of 10p coins which is 16·6 cm tall. What is the value of the money in Alex's pile of coins?

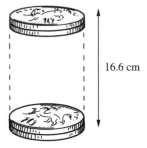

16.6 cm

2 mm

4. A British Airways Concorde leaves Paris at 07 00 and arrives in New York at 10 20.
   A 747 leaves Paris at 07 10 and flies at half the speed of the Concorde. When should it arrive in New York?

5. Percy's garden is 48 m long and 10 m wide and he wants to cover it with peat which comes in 60 kg sacks.
   10 kg of peat covers an area of 20 m². How many sacks of peat are needed for the whole garden?

6. Find two numbers which multiply together to give 60 and which add up to 19.

7. A shopkeeper buys coffee beans at £4·20 per kg and sells them at 95p per 100 g. How much profit does he make per kg?

8. A Jaguar XJ6 uses 8 litres of petrol for every 50 km travelled. Petrol costs 90p per litre. Calculate the cost in £'s of travelling 500 km.

Exercise 2

1. A man smokes 50 cigarettes a day and a packet of 20 costs £4·20.
How much does he spend on cigarettes in six days?

2. As an incentive to tidy her bedroom, a girl is given 1p on the first day, 2p on the second day, 4p on the third day and so on, doubling the amount each day.

How much has she been given after 10 days?

3. A shopkeeper has a till containing a large number of the following coins:
  £1; 50p; 20p; 10p; 5p; 2p; 1p.
He needs to give a customer 57p in change. List all the different ways in which he can do this using no more than six coins.

4. Place the following numbers in order of size, smallest first:
  0·34; 0·334; 0·032; 0·04; 0·4.

5. A book has pages numbered 1 to 300 and the thickness of the book, without the covers, is 15 mm. How thick is each page?
[Hint: Most people get this question wrong!]

6. In an election 7144 votes were cast for the two candidates. Mr Dewey won by 424 votes. How many people voted for Dewey?

7. The tenth number in the sequence 1, 4, 16, 64 . . . . . . is 262 144.
What is (a) the ninth number,
          (b) the twelfth number?

8. Two fifths of the children in a swimming pool are boys. There are 72 girls in the pool. How many boys are there?

9. Two weights *m* and *n* are placed on scales and *m* is found to be more than 11 g and *n* is less than 7 g. Arrange the weights 8·5 g, *m* and *n* in order, lightest first.

10. A satellite link between Britain and Australia can be hired at a cost of £250 per minute from 0600 to 1400 and at £180 per minute after 1400.
The link is used to televise a football match which starts at 1330 and ends at 1500.
How much does it cost?

Exercise 3

1. Lisa is 12 years old and her father is 37 years older than her. Lisa's mother is 3·years younger than her father. How old is Lisa's mother?

2. 36 small cubes are stuck together to make the block shown and the block is then painted on the outside. How many of the small cubes are painted on:
   (a) 1 face   (b) 2 faces
   (c) 3 faces   (d) 0 faces?

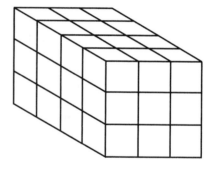

3. Find the letters in these additions.

   (a)
   ```
        8  7  A
        3  B  5
   +  C  4  2
   ─────────────
   D  8  4  1
   ```

   (b)
   ```
      A  2  4  5
      5  B  8  4
   +  1  4  C  6
   ─────────────
   E  0  5  2  D
   ```

4. Petrol costs 89·6p per litre. How many litres can be bought for £17? Give your answer to the nearest litre.

5. A flight on Concorde takes 2h 36min. How long would the same flight take on a plane travelling at half the speed of Concorde?

6. Seven oak trees were planted in Windsor when Queen Victoria was born. She died in 1901 aged 82. How old were the trees in 1993?

7. A mixed school has a total of 876 pupils.
There are 48 more boys than girls.
How many boys are there?

8. Four 4's can be used to make 12: $\dfrac{44 + 4}{4}$

(a) Use three 6's to make 2
(b) Use three 7's to make 7
(c) Use three 9's to make 11
(d) Use four 4's to make 9
(e) Use four 4's to make 3

9. A Rover 216XL travels 10 miles on a litre of petrol and petrol costs 90p per litre. In six months the car is driven a total of 5500 miles. Find the cost of the petrol to the nearest pound.

10. In a code the 25 letters from A to Y are obtained from the square using a 2 digit grid reference similar to coordinates.
So letter 'U' is 42 and 'L' is 54.
The missing letter 'Z' has code 10.

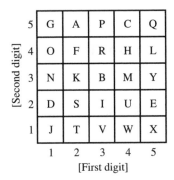

Decode the following messages:

(a) 41, 52
    13, 52, 52, 12
    43, 14, 34, 52
    22, 42, 43, 22

(b) 44, 25, 31, 52
    25
    13, 32, 45, 52
    12, 25, 53

(c) 22, 35, 42, 34, 22
    25, 34, 52
    34, 42, 33, 33, 32, 22, 44

In part (d) each pair of brackets gives one letter

(d) $\left(\frac{1}{4} \text{ of } 140\right)$, $(7^2 + 5)$, $(7 \times 8 - 4)$, $(4^2 + 3^2)$, $\left(\frac{1}{5} \text{ of } 110\right)$, $\left(26 \div \frac{1}{2}\right)$
    $(3 \times 7 + 1)$, $(83 - 31)$, $(2 \times 2 \times 2 \times 2 + 5)$
    $(100 - 57)$, $(4^2 - 2)$, (17×2), $(151 - 99)$
    $(2 \times 2 \times 2 \times 5 + 1)$, $\left(\frac{1}{4} \text{ of } 56\right)$, $(2 \times 3 \times 2 \times 3 - 2)$, $(5^2 - 2)$.

(e) Write your own message in code and ask a friend to decode it.

Exercise 4

1. Unifix cubes can be joined together to make different sized cuboids.

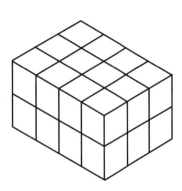 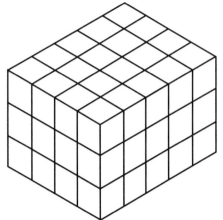

If the smaller cuboid weighs 96 g, how much does the large cuboid weigh?

2. A lorry is travelling at a steady speed of 60 m.p.h. How far does the lorry travel between 10.50 a.m. and 11.05 a.m.?

3. In a 'magic' square the sum of the numbers in any row, column or main diagonal is the same. Find x in each square

(a)

3		
8		4
7	x	

(b)

14		7	2
x		12	
	5	9	16
15			3

4. A school play was attended by 226 adults, each paying £1·50, and 188 children, each paying 80p. How much in £'s was paid altogether by the people attending the play?

5. The test results of 50 students are shown below.

Mark	5	6	7	8	9	10
Frequency	0	2	12	17	10	9

What percentage of the students scored 8 marks or more?

6. On the 30th June 1994 the day was extended by 1 second to allow for the irregularity in the speed of rotation of the Earth. A newspaper carried an article stating that people in Britain eat 54 digestive biscuits every second. How many digestive biscuits are eaten in a normal day?

7. Which of the shapes below can be drawn without taking the pen from the paper and without going over any line twice?

(a)   (b)   (c)

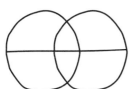  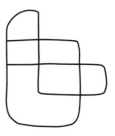

8. A corn field is a rectangle measuring 300 m by 600 m. One hectare is 10 000 m² and each hectare produces 3·2 tonnes of corn. How much corn is produced in this field?

9. Four and a half dozen eggs weigh 2970 g. How much would six dozen eggs weigh?

10. The numbers 1 to 12 are arranged on the star so that the sum of the numbers along each line is the same.

Copy and complete the star.

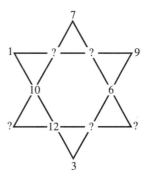

11. A jar with 8 chocolates in it weighs 160 g. The same jar with 20 chocolates in it weighs 304 g. How much does the jar weigh on its own?

12. A floor measuring 5 m by 3·6 m is to be covered with square tiles of side 10 cm. A packet of 20 tiles costs £6·95. How much will it cost to tile the floor?

13. A small boat travels 300 km on 125 litres of fuel. How much fuel is needed for a journey of 1200 km?

14. A shop keeper bought 30 books at £3·40 each and a number of C.D.'s costing £8·40 each. In all he spent £312. How many C.D.'s did he buy?

6.6 Mathematical games and crossnumbers

Biggest number: a game for the whole class

(a) Draw a rectangle like this with 4 boxes

(b) Your teacher will throw a dice and call out the number which is showing. (eg 'four')

(c) Write this number in one of the boxes.

(d) Your teacher will throw the dice again. (eg 'two')
Write the number in another box.

(e) Your teacher will throw the dice two more times (eg 'three' and then 'two') and again you write the numbers in the boxes.

(f) The object of the game is to get the biggest possible four figure number. The skill (or luck!) is in deciding which box to use for each number.
You score one point if you have written down the largest four digit number which can be made from the digits thrown on the dice. In the example above you score a point if you have 4322 and no points for any other number.
The game can also be played with 5 boxes or 6 boxes for variety.

Boxes: a game for two players

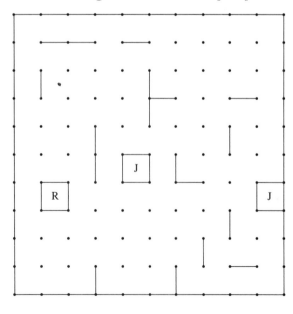

- Draw around the border of a 10 × 10 square on dotty paper (you can also use squared paper).
- Two players take turns to draw horizontal or vertical lines between any two dots on the grid.
- A player wins a square (and writes his initial inside the square) when he draws the fourth side of a square.
- After winning a square a player has one extra turn.
- The winner is the player who has most squares at the end.

In the game above J has two squares so far and R has one square.

Crossnumbers

Make three copies of the pattern below and complete the puzzles using the clues given. To avoid confusion it is better not to write the small reference numbers 1, 2–18 on your patterns.

Part A

Across	Down
1. Days in a year	**1.** 6^2
3. $6524 - 4018$	**2.** 7×72
5. 20% of 400	**4.** $285 + 338$
6. $43\,328 \div 8$	**7.** $8^2 \times 3$
8. 82·74 to the nearest whole number	**8.** $269 + 270 + 271$
9. $126 \div 7$	**9.** $5 \times 5 \times 5 \times 10 + 1$
10. $4^2 + 5^2$	**11.** $2 \times 3 \times 5 \times 7$
11. $164 + 57 + 8$	**12.** 967×9
13. Half of a half of 104	**14.** $1000 - 352$
15. $10^3 + 10^2 + 1$	**16.** Two fifths of 45
17. $4 \times (58 + 6 \times 7)$	
18. Next in the sequence 8, 16, 32, 64	

Part B

Across

1. 3·25 m in cm
3. 4567 − 123
5. Area of a square of side 7 cm
6. $50^2 + 555$
8. Total of the numbers on a dice
9. One fifth of 475
10. Find n, if $n − 23 = 37$
11. Angle sum of a triangle
13. Next in the sequence 3, 7, 15, 31
15. $100 \times 100 − 100$
17. $5^4 − 5$
18. Find n, if $\dfrac{n}{85} = 10$

Down

1. $2 \times 2 \times 2 \times 2 \times 2$
2. 1% of 50 000
4. $41 + 10 \times 41$
7. $4116 \div 7$
8. 9×23
9. $10\,001 − 2$
11. $11^2 − 5^2 + 2^2$
12. 3·3 km in metres
14. Angle sum of a quadrilateral
16. $10^2 − 1^2$

Part C

Across

1. Next square number after 100
3. $15 + 200 \times 7$
5. Minutes between 1.55 pm and 2.50 pm
6. 7416 − 4533
8. $\frac{4}{5}$ as a percentage
9. Smallest two digit prime number
10. $1^1 + 2^2 + 3^3$
11. $180 − 65 \div 5$
13. Factor of 60
15. 6874 to the nearest 100
17. Find n, if $n \div 11 = 11$
18. Number of 2p coins in £10

Down

1. Half of a third of 66
2. Perimeter of a square of side 27 cm
4. Next in the sequence 70, 140, 280
7. Double 125 plus treble 202
8. $30^2 − 2^6 − 3^2$
9. William the Conqueror
11. Maximum score with three darts
12. $\frac{3}{7}$ of 3528
14. 17×30
16. Multiple of 8

Part D

Design you own crossnumber puzzle. Start with the answers and
then write clues to the puzzle.
Try to make your clues as varied and interesting as possible.

Part 7

7.1 Numeracy tests

This section contains two numeracy tests each with 25 questions. A calculator is not allowed with either test.

Numeracy test 1

1. Write the number two thousand, six hundred and fifty-seven in figures.

2. Write the number 703 in words.

3. What is the value of the underlined figure in this number: 9813?

4. What is $537 + 246$?

5. What is $16 + 27 + 48$?

6. What is $78 - 19$?

7. What is $453 - 371$?

8. If 8 km is about 5 miles, how many miles is 48 km?

9. Work out 16×8.

10. What is $56 \div 7$?

11. Work out $725 \div 5$.

12. What fraction of the whole figure is shaded in this diagram?

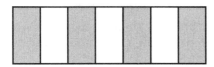

13. Write the next number in this sequence: 1, 3, 6, 10, 15, ☐.

14. Write the missing number in this sequence: 7, 18, ☐, 40.

15. Find the missing number: $36 - ☐ = 17$.

16. Find the missing number: $29 + ☐ = 44$.

17. Find the missing number: $☐ - 7 = 61$.

18. If 84% of people wear a wristwatch, what percentage does not?

19. What is 70% as a fraction?

20. What is $36 + 42 - 17$?

21. In which of the following diagrams is $\frac{5}{8}$ of the shape shaded?

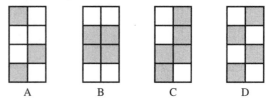

22. Write the fraction $\frac{6}{8}$ in its simplest form.

23. What fraction of the whole line is AB?

24. What fraction is 0·75?

25. What is $12·37 + 31·98$?

Numeracy test 2

1. What is $3 \cdot 14 + 2 \cdot 52 + 1 \cdot 31$?

2. What is the reading in kilograms shown in this scale?

3. *Estimate* the length of this line:

4. Each pace of an Egyptian warrior is 90 cm. How far does he walk, in km, when he walks 1 00 000 paces?

5. What is the cost of 5 chocolate bars at 32 pence each?

6. If you buy 3 tins of cat food for £2·16, how much did each tin cost?

7. If there are 60 minutes in an hour, how many minutes is 40 hours?

8. How many 20 pence coins can I exchange for £3·60?

9. A mountain bicycle costs £500 plus 10% delivery charge. How much extra do you pay for the delivery charge?

10. A personal computer costs £350. In a sale it is reduced by 20%. What is the reduction in the original price?

11. Trisha, Stella and Vikky have lunch together and agree to share the cost equally. If lunch costs £24·99, how much should each pay?

12. A metal rod is 12 cm long. A piece 1 cm 2 mm is cut off. What length of rod is left in centimetres?

13. What is 4500 grams in kilograms?

14. A cross-country course is 5 km. How far is this in metres?

15. Over a month a man drank 36 pints of beer. How many gallons is this?
(1 gallon = 8 pints)

16. What is the area of this square in square metres?

17. A rectangular bowling green is 15 metres long and 12 metres wide. What is its area in square metres?

18. What is the perimeter of this shape?

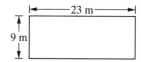

19. A train leaves St Pancras London at 13 20 and arrives in Sheffield at 15 35. How many minutes did the journey take?

20. A journey by bus takes 35 minutes. If Judith got on the bus at 14 45, at what time does she arrive?

21. A car travels at 60 miles per hour on a motorway. How far has it travelled after $2\frac{1}{2}$ hours?

22. A train covers a journey of 395 miles in 5 hours. What is its average speed in m.p.h?

23. A two hour cassette tape is used to record a radio programme. If the programme lasts 40 minutes, how much recording time is left on the cassette tape?

24. A marathon runner runs on average at 10 m.p.h. How many hours will she take to run 25 miles?

25. Three people are aged 12, 20 and 28. What is their mean age?

7.2 End of book review

Review exercise 1   Number and algebra

1. In a 'magic square' all rows (←—→) columns

$\left(\updownarrow \right)$ and diagonals $\left(\bbox{\times} \right)$ add up to the

same 'magic number'. Copy and complete this
magic square.

	6	10	15
16		5	4
	12	8	
		11	

2. Harminder has to visit a relative who lives 196 miles away. He
stops for lunch after driving 117 miles. How much further does
he still have to go?

3. In a new office building, 62 new doors are required.
   (a) If each door is fastened by 3 hinges, how many hinges are
   needed altogether?
   (b) If each hinge requires 6 screws, what is the total number of
   screws required to fit all the doors?

4. A multi-storey office block has 216 offices altogether. If there
are 9 offices on each floor, how many storeys does the building
have?

5. Numbers are missing on four of these calculator buttons. Copy
the diagram and write in numbers to make the answer 30.

$$\boxed{2}\boxed{8}\boxed{+}\boxed{}\boxed{}\boxed{-}\boxed{}\boxed{}\boxed{=}\boxed{3}\boxed{0}$$

6. Here are some number cards. $\boxed{3}$ $\boxed{4}$ $\boxed{5}$ $\boxed{2}$ $\boxed{9}$

   (a) Use two cards to make a
   fraction which is equal to $\frac{1}{3}$. $\dfrac{\square}{\square}$

   (b) Use three of the cards to make
   the smallest possible fraction. $\dfrac{\square}{\square\square}$

7. (a) How many 9 centimetre pieces of string can be cut from a
   piece of string which is 2 metres in length?
   (b) How much string is left over?

8. Look at this group of numbers ...

$$10, 19, 25, 30, 21$$

(a) Which of the numbers is a multiple of both 3 and 5?
(b) Which of the numbers is a prime number?
(c) Which of the numbers is a square number?

9. Write down these calculations and find the missing digits.

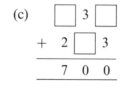

(a)
```
   5 □ 5
 + 3 7 □
 ───────
   9 0 9
```

(b)
```
   7 □ 8
 + 3 8 □
 ───────
 □ 1 5
```

(c)
```
   □ 3 □
 + 2 □ 3
 ───────
   7 0 0
```

10. The rule for the number sequences below is '*double and add 1*'. Write down each sequence and fill in the missing numbers.

(a) $1 \to 3 \to 7 \to 15 \to \square$

(b) $\square \to 5 \to 11 \to 23$

(c) $\square \to 13 \to \square \to \square$

11. Simplify the following expressions.
(a) $5n + 3 + 2n - 1$ (b) $6m + 2n - 2m + 7n$
(c) $3a + 7c - 3a + 5$ (d) $10n + 3 + 10n + 13$

12. Solve the equations.
(a) $n + 5 = 11$ (b) $n - 7 = 3$ (c) $3n = 12$
(d) $5n = 30$ (e) $15 = n + 2$ (f) $6 = n - 6$

13. This shape has $\frac{1}{3}$ shaded.

Copy each diagram and shade the given fraction.

(a)
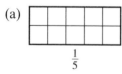
$\frac{1}{5}$

(b)
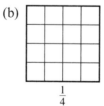
$\frac{1}{4}$

(c)
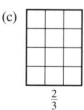
$\frac{2}{3}$

14. Simplify these fractions.
(a) $\frac{12}{16}$ (b) $\frac{20}{25}$ (c) $\frac{48}{50}$ (d) $\frac{28}{42}$

15. Look at the following numbers ...

$$-9, \quad 4, \quad 0, \quad -2, \quad +5$$

(a) Write down the positive numbers.
(b) Write down the negative numbers.
(c) Write the numbers in order, lowest to highest.
(d) Write down the difference between the highest and lowest numbers.

16. Copy and complete this table showing equivalent fractions, decimals and percentages:

Fraction	Decimal	Percentage
	0·5	
$\frac{1}{4}$		
		75%

17. Which is larger ...
   (a) $\frac{3}{10}$ of £50   or   (b) 25% of £40?

18. Here is a sequence of diagrams showing an arrangement of counters ...

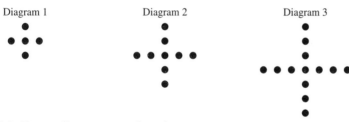

Diagram 1   Diagram 2   Diagram 3

(a) Draw diagram number 4.
(b) Copy and complete this table for the diagrams so far.

Diagram Number	Counters used
1	5
2	
3	
4	

(c) Without drawing, how many counters will be needed for diagram number 5?

(d) Write in words how you found your answer without drawing.

19. The diagrams below show three test tubes containing a liquid.

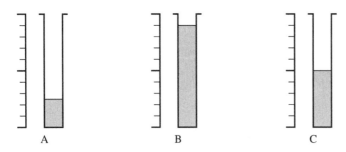

A   B   C

(a) Which of the test tubes above is 0·9 full?
(b) Which of the test tubes is $\frac{1}{4}$ full?
(c) Which of the test tubes is 50% full?

20. Look at the following input/output machine ...

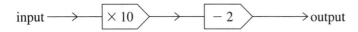

input ⟶ ×10 ⟶ −2 ⟶ output

Copy and complete this table using the machine above:

	Input	Output
	3	28
(a)	4	
(b)	7	
(c)	10	
(d)		108
(e)		148

21. An ice cream and a can of drink together cost 85p.
Two ice creams and a can of drink together cost £1·40.
(a) How much does one ice cream cost?
(b) How much would you pay for three ice creams and two cans of drink?

22. Find the number I am thinking of in each part:
(a) If I take away 13 from it, I get 44.
(b) If I double it, I get 350.
(c) If I divide it by 10, I get 3·2.
(d) If I double the number and take away 12, I get 40.
(e) If I treble the number and add 7, I get 8.

Review exercise 2   Shape and space

1. Tara and Quentin had these shapes and they were asked to sort the shapes into two groups.

Tara chose shapes A, C and E. She gave Quentin shapes B, D and F.
   (a) Who should have this shape, Tara or Quentin?
   (b) Give a reason.

2. Here are 6 objects.

Shape 1   Shape 2   Shape 3   Shape 4   Shape 5   Shape 6

   (a) For shape 2, shape 3 and shape 5 write down the number of
      (i) faces   (ii) edges   (iii) vertices.
   (b) Write down the correct mathematical name for each of the six shapes.

3. Listed below are various items that can be measured. Copy the list and insert next to each item the most suitable unit of measurement.
   (a) The fuel tank of an aircraft.
   (b) The mass of a packet of crisps.
   (c) The height of your bedroom.
   (d) The distance from London to Edinburgh.
   (e) The amount of cough mixture on a teaspoon.
   (f) The width of a postage stamp.

Units
1. centimetres
2. millilitres
3. grams
4. kilometres
5. litres
6. metres

4. Draw a grid like this ...
   (a) Plot these points on the grid and join them up in the order given:
   (2, 2), (3, 3), (3, 4),
   (2, 5), (5, 5), (4, 4),
   (4, 3), (5, 2), (2, 2)
   (b) How many lines of symmetry does the shape have?

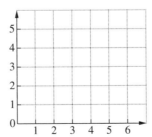

5. Calculate the area of each shape.

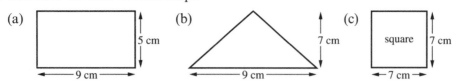

(a)   5 cm   9 cm   (b)   7 cm   9 cm   (c)   square   7 cm   7 cm

6. On squared paper draw these shapes:
(a) a quadrilateral with just one right angle
(b) an isosceles triangle
(c) a quadrilateral with no right angles and no parallel sides.

7. Draw the shape on squared paper.
Draw the new position after it is
turned clockwise through one right
angle around the point A.

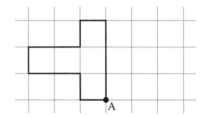

8. (a) Points A, D and E are three vertices of a
rectangle. Write down the coordinates of
the other vertex.
(b) C, E and D are three vertices of a square.
Write down the coordinates of the other
vertex.
(c) B, C and E are three vertices of a
parallelogram. Write down the
coordinates of the other vertex.

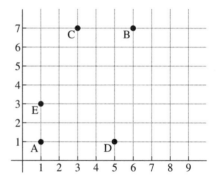

9. Draw, as accurately as you can,
the triangle shown.
Measure the length marked L.

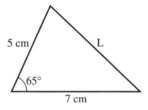

5 cm   L   65°   7 cm

10. ABCD is a rectangle.
(a) Write down the coordinates of A.

(b) M is mid-way between A and B.
What are the coordinates of M?

(c) N is in the middle of the rectangle.
What are the coordinates of N?

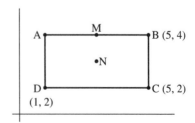

A   M   B (5, 4)   •N   D   C (5, 2)   (1, 2)

11.

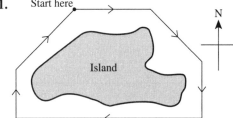

A ship is sailing around an island.
Copy and complete the missing compass
directions of the ship's journey.

East   then ☐ then ☐ then ☐ then ☐ then ☐

12. In each of the following diagrams, mirror lines are shown as
broken lines. Copy each diagram and complete the reflections.

  (a)   (b)   (c)

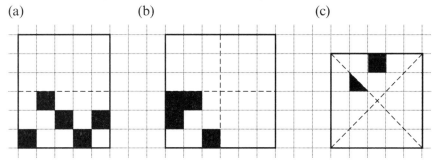

13. Here is a diagram of a designer's logo
for 'speedo' training shoes:

  (a) Make an accurate drawing of the logo
       using a ruler, pencil and protractor.

  (b) Measure the length AB on your drawing.

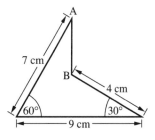

14.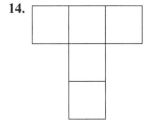

The T-shape is made from five squares
and has a total area of $45 \, cm^2$.
Work out the perimeter of the shape.

Review exercise 3　Handling data and probability

1. Here is a table showing the percentage of votes for the main political parties in the 1997 General Election predicted by various polling organisations:

Organisation	Labour vote (%)	Conservative vote (%)	Lib Dem vote (%)	Others (%)	Labour lead over Conservative (%)
Harris	48	31	15	6	17
NOP	50	28	14	8	22
ICM	43	33	18	6	10
Gallup	46	33	16	5	13
MORI	47	29	19	5	18
Poll of polls	47	31	16	6	16
Actual result	44	31	17	8	13

(a) Which organisations correctly predicted the Conservative vote?

(b) Which organisation was closest to predicting the Labour vote?

(c) Which organisation correctly predicted the Labour lead over the Conservatives?

(d) Represent the actual result of the election on a bar chart.

2. Eggs are sorted into size by weight. The weight is then converted into an egg size. The sizes range from 1 to 7.
Here are the weights of eggs produced by a farmer's chickens:

65, 56, 62, 69, 64, 51, 53, 57, 60, 59,
45, 59, 50, 57, 54, 58, 53, 59, 55, 58,
56, 46, 55, 44, 61, 55, 52, 70, 60, 56,
70, 66, 62, 42, 49, 63, 50, 57, 64, 72.

Copy and complete this table:

Weight (grams)	Size	Tally	Frequency
Under 45 g	7		
45–49	6		
50–54	5		
55–59	4		
60–64	3		
65–69	2		
70 g or over	1		

3. This chart shows the number of packets of different flavours of crisps sold by a shop.

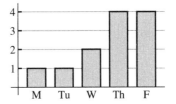

	M	Tu	W	Th	F
Ready Salted	3	1	2	4	0
Salt 'n Vinegar	4	2	5	3	1
Cheese 'n Onion	5	1	3	1	4
Roast Beef	3	2	6	4	1
Prawn	1	1	2	4	4

(a) How many packets of crisps were sold on Wednesday?

(b) Each packet of Ready Salted crisps costs 15p. How much was spent on Ready Salted crisps in the whole week?

(c) This is a graph of one flavour of crisps.
Which flavour is it?

4. In a survey the children at a school were asked to state their favourite sport in the Olympics.
(a) Estimate what fraction of the children chose gymnastics.
(b) There are 120 children in the school. Estimate the number of children who chose athletics.

5. This bar line graph shows the number of bedrooms in the houses in one road.
(a) How many houses had 4 bedrooms?
(b) How many houses are in the road?
(c) Why would it not be sensible to join the tops of the bars to make a line graph?

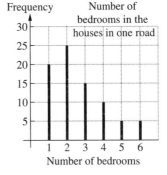

6. Some keen gardeners collect rain water from the roofs of their homes into rain barrels. They use the water from the barrel when the ground is dry to save using tap water.
Look at this graph and write down what you think is happening. Use the labels A, B, C ...

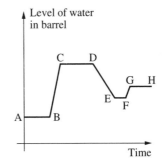

7. One card is selected at random from a normal pack of 52 playing cards. Find the probability of selecting:
   (a) the king of diamonds
   (b) an ace
   (c) a red card.

8. Here are two spinners
   Say whether the following
   statements are true or false.
   Explain why.

   Gill's spinner   Nick's spinner

   (a) 'Gill is more likely than Nick to spin a 4.'
   (b) 'Gill and Nick are equally likely to spin an even number.'
   (c) 'If Nick spins his spinner eight times he is bound to get at least one 8.'

9. A bag contains 1 blue ball, 3 red balls and 7 white balls.

   (a) If I select a ball at random from the bag without looking, what colour ball am I most likely to select?
   (b) What is the probability I select:
      (i) a white ball?
      (ii) a red ball?
      (iii) a green ball?
      (iv) a blue ball?

10. A bag contains 4 balls. The probability of selecting a white ball from the bag is 0·5. A white ball is taken from the bag and left on one side.
    What is the probability of selecting a white ball from the bag now?

11. (a) Find the mean of the numbers   2, 5, 3, 7, 9
    (b) Find the median of the numbers   6, 8, 1, 5, 9, 7, 9
    (c) Find the mode of the numbers   1, 3, 2, 4, 3, 2, 1, 3
    (d) Find the range of the numbers   3, 2, 7, 20, 11, 4

12. Karen has 5 cards.
    The mean of the five cards is 9.
    The range of the five cards is 4.
    What number are on the other two cards?

    9   9   9   ☐   ☐

Practice test 1

1. Work out:

(a)　　£3·87
　　　+ £2·43
　　　————

(b)　　£5·00
　　　− £1·67
　　　————

(c)　　£3·75
　　　×　　3
　　　————

(d) 4)£2·16

2. Look at the following numbers ...　　2,　3,　8,　9,　11,　15

(a) How many numbers are odd?
(b) How many numbers are even?
(c) Write down the prime numbers.
(d) Write down the number that is a multiple of five.
(e) Write down the numbers that are factors of twenty-four.
(f) Write down the number that is a square number.

3. In how many ways can you join the square X to shape Y along an edge so that the final shape has line symmetry?

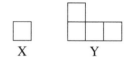

X　　　　Y

4. Here is a table of temperatures at 06·00 on the same day.

(a) What is the difference in temperature between Rome and London?
(b) At 12·00 the temperature in New York has risen by 5°C. What is the temperature in New York at 12·00?

London	−5°C
Paris	−3°C
Rome	+1°C
Melbourne	+11°C
New York	−8°C

5. Write the missing numbers in the following sequences ...

(a) 1,　8,　15,　22,　☐,　☐ ...

(b) 1,　3,　7,　15,　☐,　☐ ...

(c) Write down the rule you used to find your answer in (a).

(d) Write down the rule you used to find your answer in (b).

6. Write each of the following in the units shown, using decimals when needed.

(a) 2 m 35 cm = ☐ m

(b) 350 g = ☐ kg

(c) 0·62 m = ☐ cm

(d) 3·3 kg = ☐ g

(e) 44 cm = ☐ m

(f) 27 mm = ☐ cm

7. In the following diagrams write down the value of the angles marked with letters.

(a) 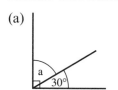 (b) 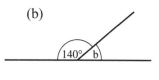 (c) 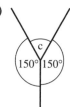 (d)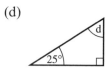

8. Find the value of each letter in the following equations
   (a) $g - 4 = 6$
   (b) $n + 3 = 70$
   (c) $2p = 16$
   (d) $r \div 3 = 21$

9. Solve the following balance puzzle, writing your answer x = ...

10. What six coins make eighty-eight pence?

11. What fraction of one complete turn is one right angle?

12. A recipe uses 3 eggs and 2 apples for every cake.
A chef has an order for several cakes.
He uses 24 eggs. How many apples does he use?

13. The diagram opposite shows a room which is to be carpeted.
   (a) Find the area of carpet required to cover the floor.
   (b) What is the perimeter of the room?

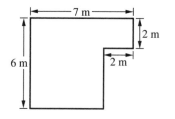

14. In the diagram opposite ... ⟶
   (a) Measure angle $A\widehat{B}D$ using a protractor.
   (b) Measure angle $A\widehat{C}B$ using a protractor.
   (c) What is the length of the line DB in centimetres?
   (d) What is the length of the line AB in millimetres?
   (e) What type of triangle is $\triangle ABC$?
   (f) How many triangles can you see in the diagram?
   (g) What do all the angles in any triangle add up to?

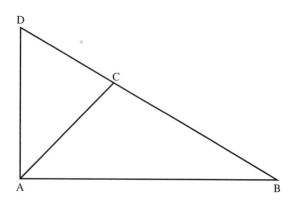

15. The line graph below shows the fuel gauge reading of a car at different times throughout a day ...

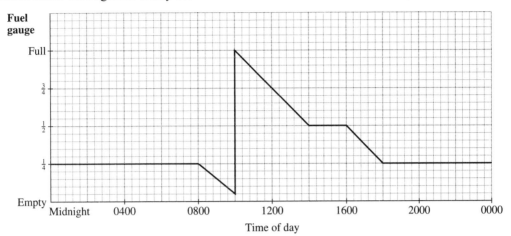

(a) Was the car moving or stationary between midnight and 8·00 am?

(b) What happened to the car at 10·00 am?

(c) How much petrol was used between 10·00 am and 2·00 pm?

(d) At what time in the evening was the car put in the garage?

16. Work out

(a) $\frac{1}{4}$ of £24 = ?　　(b) $\frac{5}{6}$ of £36 = ?　　(c) 25% of £480 = ?

(d) $\frac{3}{4}$ of £80 = ?　　(e) 25% of £90 = ?　　(f) 12% of £1000 = ?

17. Draw the two patterns on the right and shade in one more square so that the final patterns have reflective symmetry.

18. Write down the probability of the following events occurring ...

(a) When a fair coin is tossed it will come down 'heads'

(b) You will roll a 'six' on a fair dice.

(c) From a bag containing six red balls and one yellow ball, you select a red ball

18. What fraction of the area of the rectangle is the area of the triangle?

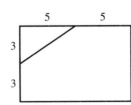

Practice test 2

1. Work out the total cost.

13 kg of sand at 57p per kg.
2 tape measures at £4·20 each
2000 screws at 80p per hundred
250 g of varnish at £6·60 per kg

2. Use a calculator to work out the following and give your answers correct to 1 decimal place.

(a) $8·62 - \dfrac{1·71}{0·55}$ (b) $\dfrac{8·02 - 6·3}{1·3^2 + 4·6}$ (c) $\dfrac{5·6}{1·71} - \dfrac{9·7}{11·3}$

3. A normal pack of 52 playing cards (without jokers) is divided into two piles

Pile A has all the picture cards (Kings, Queens, Jacks) 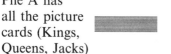 Pile B has the rest of the pack.

Find the probability of selecting
(a) any 'three' from pile B
(b) the King of hearts from pile A
(c) any red seven from pile B.

4. In each of the following diagrams, lines of symmetry are shown by broken lines. Copy and complete each diagram.

(a)   (b)   (c)

5. Draw the two patterns on the right and shade in more squares so that the final patterns have rotational symmetry of order 2.

6. Write down five consecutive numbers whose mean value is 42.

7. There were ten children on a coach journey. The mean age of the children was 11 and the range of their ages was 4. Write each statement below and then write next to it whether it is *True*, *Possible* or *False*.
   (a) The youngest child was 9 years old.
   (b) Every child was 11 years old.
   (c) All the children were at least 10 years old

8. In number walls each brick is made by adding the two bricks underneath it.

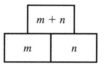

   Fill in the missing expressions on these walls

   (a) 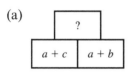 (b) 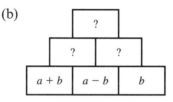 (c)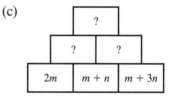

9. These nets form cubical dice. Opposite faces of a dice always add up to 7. Write down the value of a, b, c, d, e, and f so that opposite faces add up to 7.

10. Work out the areas of A, B, C, ..., I in the shapes below. The dots are 1 cm apart.

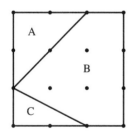 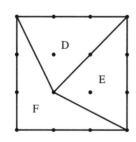 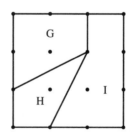

11. Copy and complete the magic squares

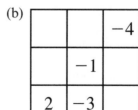

Practice test 3

1. Sketch a cuboid with dimensions 3 cm by 4 cm by 5 cm.
   Calculate the total surface area of the cuboid.

2. The same operations are in each chain of number machines

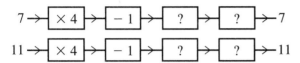

   Find the missing operations.

3. (a) Suppose the '5' button on your calculator does not work.
       Show how you can make your calculator show the number
       345.
   (b) Suppose none of the numbers 1, 3, 5, 7, 9 work. Show how
       you can make your calculator show the number 115.

4. (a) Copy the diagram.
   (b) Rotate triangle 1 90° clockwise around
       the point (0, 0). Label the image △2.
   (c) Rotate triangle 1 90° anti-clockwise around
       the point (4, 3). Label the image △3.

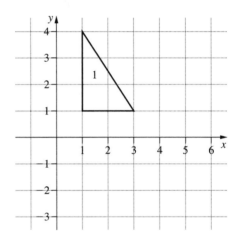

5. Which fraction is closer to one: $\frac{7}{8}$ or $\frac{8}{7}$?
   Show your working.

6. The price of a dress costing £45 was decreased by 10%.
   Six months later the price was increased by 10%.
   Calculate the final price of the dress.

7. Three friends share a prize of £5000 in the ratio 2:3:5.
   How much was the smallest share?

8. Draw a net for a cuboid 2 cm × 3 cm × 4 cm.

9. Copy and complete by filling in the boxes. You can use any of the numbers 1, 2, 3, 4, 5 but you cannot use a number more than once.

(a) $\Box + \Box - \Box = 7$

(b) $(\Box + \Box) \div \Box = 3$

(c) $(\Box + \Box) \div (\Box - \Box) = 1\frac{1}{2}$

(d) $(\Box + \Box + \Box) \times \Box = 33$

10. Look at the diagram.
(a) Write down the ratio shaded length : unshaded length.

(b) As a percentage, what proportion of the diagram is shaded?

11. The star shape is made from four triangles like the one shown.
(a) Calculate the area of the star shape.
(b) Calculate the perimeter of the star shape.

 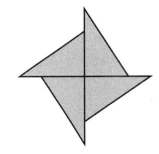

12. On a coordinate grid, plot the points A(1, 4) B(2, 1) C(5, 2)
What are the coordinates of D if ABCD is a square?

13. Two books cost £13·50 in total. One book is one-and-a-half times the price of the other. How much does each book cost?

14. In the box is a formula for working out heights.
Lindsey's mother is 162 cm tall and her father is 180 cm tall. What is the greatest height to which Lindsey is likely to grow?

> Add the height of each parent.
> Divide by 2
> Add 6 cm to the result.
>
> A girl is likely to be this height plus or minus 7 cm.

15. A map has a scale of 1 cm to 5 km.
A lake appears 3·2 cm long on the map. How long is the actual lake in km?

16. There are eight balls in a bag. The probability of taking a white ball from the bag is 0·5.
A white ball is taken from the bag and put on one side.
What is the probability of taking a white ball from the bag now?

INDEX